MATH

Mc
Graw
Hill
Education

connectED.mcgraw-hill.com

STEM McGraw-Hill is committed to providing instructional materials in Science, Technology, Engineering, and Mathematics (STEM) that give all students a solid foundation, one that prepares them for college and careers in the 21st century.

Send all inquiries to:
McGraw-Hill Education
STEM Learning Solutions Center
8787 Orion Place
Columbus, OH 43240

ISBN: 978-0-07-664150-5
MHID: 0-07-664150-3

Printed in the United States of America.

6 7 8 9 RMN 16

CONTENTS IN BRIEF

Organized by Focal Areas

Your assignment's due tomorrow...
but your book is in your locker!

NOW WHAT?

Even in crunch time, with ConnectED, we've got you covered!

With ConnectED, you have instant access to all of your study materials—anytime, anywhere. From homework materials to study guides—it's all in one place and just a click away. ConnectED even allows you to collaborate with your classmates and use mobile apps to make studying easy.

Resources built for you—available 24/7:

- Your eBook available wherever you are

- Personal Tutors and Self-Check Quizzes whenever you need them

- An Online Calendar with all of your due dates

- eFlashcard App to make studying easy

- A message center to stay in touch

Reimagine Learning

Go Online!
connectED.mcgraw-hill.com

Vocab
Learn about new vocabulary words.

Watch
Watch animations and videos.

Tutor
See and hear a teacher explain how to solve problems.

Tools
Explore concepts with virtual manipulatives.

Check
Check your progress.

eHelp
Get targeted homework help.

Worksheets
Access practice worksheets.

Chapter 1
Rational Numbers and the Coordinate Plane

Go to page 93 to learn about a 21st Century Career in
Art!

Chapter 2
Multiply and Divide Rational Numbers

Go to page 187 to learn about a 21st Century Career in
Design!

Chapter 3
Operations with Integers

Go to page 257 to learn about a 21st Century Career in **Astronomy!**

Chapter 4
Understand Proportions

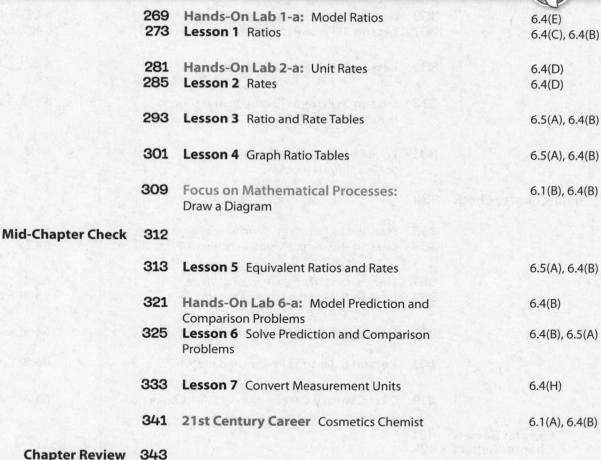
Go to page 341 to learn about a 21st Century Career in **Chemistry!**

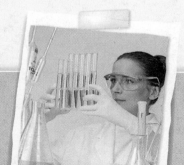

Chapter 5
Apply Proportions to Percent

Go to page 419 to learn about a 21st Century Career in **Movies!**

Chapter 6
Multiple Representations

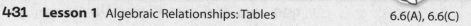

Go to page 487 to learn about a 21st Century Career in
Atmospheric Science!

Chapter 7
Algebraic Expressions

Go to page 577 to learn about a 21st Century Career in **Engineering!**

Chapter 8
Equations and Inequalities

Go to page 661 to learn about a 21st Century Career in **Music!**

Chapter 9
Represent Geometry with Algebra

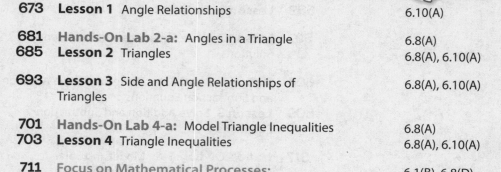

Go to page 767 to learn about a 21st Century Career in **Community Planning!**

Chapter 10
Statistical Measures and Displays

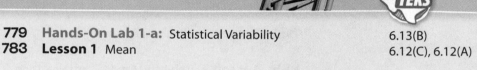

Go to page 871 to learn about a 21st Century Career in
Environmental Science!

Chapter 11 Personal Financial Literacy

TEKS

Texas Essential Knowledge and Skills, Grade 6

Track Your TEKS Progress

The knowledge and skills that you will learn this year are listed on these pages. Throughout the year, your teacher will ask you to rate how confident you feel about your knowledge of each one. Don't worry if you have no clue **before** you learn about them. You will rate your knowledge before and after you learn them. Your teacher will provide you with more instructions. Watch how your knowledge and skills grow as the year progresses!

😞 I have no clue.　　😐 I've heard of it.　　🙂 I know it!

6.1 Mathematical Process Standards	Before			After		
	😞	😐	🙂	😞	😐	🙂
The student uses mathematical processes to acquire and demonstrate mathematical understanding. The student is expected to:						
6.1(A) Apply mathematics to problems arising in everyday life, society, and the workplace;						
6.1(B) Use a problem-solving model that incorporates analyzing given information, formulating a plan or strategy, determining a solution, justifying the solution, and evaluating the problem-solving process and the reasonableness of the solution;						
6.1(C) Select tools, including real objects, manipulatives, paper and pencil, and technology as appropriate, and techniques, including mental math, estimation, and number sense as appropriate, to solve problems;						
6.1(D) Communicate mathematical ideas, reasoning, and their implications using multiple representations, including symbols, diagrams, graphs, and language as appropriate;						
6.1(E) Create and use representations to organize, record, and communicate mathematical ideas;						
6.1(F) Analyze mathematical relationships to connect and communicate mathematical ideas; and						
6.1(G) Display, explain, and justify mathematical ideas and arguments using precise mathematical language in written or oral communication.						

		Before			After		

6.2 Number and Operations

The student applies mathematical process standards to represent and use rational numbers in a variety of forms. The student is expected to:

6.2(A)	Classify whole numbers, integers, and rational numbers using a visual representation such as a Venn diagram to describe relationships between sets of numbers;
6.2(B)	Identify a number, its opposite, and its absolute value;
6.2(C)	Locate, compare, and order integers and rational numbers using a number line;
6.2(D)	Order a set of rational numbers arising from mathematical and real-world contexts; and
6.2(E)	Extend representations for division to include fraction notation such as a/b represents the same number as $a \div b$ where $b \neq 0$.

6.3 Number and Operations

The student applies mathematical process standards to represent addition, subtraction, multiplication, and division while solving problems and justifying solutions. The student is expected to:

6.3(A)	Recognize that dividing by a rational number and multiplying by its reciprocal result in equivalent values;
6.3(B)	Determine, with and without computation, whether a quantity is increased or decreased when multiplied by a fraction, including values greater than or less than one;
6.3(C)	Represent integer operations with concrete models and connect the actions with the models to standardized algorithms;
6.3(D)	Add, subtract, multiply, and divide integers fluently; and
6.3(E)	Multiply and divide positive rational numbers fluently.

		Before			After		

6.4 Proportionality

The student applies mathematical process standards to develop an understanding of proportional relationships in problem situations. The student is expected to:

6.4(A)	Compare two rules verbally, numerically, graphically, and symbolically in the form of $y = ax$ or $y = x + a$ in order to differentiate between additive and multiplicative relationships;						
6.4(B)	Apply qualitative and quantitative reasoning to solve prediction and comparison of real-world problems involving ratios and rates;						
6.4(C)	Give examples of ratios as multiplicative comparisons of two quantities describing the same attribute;						
6.4(D)	Give examples of rates as the comparison by division of two quantities having different attributes, including rates as quotients;						
6.4(E)	Represent ratios and percents with concrete models, fractions, and decimals;						
6.4(F)	Represent benchmark fractions and percents such as 1%, 10%, 25%, 33 1/3%, and multiples of these values using 10 by 10 grids, strip diagrams, number lines, and numbers;						
6.4(G)	Generate equivalent forms of fractions, decimals, and percents using real-world problems, including problems that involve money; and						
6.4(H)	Convert units within a measurement system, including the use of proportions and unit rates.						

6.5 Proportionality

The student applies mathematical process standards to solve problems involving proportional relationships. The student is expected to:

6.5(A)	Represent mathematical and real-world problems involving ratios and rates using scale factors, tables, graphs, and proportions;						
6.5(B)	Solve real-world problems to find the whole given a part and the percent, to find the part given the whole and the percent, and to find the percent given the part and the whole, including the use of concrete and pictorial models; and						
6.5(C)	Use equivalent fractions, decimals, and percents to show equal parts of the same whole.						

6.6 Expressions, Equations, and Relationships	Before			After		
The student applies mathematical process standards to use multiple representations to describe algebraic relationships. The student is expected to:						
6.6(A) Identify independent and dependent quantities from tables and graphs;						
6.6(B) Write an equation that represents the relationship between independent and dependent quantities from a table; and						
6.6(C) Represent a given situation using verbal descriptions, tables, graphs, and equations in the form $y = kx$ or $y = x + b$.						

6.7 Expressions, Equations, and Relationships	Before			After		
The student applies mathematical process standards to develop concepts of expressions and equations. The student is expected to:						
6.7(A) Generate equivalent numerical expressions using order of operations, including whole number exponents and prime factorization;						
6.7(B) Distinguish between expressions and equations verbally, numerically, and algebraically;						
6.7(C) Determine if two expressions are equivalent using concrete models, pictorial models, and algebraic representations; and						
6.7(D) Generate equivalent expressions using the properties of operations: inverse, identity, commutative, associative, and distributive properties.						

	Before			After		

6.8 Expressions, Equations, and Relationships

The student applies mathematical process standards to use geometry to represent relationships and solve problems. The student is expected to:

		Before			After		
6.8(A)	Extend previous knowledge of triangles and their properties to include the sum of angles of a triangle, the relationship between the lengths of sides and measures of angles in a triangle, and determining when three lengths form a triangle;						
6.8(B)	Model area formulas for parallelograms, trapezoids, and triangles by decomposing and rearranging parts of these shapes;						
6.8(C)	Write equations that represent problems related to the area of rectangles, parallelograms, trapezoids, and triangles and volume of right rectangular prisms where dimensions are positive rational numbers; and						
6.8(D)	Determine solutions for problems involving the area of rectangles, parallelograms, trapezoids, and triangles and volume of right rectangular prisms where dimensions are positive rational numbers.						

		Before			After		
6.9 Expressions, Equations, and Relationships		☹	😐	☺	☹	😐	☺
The student applies mathematical process standards to use equations and inequalities to represent situations. The student is expected to:							
6.9(A)	Write one-variable, one-step equations and inequalities to represent constraints or conditions within problems;						
6.9(B)	Represent solutions for one-variable, one-step equations and inequalities on number lines; and						
6.9(C)	Write corresponding real-world problems given one-variable, one-step equations or inequalities.						

		Before			After		
6.10 Expressions, Equations, and Relationships		☹	😐	☺	☹	😐	☺
The student applies mathematical process standards to use equations and inequalities to solve problems. The student is expected to:							
6.10(A)	Model and solve one-variable, one-step equations and inequalities that represent problems, including geometric concepts; and						
6.10(B)	Determine if the given value(s) make(s) one-variable, one-step equations or inequalities true.						

	Before			After		

6.11 Measurement and Data

The student applies mathematical process standards to use coordinate geometry to identify locations on a plane. The student is expected to:

Graph points in all four quadrants using ordered pairs of rational numbers.

6.12 Measurement and Data

The student applies mathematical process standards to use numerical or graphical representations to analyze problems. The student is expected to:

6.12(A) Represent numeric data graphically, including dot plots, stem-and-leaf plots, histograms, and box plots;

6.12(B) Use the graphical representation of numeric data to describe the center, spread, and shape of the data distribution;

6.12(C) Summarize numeric data with numerical summaries, including the mean and median (measures of center) and the range and interquartile range (IQR) (measures of spread), and use these summaries to describe the center, spread, and shape of the data distribution; and

6.12(D) Summarize categorical data with numerical and graphical summaries, including the mode, the percent of values in each category (relative frequency table), and the percent bar graph, and use these summaries to describe the data distribution.

6.13 Measurement and Data

The student applies mathematical process standards to use numerical or graphical representations to solve problems. The student is expected to:

6.13(A) Interpret numeric data summarized in dot plots, stem-and-leaf plots, histograms, and box plots; and

6.13(B) Distinguish between situations that yield data with and without variability.

	Before			After		
6.14 Personal Financial Literacy	☹	😐	🙂	☹	😐	🙂
The student applies mathematical process standards to develop an economic way of thinking and problem solving useful in one's life as a knowledgeable consumer and investor. The student is expected to:						
6.14(A) Compare the features and costs of a checking account and a debit card offered by different local financial institutions;						
6.14(B) Distinguish between debit cards and credit cards;						
6.14(C) Balance a check register that includes deposits, withdrawals, and transfers;						
6.14(D) Explain why it is important to establish a positive credit history;						
6.14(E) Describe the information in a credit report and how long it is retained;						
6.14(F) Describe the value of credit reports to borrowers and to lenders;						
6.14(G) Explain various methods to pay for college, including through savings, grants, scholarships, student loans, and work-study; and						
6.14(H) Compare the annual salary of several occupations requiring various levels of post-secondary education or vocational training and calculate the effects of the different annual salaries on lifetime income.						

Mathematical Processes Handbook

Texas Essential Knowledge and Skills

Targeted TEKS
6.1 The student uses mathematical processes to acquire and demonstrate mathematical understanding.

Mathematical Processes
6.1, 6.1(A), 6.1(B), 6.1(C), 6.1(D), 6.1(E), 6.1(F), 6.1(G)

Essential Question

WHAT processes help me learn and talk about math?

1

What You'll Learn

MP The mathematical process standards listed below will help you to become a successful problem solver and to use math effectively in your daily life. Throughout this handbook, you will learn about each of these mathematical processes and how they are integrated in the chapters and lessons of this book.

Apply the Mathematical Processes to Every Lesson

Use the chart at the beginning of each lesson throughout this text to select which processes you used to solve a particular problem.

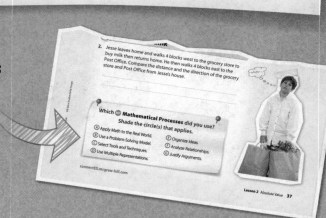

Apply Math to the Real World

When am I EVER going to use this?

Suppose you receive gift cards to an online store for your birthday. Great-aunt Hilda sends you a $10 gift card, Uncle Norman sends you a $25 gift card and your grandparents send you a $50 gift card. You've had your eye on five MP3 downloads, three games, and a wireless game controller. What can you buy? Well, NOW you are going to use some of what you learned in class.

Item	Cost ($)
MP3 download	0.99
Game 1	47.91
Game 2	17.61
Game 3	27.95
Game controller	60.00

Texas Essential Knowledge and Skills
Targeted TEKS
6.1(A) Apply mathematics to problems arising in everyday life, society, and the workplace.

1. What skill(s) would you use to see how much you can spend?

   _____

2. What skill(s) would you use to see how much the items will cost?

   _____

3. How do the two amounts compare?

   _____

4. Using as much of the gift cards that you can, what can you buy?

   _____

   _____

5. List three skills you learned in math class last year. Then list a real-world situation where you would use each skill.

Skill 1
_____
_____
_____
_____

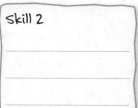

Skill 2
_____
_____
_____
_____

Skill 3
_____
_____
_____
_____

List the skills needed to solve each exercise. Then solve.

6. The Titan roller coaster in Arlington, Texas has the seventh longest drop of all roller coasters in the world. The ride can accommodate 1,600 riders per hour. A digital sign states there are 345 people in line. If you get into line, about how many minutes will it take you to get to the front of the line?

_____

_____

7. Whew! Was this year the hottest year on record? Research and graph the record monthly high temperatures for your town. Then describe how this year's temperatures compare to the record temperatures.

_____

_____

_____

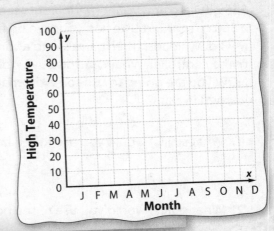

8. You have just arrived at summer camp. In your cabin, the counselor has each camper perform the super-secret handshake with every other person in the cabin. You and another person are in the cabin, so there is one handshake. Another person arrives, and another, until there are 14 people in the cabin. How many handshakes will there be in all?

_____

_____

(F)ind it in Your Book!

MP **Apply Math to the Real World**

Look at Chapter 1. Write the page number(s) where you find these examples of Mathematical Process A.

_____ Apply Math to the Real World exercises

_____ Graphic Novels

_____ 21st Century Career

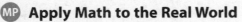

Use a Problem-Solving Model

How do I begin solving this problem?

Texas Essential Knowledge and Skills

Targeted TEKS
6.1(B) Use a problem-solving model that incorporates analyzing given information, formulating a plan or strategy, determining a solution, justifying the solution, and evaluating the problem-solving process and the reasonableness of the solution.

Yolanda will put 72 photos in a scrapbook. She will put the same number of photos on each of 6 pages. Four photos will be in each row. How many rows will be on each page?

You can use the four-step problem-solving plan. Let's study each step.

1. **Analyze** Read the problem. Circle the information that you are given and underline what you are trying to determine.

2. **Plan** Decide on an appropriate strategy to use. Some strategies are listed below.

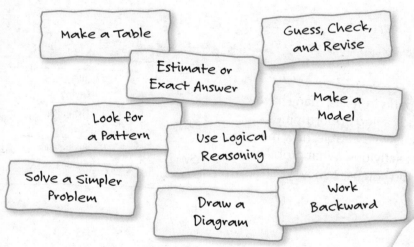

Make a Table

Guess, Check, and Revise

Estimate or Exact Answer

Make a Model

Look for a Pattern

Use Logical Reasoning

Solve a Simpler Problem

Draw a Diagram

Work Backward

What strategy will you use to solve the problem above?

_____

3. **Solve** Apply your strategy to solve the problem.

_____

4. **Justify and Evaluate** Determine if your solution is accurate and makes sense. Explain.

_____

_____

Solve each problem by using the four-step problem-solving model.

5. Tina bought some nail polish and lip gloss at the store. The nail polish cost $4.50 per bottle and lip gloss cost $7 per tube. Tina bought 9 items and paid $50.50. How many of each item did she buy?

   a. **Analyze** Circle the information you know and underline what you are trying to find. Is there any information you will not use? _____

   b. **Plan** What strategy will you use to solve this problem?

   _____

   c. **Solve** Solve the problem. Show your steps below. What is the solution?

   _____

   d. **Justify and Evaluate** Does your answer make sense? Can you solve the problem another way to check your work?

   _____

6. Of the 100 state parks in Texas, many have fishing, biking and caving opportunities. Based on the results in the table, how many parks allow these activities? What problem solving strategy did you use? Show your steps below.

Fishing	68	Biking and Caving	2
Biking	46	Fishing and Caving	0
Caving	4	Biking and Fishing	36

   _____

Find it in Your Book!

MP Use a Problem-Solving Model

Look at Chapter 1. Write the page number(s) where you find these examples of Mathematical Process B.

_____ Use a Problem-Solving Model exercises

_____ Multi-Step Problem-Solving exercises

_____ Focus on Mathematical Processes lesson

Select Tools and Techniques

Texas Essential Knowledge and Skills

Targeted TEKS
6.1(C) Select tools, including real objects, manipulatives, paper and pencil, and technology as appropriate, and techniques, including mental math, estimation, and number sense as appropriate, to solve problems.

How likely is it that a baseball player will hit a homerun using a hockey stick?

Since he is using a hockey stick as a bat, he's not very likely to make any hit, much less a homerun! So, let's investigate how to choose and use the proper tools and techniques to solve math problems.

1. To build a hockey goal cage, you might use a hammer or a drill. While you wouldn't use a hammer or a drill to solve a math problem, you might use some of the tools and techniques listed below. Complete the graphic organizer by adding some of your own tools and techniques.

Math Tools and Techniques

Tools	
counters	algebra tiles
ruler	computer

Techniques	
estimation	choose the correct unit
draw a diagram	mental math

2. Suppose you want to build a hockey goal cage and need to determine how much the materials will cost. List three tools or techniques that you could use to determine the total cost of the materials.

_____

3. Describe a situation in which you might use estimation.

_____

_____

_____

It's Your Turn!

For Exercises 4–7, select the tools and/or techniques you could use to solve each problem. Then write the corresponding letter(s) of each tool or technique.

Tools	Techniques
A. paper and pencil	F. draw a diagram
B. calculator	G. estimation
C. measuring tape/ruler	H. mental math
D. Internet	I. number sense
E. virtual manipulatives	J. make a prediction

4. Yikes, the supply list for school is huge! You need to buy everything on the list. How much will it all cost?

_____

5 spiral notebooks	10 pens
3-ring binder	3 pencils
notebook paper	dictionary
4 highlighters	10 folders
scientific calculator	flash drive

5. You want to bake a cake for your best friend's birthday. How much will it cost to buy all of the ingredients?

_____

6. The table shows the different admission prices to Space Center Houston. You and your family want to spend the day at the Space Center, have lunch, and buy a souvenir. How much money should you take?

_____

Space Center Houston	
Ticket Prices	
Adult	$22.95
Children (4–11)	$18.95
Seniors	$21.95

Find it in Your Book!

MP Select Tools and Techniques

Look at Chapter 1. Write the page number(s) where you find these examples of Mathematical Process C.

_____ Select Tools and Techniques exercises

_____ Hands-On Labs

Use Multiple Representations

How many different names do you have?

Your family, friends, and teachers may call you by different names. You might be Susanna, Suzie, Sue, or Miss Wilson. All of these names still represent *you*. In math, we also use different ways to represent the same idea. We can use words, graphs, tables, numbers, symbols, or diagrams.

Texas Essential Knowledge and Skills

Targeted TEKS
6.1(D) Communicate mathematical ideas, reasoning, and their implications using multiple representations, including symbols, diagrams, graphs, and language as appropriate.

1. How can you represent the number 0.25 using words?

_____

2. How can you represent the number 0.25 using a fraction?

_____

3. Suppose you and your friends ordered four pizzas. Together, a total of 3 pizzas were eaten. Complete the graphic organizer to represent the fraction of the pizzas that were eaten.

Diagram	Numbers	Words
$\frac{1}{4}$ $\frac{1}{4}$ $\frac{1}{4}$	$\dfrac{\square}{\square}$, 0.75, $\boxed{}$%	three-_____ _____ out of four _____-five percent

4. Draw a fraction circle to show the relationship between the amount of pizza you and your friends ate and the total amount of pizza ordered. Explain why the fraction circle is a good representation.

_____

_____

_____

Use the multiple representations shown to solve each problem.

5. You are downloading MP3 singles onto your computer. The singles are $0.99 each.

   a. **Tables** Complete the table to show the cost of 1, 2, 3, 4, and 5 singles.

Number of Singles, s	Cost, c ($)

   b. **Graph** Graph the ordered pairs (number of singles, cost) on the coordinate plane.

   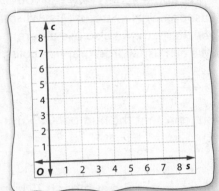

6. One of the major East-West highways in Texas is I–10. Luna's family is driving along I–10. The table shows the time, in hours, traveled and the total distance, in miles, traveled.

Time t (h)	Distance d (mi)
1	68
2	136
3	204
4	272
5	340

   a. **Tables** Use the table to determine the total distance traveled after 7 hours. _____

   b. **Words** Describe the relationship between time and distance traveled.

   _____

   _____

Find it in Your Book!

MP **Use Multiple Representations**

Look at Chapter 6. Write the page number(s) where you find these examples of Mathematical Process D.

_____ Use Multiple Representations exercises

How will being organized help me learn and understand math?

If you don't take notes in an organized way, the concepts you are learning might not make sense or seem connected. Graphic organizers are visual ways to organize information. They can be used to compare and contrast concepts or terms. They can also be used to summarize ideas.

Texas Essential Knowledge and Skills
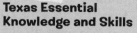

Targeted TEKS
6.1(E) Create and use representations to organize, record, and communicate mathematical ideas.

1. The chart shows some graphic organizers you may have learned before. Circle the ones that you have used before in other classes.

Types of Graphic Organizers		
concept map	timeline	flowchart
spider map	Venn diagram	web
fishbone map	compare and contrast map	K-W-L chart

2. Use the Internet or another source to research the organizers with which you are not familiar. Write a brief description of one of those organizers below.

_____

_____

_____

3. Suppose you wanted to record notes about the steps needed to build a fence in the backyard for your dog. What kind of graphic organizer could you create?

_____

_____

4. Another kind of graphic organizer is a Foldable. Foldables are three-dimensional graphic organizers that help you create study guides. Look through Chapter 1 in your text. Describe the Foldable you will create for this chapter. How do you think it will help you organize the information you will learn in Chapter 1?

_____

_____

_____

5. Turn to page 28 in your text. Find the vocabulary term _integer_ and complete the graphic organizer for that term.

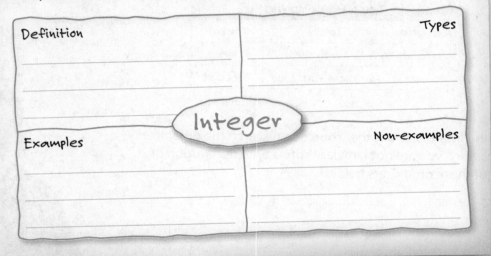

Definition

Types

Integer

Examples

Non-examples

Find it in Your Book!

MP **Organize Ideas**

Look at Chapter 1. Write the page number(s) where you find these examples of Mathematical Process E.

_____ Organize Ideas exercises

_____ Foldables

_____ Graphic Organizers

Analyze Relationships

Texas Essential Knowledge and Skills

Targeted TEKS

6.1(F) Analyze mathematical relationships to connect and communicate mathematical ideas.

Do you have a friend that is a friend of another friend?

Maybe your best friend's parent is also your basketball coach. Relationships are often connected in your personal life. In math, relationships are also connected.

1. Let's look at some relationships. The table shows the dimensions, in different units, of a basketball court. Use the relationship between feet, yards, and inches to complete the table.

Length	Width	Perimeter	Area
74 ft	42 ft	ft	ft^2
yd	yd	yd	yd^2
in.	in.	in.	in^2

2. If you are given the perimeter in feet, what should you do to obtain the perimeter in yards?

_____

3. If you are given the area in feet, what should you do to obtain the area in square yards?

_____

_____

4. If you are given the perimeter in feet, what should you do to obtain the perimeter in inches?

_____

5. If you are given the area in feet, what should you do to obtain the area in square inches?

_____

_____

6. The undergraduate enrollments in the different colleges at the University of Texas at Austin of a recent year are shown in the bar graph. How is the enrollment in the College of Engineering related to the enrollment in the College of Undergraduate Studies?

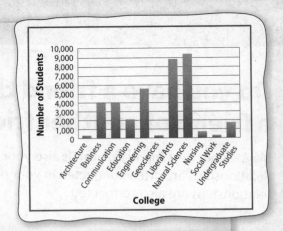

_____

7. Is the area of the rectangle shown related to the volume of the rectangular prism shown? Explain.

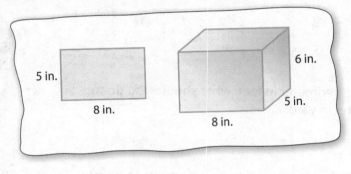

_____

_____

_____

Find it in Your Book!

MP **Analyze Relationships**

Look at Chapter 1. Write the page number(s) where you find these examples of Mathematical Process F.

_____ Analyze Relationships exercises

_____ Analyze exercises in H.O.T. problems

_____ Analyze and Reflect exercises in Hands-On Labs

Justify Arguments

Have you ever had to explain to someone why you were late?

Chances are that saying "I don't know" is not going to go over very well. You need to give a good reason why you were late. In math, you often need to justify an argument or explain your reasoning. When you use rules, definitions, or properties, you are using *deductive reasoning*. When you use examples or patterns, you are using *inductive reasoning*.

Texas Essential Knowledge and Skills

TEKS

Targeted TEKS
6.1(G) Display, explain, and justify mathematical ideas and arguments using precise mathematical language in written or oral communication.

1. The table shows some of the properties of math. Complete the table by completing the example for each property.

Commutative Property of Addition	Commutative Property of Multiplication
$5 + 8 = \boxed{} + 5$	$5 \times 8 = 8 \times \boxed{}$
Associative Property of Addition	**Associative Property of Multiplication**
$6 + (4 + 3) = (\boxed{} + 4) + 3$	$6 \times (4 \times 3) = (6 \times 4) \times \boxed{}$
Identity Property of Addition	**Identity Property of Multiplication**
$9 + 0 = \boxed{}$	$9 \times 1 = \boxed{}$

2. Complete each step to justify how you can determine $3.5 + 1.7 + 1.5$ mentally.

Step	Property
$3.5 + 1.7 + 1.5 = 1.7 + 3.5 + 1.5$	_____
$= 1.7 + (3.5 + 1.5)$	_____
$= 1.7 + \underline{}$	Add mentally.
$= \underline{}$	Add mentally.

Solve each problem. Justify your answer.

3. About 80% of the egg rolls sold in U.S. grocery stores are made in Houston, Texas. A skilled wrapper can make 4,000 egg rolls in an 8-hour day. Bettie said this is about one egg roll a minute. Is her claim reasonable? Explain.

_____

_____

_____

4. Not all products labeled cheese are all cheese! A cheese product is less than half actual cheese. Cheese food is more than half, but less than all cheese. Arturo said a 1 pound block that contained 9 ounces of cheese should be called a cheese food. Is his claim reasonable? Explain.

_____

_____

5. A department store advertised that for every $25 you spend at the store, you get $2 off your total bill. Nathanial's bill came to $154 before the discount. He figured he would get a $12 discount. Is his claim reasonable? Explain.

_____

Find it in Your Book!

MP Justify Arguments

Look at Chapter 1. Write the page number(s) where you find these examples of Mathematical Process G.

_____ Justify Arguments exercises

_____ Evaluate exercises in H.O.T. problems

Use the Mathematical Processes

Solve.

During the summer, you earn money to buy school clothes. The table shows how much money you earn for each job. This summer, you babysat for 32 hours, mowed 10 lawns, and worked at the pool for 20 hours. You spent $256.78 on school clothes.

Job	Money Earned
babysitting	$5.00/hr
lawn mowing	$15.00/lawn
pool	$6.20/hr

a. Do you have any money left? If so, how much? _____

b. You want to buy a tablet that costs $399. Do you have enough money left? If not, how many more hours would you need to babysit

to have enough to buy the tablet? _____

Look Ahead

Determine which mathematical processes you used to determine the solution. Shade the circles that apply.

Which MP **Mathematical Processes** did you use?
Shade the circle(s) that applies.

Ⓐ Apply Math to the Real World.   Ⓔ Organize Ideas.

Ⓑ Use a Problem-Solving Model.   Ⓕ Analyze Relationships.

Ⓒ Select Tools and Techniques.   Ⓖ Justify Arguments.

Ⓓ Use Multiple Representations.

Reflect

 Answering the Essential Question

Use what you learned about the mathematical processes to complete the graphic organizer. Write 3 examples that you could use for each category.

Select Tools and Techniques

1. _____
2. _____
3. _____

Organize Ideas

1. _____
2. _____
3. _____

Essential Question

WHAT processes help me learn and talk about math?

1. _____
2. _____
3. _____

Use Multiple Representations

1. _____
2. _____
3. _____
4. _____

Use a Problem-Solving Model
(List the four steps)

Answer the Essential Question. WHAT processes help me learn and talk about math?

_____

_____

_____

Chapter 1
Rational Numbers and the Coordinate Plane

Texas Essential Knowledge and Skills

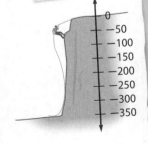

Targeted TEKS
6.2 The student applies mathematical process standards to represent and use rational numbers in a variety of forms.

Mathematical Processes
6.1, 6.1(A), 6.1(B), 6.1(C), 6.1(D), 6.1(E), 6.1(F), 6.1(G)

Essential Question

HOW are rational numbers used in real-world situations?

Math in the Real World

Rock Climbing A rock climber rappels 350 feet down a rock at Enchanted Rock State Natural Area. His starting position is represented by 0 on the number line. His ending position can be represented by −350. Locate −350 on the number line below.

Go Online!
www. connectED.mcgraw-hill.com

Watch   Worksheets   Vocab   Tutor   Tools   Check

What Tools Do You Need?

Vocab

Vocabulary

absolute value
bar notation
integer
negative integer
opposites
positive integer
quadrants
rational number
repeating decimal
terminating decimal

Review Vocabulary

Using a graphic organizer can help you to remember important vocabulary terms. Fill in the graphic organizer below for the word *decimal*. Refer to the glossary if needed.

Decimal

Definition

Math Example

Real-World Example

6.1(A), 6.4(G)

Review 5.2(B), 4.3(D)

Example 1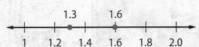

Replace the ◯ with <, >, or = to make a true statement.

1.6 ◯ 1.3

Since 1.6 is to the right of 1.3, 1.6 > 1.3.

Example 2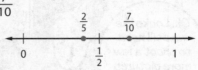

Replace the ◯ with <, >, or = to make a true statement.

$\frac{2}{5}$ ◯ $\frac{7}{10}$

Since $\frac{2}{5}$ is less than $\frac{1}{2}$ and $\frac{7}{10}$ is greater than $\frac{1}{2}$, $\frac{2}{5} < \frac{7}{10}$.

Check

Compare Decimals Replace each ◯ with <, >, or = to make a true statement.

1. 4.8 ◯ 4.80

2. 7.7 ◯ 7.5

3. 1.2 ◯ 2.1

Show your work.

Compare Fractions Replace each ◯ with <, >, or = to make a true statement.

4. $\frac{2}{11}$ ◯ $\frac{9}{10}$

5. $\frac{3}{5}$ ◯ $\frac{1}{4}$

6. $\frac{2}{3}$ ◯ $\frac{4}{6}$

7. Jahan bought $\frac{2}{3}$ pound of peanuts and $\frac{1}{4}$ pound of walnuts. Did Jahan buy more peanuts or more walnuts? _____

Which problems did you answer correctly in the Quick Check?
Shade those exercise numbers below.

(1) (2) (3) (4) (5) (6) (7)

 Use the Foldable throughout this chapter to help you learn about rational numbers.

 cut on all dashed lines ▭ fold on all solid lines tape to page 96

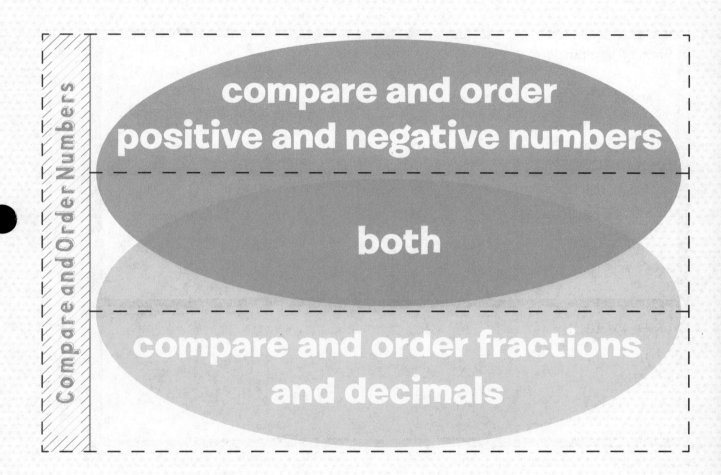

Compare and Order Numbers

compare and order positive and negative numbers

both

compare and order fractions and decimals

FOLDABLES® Use the Foldable throughout this chapter to help you learn about rational numbers.

✂ cut on all dashed lines   📄 fold on all solid lines   tape to page 96

Write About It

Write About It

Write About It

page 96

INQUIRY HOW can I use multiple representations to indicate positive and negative values?

In coastal regions, some animals live above sea level and other animals live in the ocean. A sea star can be found at an ocean depth of two feet. How can you represent an ocean depth of two feet?

What do you know? _____

_____

What do you need to find? _____

_____

Texas Essential Knowledge and Skills

Targeted TEKS
6.2(B) Identify a number, its opposite, and its absolute value.
6.2(C) Locate, compare, and order integers and rational numbers using a number line.

Mathematical Processes
6.1(C), 6.1(D), 6.1(E), 6.1(G)

Hands-On Activity

Sea level can be represented with the number 0.

To represent a location above sea level, use a positive number. A positive number can be written with or without a positive sign, such as 5 or +5.

To represent a location below sea level, use a negative number. A negative number is written with a negative sign, such as −5.

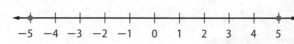

Write a number to represent an ocean depth of two feet.

Step 1 Determine if a positive sign or a negative sign should be used.

Since the location is below, or less than, sea level,

use a _____ sign.

Step 2 Determine which number to use.

Use the number ☐ to represent two feet.

So, the number ☐ represents an ocean depth of two feet.

Investigate

Work with a partner. Write the correct number to represent each location in relationship to sea level. The first one is done for you. Then draw a number line to locate each number.

Show your work.

	Animal	Elevation (ft)	Above or Below Sea Level	Number
	Fiddler Crab	3	above sea level	+3
1.	Eagle's Nest	75	above sea level	
2.	Dolphin	10	below sea level	
3.	Spider Crab	375	below sea level	
4.	Blue Heron	4	above sea level	
5.	Kelp Forest	656	below sea level	
6.	White Egret	50	above sea level	

Analyze and Reflect

7. **MP Analyze Relationships** What negative number is the same distance from 0 as the number +4? Explain. Locate both numbers on the number line below.

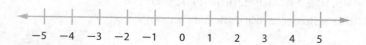

Create

8. **MP Apply Math to the Real World** Write about a real-world situation that can be described using the number −6. Describe what the number 0 would represent. What would the number −6 represent?

9. **INQUIRY** How can I use multiple representations to indicate positive and negative values?

Integers and Graphing

  Launch the Lesson: Real World ▶ Watch

The bar graph shows the amount of money remaining in the clothing budgets of four students at the end of one month. A value of —$2 means that someone overspent the budget and owes his or her parents 2 dollars. Who has the most money left? Who owes the most?

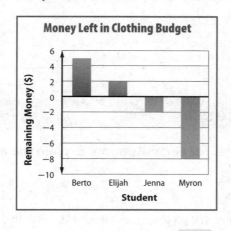

Money Left in Clothing Budget

Remaining Money ($)

Student: Berto, Elijah, Jenna, Myron

1. What number represents owing 2 dollars? ☐

2. What number represents having 2 dollars left? ☐

3. Who has the most money left? Who owes the most? Explain. What numbers represent these situations?

_____

_____

_____

 TEKS

Texas Essential Knowledge and Skills

Targeted TEKS
6.2(B) Identify a number, its opposite, and its absolute value.
6.2(C) Locate, compare, and order integers and rational numbers using a number line.

Mathematical Processes
6.1(A), 6.1(B), 6.1(C), 6.1(D), 6.1(F), 6.1(G)

Vocabulary Vocab
integer
negative integer
positive integer

Essential Question
HOW are rational numbers used in real-world situations?

 $15.00

Which Ⓜ Mathematical Processes did you use?
Shade the circle(s) that applies.

Ⓐ Apply Math to the Real World.   Ⓔ Organize Ideas.

Ⓑ Use a Problem-Solving Model.   Ⓕ Analyze Relationships.

Ⓒ Select Tools and Techniques.   Ⓖ Justify Arguments.

Ⓓ Use Multiple Representations.

Use Integers to Represent Data

Positive whole numbers, their opposites, and zero are called **integers**. To represent data that are less than 0, you can use **negative integers**. A negative integer is written with a — sign. Data that are greater than zero are represented by **positive integers**.

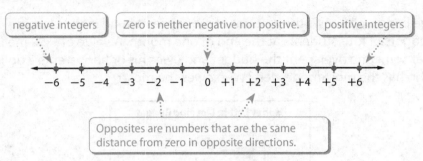

| negative integers | Zero is neither negative nor positive. | positive integers |

−6 −5 −4 −3 −2 −1   0 +1 +2 +3 +4 +5 +6

Opposites are numbers that are the same distance from zero in opposite directions.

Examples

Tutor

Generate an integer for each situation. Explain the meaning of zero in each situation.

1. a 10-yard loss

Because it represents a loss, the integer is −10. In football, the integer 0 represents no yards lost or no yards gained.

2. 4 inches of rain above normal

Because it represents above, the integer is 4. In this situation, the integer 0 represents the normal amount of rain.

3. a $48 deposit into a savings account

Because it represents an increase, the integer is _____.

In this situation, the integer 0 represents _____

_____.

> **Got It?** Do these problems to find out.

Generate an integer for each situation. Explain the meaning of zero in each situation.

a. a gain of $2 a share

b. 10 degrees below zero

Zero

The number zero can have different meanings based on real-world context. Sometimes zero represents an amount that does not change. Zero can also be used to represent real-world ideas, such as sea level.

Show your work.

a. _____

b. _____

Locate Integers on a Number Line

Integers and sets of integers can be located on a horizontal or vertical number line. To locate a point on the number line, draw a point on the number line at its location. A set of integers is written using braces, such as {2, −9, 0}.

Tutor

Examples

4. **Locate −7 on a number line.**

Draw a number line. Then draw a dot at the location that represents −7.

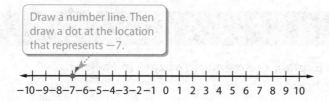

5. **Locate the set of integers {−4, 2, −1} on a number line.**

Draw a number line. Then draw a dot at the location of each integer.

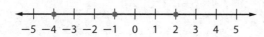

6. **Locate the set of integers {0, 2, −3} on a number line.**

Draw a number line. Then draw a dot at the location of each integer.

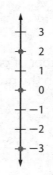

Show your work.

Got It? Do these problems to find out.

Locate each set of integers on a number line.

c. {−3, 0, −2, 4}

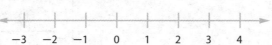

d. {8, −6, −9, 5}

d. _____

Example

7. Alaina and her dad played golf on four different days. The data set {−1, +1, −3, +2} shows Alaina's scores in relation to par. Locate the scores on the number line. Explain the meaning of zero in this situation.

Draw a number line. Then draw a dot at the location of each golf score.

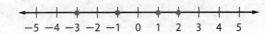

The integer 0 represents par.

Guided Practice

Generate an integer for each situation. Explain the meaning of zero in each situation. (Examples 1–3)

1. 15-yard gain _____

2. loss of 2 hours _____

Locate each integer or set of integers on a number line. (Examples 4–6)

3. −2

4. {−1, 1, 0}

5. The data set {+5, 0, −15, +20} shows the number of points Delaney scored on each hand of a card game. Locate the scores on the number line. Explain the meaning of zero in this situation. (Example 7)

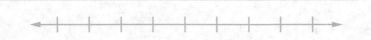

6. ❓ **Building on the Essential Question** How can you use integers to represent data?

_____

_____

_____

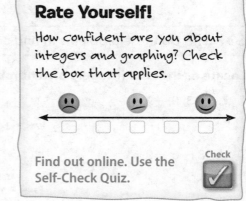

Rate Yourself!

How confident are you about integers and graphing? Check the box that applies.

Find out online. Use the Self-Check Quiz.

Check ✓

Independent Practice

6.2(B), 6.2(C), 6.1(C)

Generate an integer for each situation. Explain the meaning of zero in each situation. (Examples 1–3)

1. 3 miles below sea level _____

2. earning $45 _____

3. moving back 5 spaces on a game board _____

_____

Locate each integer or set of integers on a number line. (Examples 4–6)

4. −5

5. {2, −3, 0, 1}

6. The data set {+4, −1, −2, 0} shows a change in number of state representatives for four states after the last census. Locate the change in number of representatives on the number line. Explain the meaning of zero in this situation. (Example 7)

_____

7. **MP** **Select Tools and Techniques** The table shows the record low temperatures for several states. Locate the temperatures on a number line.

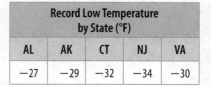

Record Low Temperature by State (°F)				
AL	AK	CT	NJ	VA
−27	−29	−32	−34	−30

8. **MP** **Select Tools and Techniques** The table shows the number of points earned for each action in a video game. While playing the video game, Kevin fell in water, jumped over a rock, touched a cactus and climbed a mountain. Locate the number of points he earned for each action on the number line.

Action	Points
fall in water	−10
walk over a bridge	+5
climb mountain	+10
jump over rock	+5
walk through quicksand	−15
touch cactus	−15

9. **MP Select Tools and Techniques** Produce a graphic organizer by writing words or symbols used to represent positive and negative integers.

Positive Integer	Negative Integer
•	•
•	•
•	•
•	•

H.O.T. Problems Higher-Order Thinking

10. **Analyze** Which number is its own opposite? _____

11. **Analyze** What is the greatest negative integer? _____

12. **Analyze** What is the least positive integer? _____

13. **Evaluate** The temperature outside is 15°F. If the temperature drops 20°, will the outside temperature be represented by a positive or negative integer? Explain your reasoning.

_____

_____

_____

14. **Analyze** Describe the characteristics of each set of numbers that make up the set of integers.

_____

_____

_____

15. **Create** Write a real-world problem in which you would need to find the number of units between −6 and 0 on a number line.

_____

_____

_____

_____

16. **Analyze** Explain how to find the number of units apart −2 and 3 are on a number line.

_____

_____

_____

_____

Multi-Step Problem Solving

17. Golf scores are measured by the number of strokes over or under par. Scores over par can be represented by a positive integer. Scores under par can be represented by a negative integer. The table shows the golf scores of four players in a golf tournament. Which golfer's score is represented by point *B* on the number line below?

Ⓐ Chase

Ⓑ Augustus

Ⓒ Etu

Ⓓ Miles

Golfer	Score
Chase	2 under par
Augustus	3 over par
Etu	1 under par
Miles	1 over par

```
              A  B     C     D
 ┼──┼──┼──┼──●──●──┼──●──┼──●──┼──┼
−5 −4 −3 −2 −1  0  1  2  3  4  5
```

Use a problem-solving model to solve this problem.

1 Analyze

Read the problem. Circle the information you know.
Underline what the problem is asking you to find.

2 Plan

What will you need to do to solve the problem? Write your plan in steps.

Step 1   Determine the number located at point _____.

Step 2   Determine the corresponding value in the table.

3 Solve

Use your plan to solve the problem. Show your steps.

Point B is located at _____. −1 is 1 _____ par. The golfer that

scored −1 is _____.

So, the correct answer is _____. Fill in that answer choice.

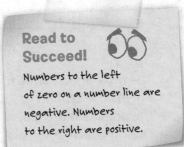

Read to Succeed!

Numbers to the left of zero on a number line are negative. Numbers to the right are positive.

4 Justify and Evaluate

How do you know your solution is accurate?

_____

_____

Use a problem-solving model to solve each problem.

18. The table shows the changes in the value of four stocks over one day. Which point on the number line represents the change in value of Stock R?

Stock	Change in Value
Stock Q	Up $2
Stock R	Down $3
Stock S	Down $1
Stock T	Up $3

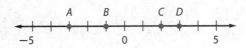

Ⓐ point A

Ⓑ point B

Ⓒ point C

Ⓓ point D

19. Monique is playing a board game where players move about the board using numbered cards. If the card is green, you move forward the number of spaces indicated on the card. If the card is red, you move backward the number of spaces indicated on the card. The number line shows the number of spaces Monique moved in her first five turns. How many red cards did Monique get in her first five turns?

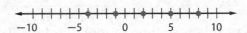

_____

20. A football team has four chances, called downs, to gain at least 10 yards. The number line shows the number of yards gained and lost in four downs of a football game.

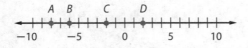

The table shows which downs correspond to the points on the graph. During which down did the team gain 2 yards?

Down	Point
1	B
2	C
3	A
4	D

_____

21. The temperature outside is 4°F. The temperature drops 6°F. Between which two points is the location of the temperature after the change?

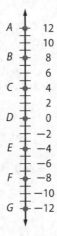

_____

Model Absolute Value

INQUIRY HOW can I use multiple representations to find two integers that are the same distance from zero?

Several hot air balloons were flying at the same height. The dashed line below represents their starting point. Which two balloons moved the same distance but in opposite directions?

Texas Essential Knowledge and Skills
Targeted TEKS
6.2(B) Identify a number, its opposite, and its absolute value.
Mathematical Processes
6.1(C), 6.1(D), 6.1(E), 6.1(F)

Hands-On Activity

In the diagram below, +8 means Balloon A climbed 8 feet and −10 means Balloon B moved down 10 feet.

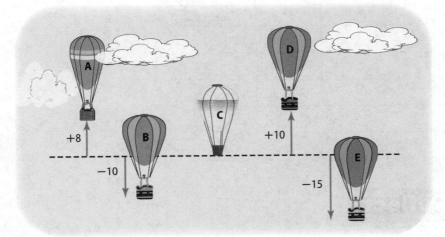

Use the diagram to compare the distance each balloon moved.

Step 1 Complete the chart to compare the distance each balloon moved from the dashed line.

Balloon	Integer	Direction	Distance Moved (ft)
C	0	none	0
D	+10		
E	−15		

Step 2 Determine which two balloons, of the five shown above, moved the same distance away from the dashed line.

So, Balloon ⬚ and Balloon ⬚ moved ⬚ feet from the dashed line.

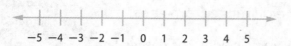

Investigate

MP Organize Ideas Use the number line to determine the distance between each integer and zero.

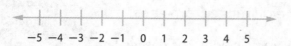

−5 −4 −3 −2 −1 0 1 2 3 4 5

1. −2 _____

2. +3 _____

Work with a partner to complete the table. The first one is done for you.

	Integer	Distance Between Integer and Zero	Opposite Integer	Distance Between Opposite Integer and Zero
	3	3	−3	3
3.	4			
4.	7			
5.	−11			
6.	−13			
7.	19			
8.	−21			

Analyze and Reflect

9. **MP Analyze Relationships** What can you conclude about the distance from zero for both an integer and its opposite? _____

_____

Create

10. **MP Use Multiple Representations** The movement of Balloon B in the activity was represented by the number −10. Express a number to represent the starting point of the balloons. How is this number shown on the diagram?

_____

11. **INQUIRY** How can I use multiple representations to find two integers that are the same distance from zero?

_____

_____

Absolute Value

Texas Essential Knowledge and Skills

Targeted TEKS
6.2(B) Identify a number, its opposite, and its absolute value.

Mathematical Processes
6.1(A), 6.1(B), 6.1(D), 6.1(F), 6.1(G)

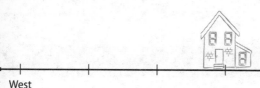 **Launch the Lesson: Vocabulary**

The distance between a number and 0 on the number line is called its **absolute value**. Each mark on the number line indicates one yard. Draw a tree three yards west of the house. Draw a mailbox three yards east of the house.

Vocabulary Vocab
absolute value
opposites

Essential Question
HOW are rational numbers used in real-world situations?

West   East

1. Compare the distance between the house and the tree to the distance between the house and the mailbox. Compare the positions of the tree and the mailbox in relation to the house.

_____

_____

_____

Real-World Link

2. Jesse leaves home and walks 4 blocks west to the grocery store to buy milk then returns home. He then walks 4 blocks east to the Post Office. Compare the distance and the direction of the grocery store and Post Office from Jesse's house.

_____

_____

 whew...

Which MP Mathematical Processes did you use?
Shade the circle(s) that applies.

Ⓐ Apply Math to the Real World.   Ⓔ Organize Ideas.

Ⓑ Use a Problem-Solving Model.   Ⓕ Analyze Relationships.

Ⓒ Select Tools and Techniques.   Ⓖ Justify Arguments.

Ⓓ Use Multiple Representations.

Identify Opposites

Positive numbers, such as 2, are graphed to the right (or above) zero on a number line. Negative numbers, such as −2, are located to the left (or below) zero on a number line.

Opposites are numbers that are the same distance from zero in opposite directions. Since 0 is not negative nor positive, 0 is its own opposite. The opposite of the opposite of a number is the number itself. For example, the opposite of the opposite of 3, −(−3), is 3.

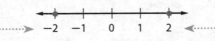

| −2 is 2 units to the left of zero. | 2 is 2 units to the right of zero. |

Tutor

Examples

1. **Identify the opposite of −5.**

Method 1 **Use a number line.**

Draw a number line and locate −5.

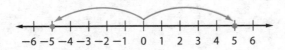

−5 is 5 units to the left of 0. The integer 5 is 5 units to the right of 0.

So, 5 is the opposite of −5.

Method 2 **Use symbols.**

The integer −5 uses the negative symbol.

The opposite of a negative symbol is a positive symbol.

So, the opposite of −5 is +5, or 5.

. . . .

2. **Identify the opposite of the opposite of 4.**

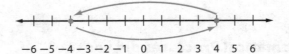

The opposite of 4 is −4. The opposite of −4 is 4.

So, 4 is the opposite of the opposite of 4.

Show your work.

Got It? Do these problems to find out.

a. Identify the opposite of 3.

b. Identify the opposite of the opposite of −2.

a. _____

b. _____

Absolute Value

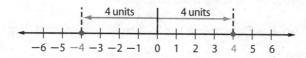

Words The absolute value of a number is the distance between the number and zero on a number line.

Model

4 units   4 units

−6 −5 −4 −3 −2 −1 0 1 2 3 4 5 6

Symbols $|4| = 4$ The absolute value of 4 is 4.

$|-4| = 4$ The absolute value of −4 is 4.

The integers −4 and 4 are each 4 units from 0, even though they are on opposite sides of 0. $|-4|$ is read *absolute value of negative four*.

Tutor

Examples

Absolute Value
Since distance cannot be negative, the absolute value of a number is always positive or zero.

3. Evaluate $|-7|$.

7 units

−8 −7 −6 −5 −4 −3 −2 −1 0 1 2 3

The graph of −7 is 7 units from 0 on the number line.

So, $|-7| = 7$.

4. Evaluate $|5| + |-6|$.

$|5| + |-6| = 5 + |-6|$ The absolute value of 5 is 5.

$= 5 + 6$ The absolute value of −6 is 6.

$= 11$ Simplify.

5. Evaluate $|-7| - |3|$.

$|-7| - |3| = \boxed{} - \boxed{}$ Identify the absolute value of −7 and 3.

$= \boxed{}$ Simplify.

Show your work.

Got It? Do these problems to find out.

c. $|14|$ **d.** $|-9| + |3|$ **e.** $|-8| - |-2|$

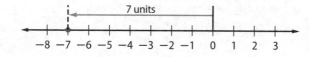

c. _____

d. _____

e. _____

Multi-Step Example

6. A seagull is flying 25 feet above sea level. Neveah is diving 15 feet below sea level. A fish is swimming 50 feet below sea level. Which is greater, the distance between Neveah and the seagull or Neveah and the fish?

> **Step 1** Determine the distance between Neveah and the seagull.
>
> $|25| + |-15|$ Neveah is below sea level. Seagull is above sea level.
>
> $= 25 + 15$ $|25| = 25$ and $|-15| = 15$
>
> $= 40$ Add.

> **Step 2** Determine the distance between Neveah and the fish.
>
> $|-50| - |-15|$ Neveah and the fish are both below sea level.
>
> $= 50 - 15$ $|-50| = 50$ and $|-15| = 15$
>
> $= 35$ Subtract.

Since $40 > 35$, the distance between Neveah and the seagull is greater.

Guided Practice

1. Identify the opposite of 0. (Example 1)

_____

 Show your work.

2. Identify the opposite of the opposite of 6. (Example 2)

_____

Evaluate each expression. (Examples 3–5)

3. $|-5| =$ _____

4. $|20| - |-3| =$ _____

5. $|-16| + |-12| =$ _____

6. A game show contestant lost 15 points. He answered another question incorrectly and lost another 15 points. How many total points has he lost? (Example 6)

_____

7. ❓ **Building on the Essential Question** How can absolute value help you to understand the size of a quantity? Give an example. _____

_____

_____

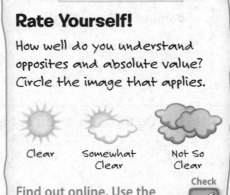

Rate Yourself!

How well do you understand opposites and absolute value? Circle the image that applies.

Clear   Somewhat Clear   Not So Clear

Find out online. Use the Self-Check Quiz.

Check

Ingram Publishing/SuperStock   Copyright © McGraw-Hill Education

40 **Chapter 1** Rational Numbers and the Coordinate Plane

Independent Practice

Identify the opposite of each integer. (Example 1)

1. 6 _____

2. −3 _____

3. 0 _____

Show your work.

Identify the opposite of the opposite of each integer. (Example 2)

4. 12 _____

5. −9 _____

6. −17 _____

Evaluate each expression. (Examples 3–5)

7. $|-14| =$ _____

8. $|31| - |-1| =$ _____

9. $|-15| + |-6| =$ _____

10. Financial Literacy Jayson spent $18 on a shirt. Then he spent $24 on a pair of pants. What is the total amount he spent? (Example 6) _____

11. Lilly saw a jelly fish at 6 feet below sea level. She saw a bright blue fish at 10 feet below sea level. What is the distance between the blue fish and the jelly fish? (Example 6) _____

12. **STEM** The table shows the melting points of various elements. Is the absolute value of the melting point of neon greater than or less than the absolute value of the melting point of hydrogen? _____

13. **STEM** The surface of Jupiter is made of colorful clouds created by various chemicals in the atmosphere. The temperature at the top of the clouds is −230°F. The temperature below the clouds is 70°F. Which temperature has the lower absolute value? _____

Element	Melting Point (°C)
Hydrogen	−259
Neon	−248
Oxygen	−218

MP Analyze Relationships **Evaluate each expression.**

14. $-|3| =$ _____

15. $|5 + 9| =$ _____

16. $|17 - 8| =$ _____

17. Find the Error Mei is evaluating an expression using absolute value. Determine her mistake and correct it.

$|-14| = -14$

 H.O.T. Problems Higher-Order Thinking

18. Evaluate Identify the phrase that *cannot* be described by the same absolute value as the other three. Explain your reasoning.

| a loss of 8 pounds | 8 miles above sea level | giving away $8 | 18° below normal |

Evaluate Determine whether each statement is *always, sometimes,* or *never* true. Explain.

19. The absolute value of a positive integer is a negative integer.

20. If *a* and *b* are integers and $a > b$, then $|a| > |b|$.

21. Analyze Explain why the absolute value of a number is never negative.

22. Analyze Explain why an account balance less than −40 dollars represents a debt greater than 40 dollars.

23. Evaluate Is −*n* always, sometimes, or *never* a positive number? Explain.

Name _____

Multi-Step Problem Solving

24. The graph shows the freezing and boiling points of water in degrees Fahrenheit. How much greater is the absolute value of the boiling point of water than the absolute value of the freezing point of water?

Ⓐ −32

Ⓑ 0

Ⓒ 180

Ⓓ 244

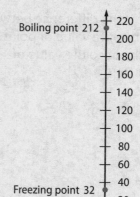

Boiling point 212 — 220
— 200
— 180
— 160
— 140
— 120
— 100
— 80
— 60
— 40
Freezing point 32 — 20
0 — 0

Use a problem-solving model to solve this problem.

1 Analyze

Read the problem. Circle the information you know. Underline what the problem is asking you to find.

2 Plan

What will you need to do to solve the problem? Write your plan in steps.

Step 1 Determine the absolute value of the boiling point of water and the absolute value of the freezing point of water.

Step 2 Subtract to find how much greater.

3 Solve

Use your plan to solve the problem. Show your steps.

Boiling point of water $|212| =$ _____

Freezing point of water $|32| =$ _____

So, the absolute value of the boiling point of water is _____ − _____

or _____ degrees greater than the absolute value of the freezing point of water. Choice C is correct. Fill in that answer choice.

> **Read to Succeed!**
> Absolute value is the distance a number is from zero and is always positive.

4 Justify and Evaluate

How do you know your solution is accurate?

_____

_____

_____

N = Number and Operations   MP = Mathematical Processes

Use a problem-solving model to solve each problem.

25. What is the difference between the absolute value of point *B* and the absolute value of point *D*?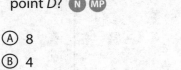

Ⓐ 8

Ⓑ 4

Ⓒ 0

Ⓓ −4

26. The table shows the account balances of five students.

Student	Balance ($)
Yen	−9
Mark	11
Aisha	−3
Wendy	10
Ross	6

What is the difference between the absolute value of Wendy's balance and the absolute value of Yen's balance, in dollars? Ⓝ ⓂⓅ

27. The graph shows the path Chante walked, beginning at point *A*. The distance between two tick marks represents 1 meter. Chante walked 3 meters east to point *B* and then 5 meters east to point *C*. How many meters west must Chante walk from point *C* to be at the point represented by the opposite of *C*? Ⓝ ⓂⓅ

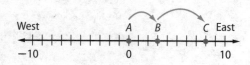

28. Is the opposite of the absolute value of a number *always*, *sometimes*, or *never* equal to the absolute value of the opposite of a number? Explain your response and give examples. Ⓝ ⓂⓅ

Ⓝ = Number and Operations   ⓂⓅ = Mathematical Processes

Compare and Order Integers

Launch the Lesson: Real World ▶ Watch

Texas Essential Knowledge and Skills

Targeted TEKS
6.2(C) Locate, compare, and order integers and rational numbers using a number line.

Mathematical Processes
6.1(A), 6.1(B), 6.1(C), 6.1(D), 6.1(F), 6.1(G)

Fairbanks is located in interior Alaska. The average temperature for several months is shown. The average temperature for December is −6.5°F and the average temperature for March is 11°F. How can we compare these temperatures?

Essential Question

HOW are rational numbers used in real-world situations?

1. Label December and March on the thermometer.

2. Shade the thermometer to represent February's temperature.

3. Which months have a greater average temperature than February?

_____

4. Which months have a lower average temperature than February?

_____

5. Complete the inequality to compare the temperatures of November and February.

3 > ☐

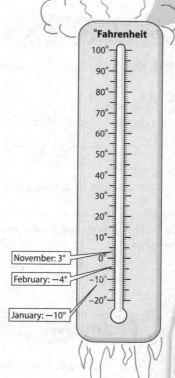

Which MP Mathematical Processes did you use?
Shade the circle(s) that applies.

Ⓐ Apply Math to the Real World. Ⓔ Organize Ideas.

Ⓑ Use a Problem-Solving Model. Ⓕ Analyze Relationships.

Ⓒ Select Tools and Techniques. Ⓖ Justify Arguments.

Ⓓ Use Multiple Representations.

Compare Integers

To compare integers, you can compare the signs as well as the magnitude, or size, of the numbers. Greater numbers are graphed farther to the right.

Compare the signs.

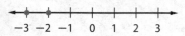

Positive numbers are greater than negative numbers. So, $2 > -3$.

Compare the position on the number line.

Since -2 is farther to the right, $-2 > -3$.

Example

Tutor

Fill in the ◯ with $<$, $>$, or $=$ to make a true sentence.

1. $12 \bigcirc -4$

Locate 12 and -4 on a number line. Then compare.

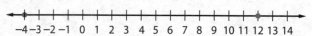

Since 12 is to the right of -4, $12 > -4$.

Got It? Do these problems to find out.

   a. $-3 \bigcirc -5$ **b.** $-5 \bigcirc 0$ **c.** $6 \bigcirc -1$

Example

Tutor

2. Justin has a score of -4 on a trivia game. Desiree's score is -5. Express the comparison of the scores as an inequality. Explain the meaning of the inequality.

   $-4 > -5$ -4 is farther to the right on a number line than -5.

   Since $-4 > -5$, Justin has a higher score than Desiree.

Got It? Do this problem to find out.

   d. The temperature on Tuesday was 2°F. The temperature on Wednesday was -2°F. Express the comparison of the temperatures as an inequality. Explain the meaning of the inequality.

Absolute Value

Although -5 is the least value in Example 2, it represents the greater point deficit.

$|-5| > |-4|$

Show your work.

d. _____

Order Integers

You can use a number line to order a set of integers. Integers can be ordered from least to greatest or from greatest to least.

Example

3. Order the set {−9, 6, −3, 0} from least to greatest.

Method 1 Use a number line.

Locate the numbers on a number line.

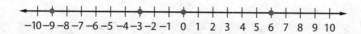

The order from left to right is −9, −3, 0, and 6.

Method 2 Compare signs and values.

Compare negative numbers. Then compare positive numbers.

The negative integers are ⬜ and ⬜.

⬜ < ⬜

The integer ⬜ is neither positive nor negative.
The positive integer is ⬜.

So, the order from least to greatest is ⬜, ⬜, ⬜, and ⬜.

Got It? Do these problems to find out.

e. Order the set {−4, 3, 11, −25} from greatest to least.

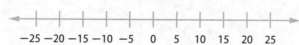

f. Order the set {−18, 30, 12, −6, 3} from least to greatest.

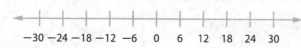

Absolute Value

Since absolute value is always positive, it is not used to compare and order integers.

e. _____

f. _____

Example

4. **STEM** The table shows the lowest elevation for several continents. Order the elevations from least to greatest.

First, locate each integer. Then, write the integers as they appear on the number line from left to right.

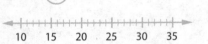

−500 −450 −400 −350 −300 −250 −200 −150 −100 −50   0

Continent	Lowest Elevation (m)
Africa	−156
Asia	−418
Australia	−12
Europe	−28
North America	−86
South America	−105

The elevations from least to greatest are −418, −156, −105, −86, −28, and −12.

Guided Practice

Fill in each ◯ with <, >, or = to make a true statement. Use a number line to compare. (Example 1)

1. 17 ◯ 31

10   15   20   25   30   35

2. −6 ◯ −10

−10 −9   −8   −7   −6   −5

3. −8 ◯ −3

−8   −7   −6   −5   −4   −3

4. Andrew and his father are scuba diving at −38 feet and Tackle Box Canyon has an elevation of −83 feet. Express the comparison of the elevations as an inequality. Explain the meaning of the inequality. (Example 2)

_____

_____

5. **STEM** The daily low temperatures in Kate's hometown last week were 2°C, −9°C, −18°C, −6°C, 3°C, 0°C, and −7°C. Use a number line to order the temperatures from greatest to least. (Examples 3 and 4)

_____

−18 −16 −14 −12 −10 −8 −6 −4 −2   0   2   4

6. ❓ **Building on the Essential Question** How can symbols and absolute value help you to order sets of integers?

_____

_____

_____

Rate Yourself!

How confident are you about comparing and ordering integers? Shade the ring on the target.

I'm on target.

I need help.

Find out online. Use the Self-Check Quiz.

Check

FOLDABLES Time to update your Foldable!

Independent Practice

6.2(C), 6.1(C), 6.1(G)
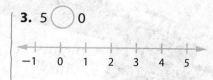

Fill in each ◯ **with <, >, or = to make a true statement. Use a number line to compare.** (Example 1)

1. −2 ◯ −4

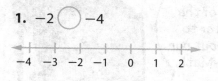

2. 1 ◯ −3

3. 5 ◯ 0

4. Amy is building a house. The basement floor is at −15 feet. The roof of the house is above the ground 25 feet. Express the comparison of heights as an inequality. Explain the meaning of the inequality. (Example 2)

_____

_____

5. The low temperature in Anchorage, Alaska, one day was −9°F. On the same day, the low temperature in Flagstaff, Arizona, was 26°F. Express the comparison of the temperatures as an inequality. Explain the meaning of the inequality. (Example 2)

_____

_____

Use a number line to order each set of integers from least to greatest. (Example 3)

6. {15, −17, 11, 6, −3}

_____

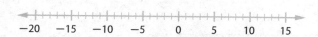

7. {−55, 143, 18, −79, 44, 101}

_____

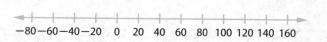

8. The table indicates Xavier's cell phone use over the last four months. Positive values indicate the number of minutes he went over his allotted time, and negative values indicate the number of minutes he was under. Arrange the months from least to most minutes used. (Example 4)

_____

Month	Time (min)
February	−156
March	12
April	0
May	−45

9. (MP) **Select Tools and Techniques** Refer to the table and the following information. The apparent magnitude of an object measures how bright the object appears to the human eye. A negative magnitude identifies a brighter object than a positive magnitude.

a. Which object appears the brightest to the human eye?

_____

b. Order the objects from the brightest to the faintest.

_____

_____

c. Determine the least apparent magnitude of this data set.

_____

Object	Approximate Apparent Magnitude
100-Watt Bulb	−19
Alpha Centauri	4
Andromeda Galaxy	0
Full Moon	−13
Sun	−27
Venus	−5

10. **MP** **Justify Arguments** Refer to the graphic novel frame below for exercises a–c.

a. If about 32,680 kilobytes of memory is still available, how many more pictures can they take? _____

b. Write an inequality to compare the number of pictures taken during school to the number of pictures taken after school. _____

c. Explain the meaning of the inequality. _____

H.O.T. Problems   Higher-Order Thinking

11. **Create** Write a real-world situation to explain the inequality −$15 < $7. _____

_____

12. **Analyze** Explain why −11 is less than −7, but |−11| is greater than |−7|.

_____

_____

13. **Analyze** Order the fractions $-\frac{1}{2}, \frac{5}{2}, -\frac{12}{4}, \frac{1}{6}$, and $\frac{7}{8}$ from least to greatest. _____

14. **Evaluate** Determine all integers that make $|n| < 3$ a true statement. Locate the integers on a number line. _____

Multi-Step Problem Solving

15. The table shows the freezing points in degrees Celsius of four substances. Which substance(s) have greater freezing points than aniline?

Substance	Freezing Point (°C)
Aniline	−6
Acetic acid	17
Acetone	−95
Water	0

Ⓐ water only

Ⓑ acetic acid only

Ⓒ acetic acid, acetone, and water

Ⓓ acetic acid, water

Use a problem-solving model to solve this problem.

1 Analyze

Read the problem. Circle the information you know. Underline what the problem is asking you to find.

2 Plan

What will you need to do to solve the problem? Write your plan in steps.

Step 1   Locate the numbers on a _____.

Step 2   Compare the numbers based on their location on the number line.

3 Solve

Use your plan to solve the problem. Show your steps.

Locate the values on a number line.

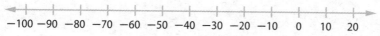

Compare the numbers.

The numbers greater than −6 are 0 and 17, which correspond to water

and acetic acid. Choice _____ is correct. Fill in that answer choice.

Read to Succeed!

Make sure to read the directions carefully.

4 Justify and Evaluate

How do you know your solution is accurate?

_____

_____

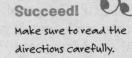 = Number and Operations   = Mathematical Processes

More Multi-Step Problem Solving

Use a problem-solving model to solve each problem.

16. Golf scores are measured as over or under par. The winner has the least score. The table shows the golf scores of five players.

Golfer	Score
Jamal	2 under par
Zaire	1 over par
Dante	even
Alexandra	3 under par
Ajay	4 over par

Which lists the players in order from first place to fifth place? N MP

Ⓐ Dante, Zaire, Jamal, Alexandra, Ajay

Ⓑ Alexandra, Jamal, Dante, Zaire, Ajay

Ⓒ Ajay, Zaire, Dante, Jamal, Alexandra

Ⓓ Dante, Alexandra, Jamal, Zaire, Ajay

17. The table shows the rise and fall in the value of a certain stock over five days. Which day shows the greatest fall in stock value? N MP

Day	Change in Stock Value ($)
1	$-1\frac{1}{8}$
2	$4\frac{3}{8}$
3	$6\frac{1}{2}$
4	$-3\frac{1}{4}$
5	$1\frac{3}{4}$

18. When a football player causes a penalty during a game, the team can lose 5, 10, or 15 yards on the play. The table shows the players, by jersey number, and the number of penalty yards the team was given based on each player's penalties. How many players caused more penalty yards than the player with jersey number 10? N MP

Player (jersey number)	Penalty Yards
12	-15
8	-25
28	-30
17	-10
10	-20
48	-5

19. Order the numbers from greatest to least. Explain how you know which number is the greatest. N MP

$\frac{1}{2}, -|-3|, -0.5, |-2|, -1$

Mathematical Process
6.1(B) Use a problem-solving model that incorporates analyzing given information, formulating a plan or strategy, determining a solution, justifying the solution, and evaluating the problem-solving process and the reasonableness of the solution.

Targeted TEKS 6.3(E)

Cabin Fever

At a summer camp, there are 180 campers with 12 campers in each cabin. Each cabin eats in 15-minute intervals, with a different cabin sitting down to eat every 5 minutes.

If lunch starts at 11:00 A.M., what time does lunch end?

Analyze What are the facts?

- 180 campers with 12 campers in each cabin
- Each cabin eats in 15-minute intervals overlapping every 5 minutes starting at 11:00 A.M.

Plan What is your strategy to solve this problem?

I will _____

_____

Solve How can you apply the strategy?

Use division to find the number of cabins.

180 ÷ 12 = _____   There are _____ cabins.

Draw a number line showing 11:00 A.M. as the beginning of the first lunch. Since cabins overlap every 5 minutes, use 5 minutes as the scale. Each cabin gets 15 minutes for lunch, and a new cabin starts lunch every 5 minutes. Draw line segments to show each cabin.

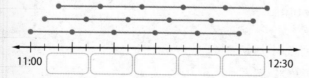

The final cabin finishes lunch at _____ P.M.

Justify and Evaluate How do you know if your solution is accurate?

Make a list of the times each cabin begins lunch, starting at 11:00 and adding 5 minutes each time.

11:05, 11:10, 11:15, … , 12:10. The last cabin starts at 12:10, so lunch ends at 12:25 P.M.

How Many Prizes?

Cathy is waiting backstage to appear on "Guess Your Prize!" The stage is filled with prizes ranging in price from $500 to $1,000. She is allowed to keep each prize with a price tag that has digits with a sum of 10. How many prizes can Cathy keep?

Analyze

Read the problem. Circle the information you know. Underline what the problem is asking you to find.

Plan

What is your strategy to solve this problem?

I will _____

Solve

How can you apply the strategy?

There are _____ prize amounts.

Justify and Evaluate

How do you know your solution is accurate?

_____

_____

Multi-Step Problem Solving

Collaborate

**Work with a small group to solve the following problems.
Show your work on a separate piece of paper.**

1. Walking

Megan uses a pedometer to find how many steps she takes each school day. She took 32,410 steps over the course of 5 days. She took the same number of steps each day and each step is 28 inches.

How many miles did she walk on Monday? Round to the nearest hundredth. (Hint: There are 5,280 feet in one mile.)

2. Savings

James is earning money to buy a $100 bicycle. For each dollar James earns, his mother has agreed to give him $1. So far, he has earned $14 mowing lawns and $7 washing cars.

How much more must James earn in order to buy the bicycle?

3. Money

Mrs. Eddington is buying a new big-screen television. She made an initial payment of $50 and paid a total of $890 over 12 months.

How much did she pay each month?

Use any strategy!

4. Pizza

Joey's Pizza sells large cheese pizzas for $12.59. Each additional topping costs $0.49. The Basketball Boosters bought 12 large pizzas, each with 3 toppings. There are 8 slices per pizza.

How much does it cost per slice? Round to the nearest cent.

Copyright © McGraw-Hill Education   Creative Crop/Getty Images

Focus on Mathematical Processes The Four-Step Plan   **55**

Vocabulary Check

1. Define *negative integer*. Give an example of a negative integer. Then give its opposite. **TEKS** 6.2(B), 6.1(B)

_____

_____

Key Concept Check

2. Complete the graphic organizer by placing the following integers in the appropriate place in the table. **TEKS** 6.2(B), 6.1(E)

$$-3, \quad 0, \quad |-1|, \quad 7, \quad 2, \quad -9, \quad |3|, \quad 8, \quad -|-5|$$

Negative	Neither	Positive
		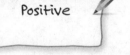

3. Hailey, Priya, and Shetal are auditioning for the same role. Hailey auditions at 10 minutes before 4 P.M., Priya auditions 30 minutes before Hailey, and Shetal auditions at 5 minutes before 4 P.M. Order the three by who will audition first.

TEKS 6.2(C), 6.1(B) _____

Multi-Step Problem Solving

4. The table shows the overnight low temperatures for a four-day period. The low temperature on Wednesday was between the second and third highest temperatures of the ones shown, when placed in order. Which of the following is a possible temperature for Wednesday? **N** **MP**

Temperature (°F)	
Thursday	−8
Friday	7
Saturday	18
Sunday	−8

Ⓐ −10°F   Ⓒ 8°F

Ⓑ 0°F   Ⓓ 20°F

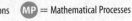
N = Number and Operations   **MP** = Mathematical Processes

Decimals and Fractions

The instruments below show the part of students in the school orchestra that play each type of instrument. How can you write each part as a fraction?

Brass 0.25

1. Express 0.25 in word form: _____

2. Express 0.25 as a fraction: ⬚/⬚

Percussion  0.15

3. Express 0.15 in word form: _____

4. Express 0.15 as a fraction: ⬚/⬚

Strings 0.31

5. Express 0.31 in word form: _____

6. Express 0.31 as a fraction: ⬚/⬚

Woodwind 0.29

7. Express 0.29 in word form: _____

8. Express 0.29 as a fraction: ⬚/⬚

 Texas Essential Knowledge and Skills

Targeted TEKS
6.4(G) Generate equivalent forms of fractions, decimals, and percents using real-world problems, including problems that involve money. *Also addresses 6.2(E).*

Mathematical Processes
6.1(A), 6.1(B), 6.1(C), 6.1(F), 6.1(G)

^{Vocab}
Vocabulary
rational number

Essential Question
HOW are rational numbers used in real-world situations?

Which MP **Mathematical Processes** did you use?
Shade the circle(s) that applies.

Ⓐ Apply Math to the Real World.
Ⓑ Use a Problem-Solving Model.
Ⓒ Select Tools and Techniques.
Ⓓ Use Multiple Representations.
Ⓔ Organize Ideas.
Ⓕ Analyze Relationships.
Ⓖ Justify Arguments.

Express Decimals as Fractions and Mixed Numbers

Decimals like 0.25, 0.15, 0.31, and 0.29 can be expressed as fractions with denominators of 10, 100, 1,000, and so on. Any number that can be expressed as a fraction is a **rational number**.

Decimals like 3.25, 26.82, and 125.54 can be expressed as mixed numbers in simplest form.

Tutor

Examples

Express each decimal as a fraction in simplest form.

1. **0.6**

The place-value chart shows that the place value of the last decimal place is tenths.

$0.6 = \dfrac{6}{10}$ Say *six tenths.*

$= \dfrac{\overset{3}{\cancel{6}}}{\underset{5}{\cancel{10}}}$ Simplify. Divide the numerator and denominator by the GCF, 2.

$= \dfrac{3}{5}$

1,000	100	10	1	0.1	0.01	0.001
thousands	hundreds	tens	ones	tenths	hundredths	thousandths
O	O	O	O	.6	O	O

2. **0.45**

$0.45 = \dfrac{45}{100}$ Say *forty-five hundredths.*

$= \dfrac{\overset{9}{\cancel{45}}}{\underset{20}{\cancel{100}}}$ Simplify.

$= \dfrac{9}{20}$

1,000	100	10	1	0.1	0.01	0.001
thousands	hundreds	tens	ones	tenths	hundredths	thousandths
O	O	O	O	.4	5	O

3. **0.375**

$0.375 = \dfrac{375}{1,000}$ Say *three hundred seventy-five thousandths*

$= \dfrac{\overset{3}{\cancel{375}}}{\underset{8}{\cancel{1,000}}}$ Simplify.

$= \dfrac{3}{8}$

1,000	100	10	1	0.1	0.01	0.001
thousands	hundreds	tens	ones	tenths	hundredths	thousandths
O	O	O	O	.3	7	5

Show your work.

a. _____

b. _____

c. _____

Got It? Do these problems to find out.

a. 0.8   b. 0.28   c. 0.125

Example

Tutor

4. The average length of a conch shell is 9.85 inches. Express 9.85 as a mixed number in simplest form.

$9.85 = 9\frac{85}{100}$ Say *nine and eighty-five hundredths.*

$= 9\frac{\overset{17}{\cancel{85}}}{\underset{20}{\cancel{100}}}$ or $9\frac{17}{20}$ in.   Simplify.

Got It? Do this problem to find out.

d. It takes approximately 4.65 quarts of milk to make a pound of cheese. Express this amount as a mixed number in simplest form.

Show your work.

d. _____

Express Fractions and Mixed Numbers as Decimals

For fractions with denominators that are factors of 10, 100, or 1,000, you can generate equivalent fractions with these denominators.

Example

Tutor

5. Express $\frac{9}{12}$ as a decimal.

Method 1 Generate an equivalent fraction.

$\overset{\div 3}{\frac{9}{12}} = \frac{3}{4} \qquad \overset{\times 25}{\frac{3}{4}} = \frac{75}{100}$
$\underset{\div 3}{} \qquad \underset{\times 25}{}$

Simplify $\frac{9}{12}$. Then multiply the numerator and denominator of $\frac{3}{4}$ by 25.

$= 0.75$ Read 0.75 as *seventy-five hundredths.*

Method 2 Divide the numerator by the denominator.

$$\frac{9}{12} \dashrightarrow \begin{array}{r} 0.75 \\ 12\overline{)9.00} \\ -\,84 \\ \hline 60 \\ -\,60 \\ \hline 0 \end{array}$$

To divide 9 by 12, place a decimal point after 9 and annex as many zeros as necessary to complete the division.

e. _____

f. _____

Got It? Do these problems to find out.

e. $\frac{3}{5}$ **f.** $\frac{14}{25}$ **g.** $\frac{102}{250}$

g. _____

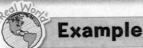

Example

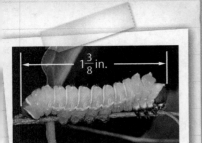
1 3/8 in.

Tutor

6. A caterpillar can have as many as 4,000 muscles, compared to humans, who have about 600. Express the length of the caterpillar as a decimal.

$$1\frac{3}{8} = 1 + \frac{3}{8}$$ Definition of a mixed number

$$= 1 + \frac{375}{1,000}$$ Multiply the numerator and the denominator by 125.

$$= 1 + 0.375 \text{ or } 1.375$$ Read 1.375 as *one and three hundred seventy-five thousandths.*

The length of the caterpillar is 1.375 inches.

Guided Practice

Express each decimal as a fraction or mixed number in simplest form. (Examples 1–4)

1. $0.4 = $ _____

2. $0.64 = $ _____

3. $2.75 = $ _____

Show your work.

Express each fraction or mixed number as a decimal. (Examples 5 and 6)

4. $\frac{27}{75} = $ _____

5. $\frac{7}{2} = $ _____

6. $3\frac{1}{5} = $ _____

7. Mr. Ravenhead's car averages 23.75 miles per gallon of gasoline. Express this amount as a mixed number

in simplest form. (Example 4) _____

_____

8. **STEM** The Siberian tiger can grow up to $10\frac{4}{5}$ feet long.

Express this length as a decimal. (Example 6) _____

_____

9. ❓ **Building on the Essential Question** What is the relationship between fractions and decimals?

_____

_____

_____

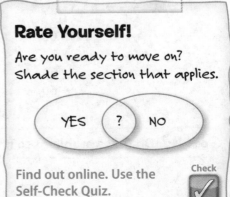

Rate Yourself!

Are you ready to move on?
Shade the section that applies.

YES   ?   NO

Find out online. Use the Self-Check Quiz.

Check ✓

Independent Practice

6.4(G), 6.1(C) TEKS

Express each decimal as a fraction in simplest form. (Examples 1–3)

Show your work.

1. $0.5 =$ _____

2. $0.7 =$ _____

3. $0.33 =$ _____

4. $0.875 =$ _____

Express each fraction or mixed number as a decimal. (Examples 5 and 6)

5. $\frac{77}{200} =$ _____

6. $\frac{1}{20} =$ _____

7. $\frac{12}{75} =$ _____

8. $8\frac{21}{40} =$ _____

9. **STEM** Mercury orbits the Sun in $87\frac{24}{25}$ Earth days. Venus orbits the Sun in $224\frac{7}{10}$ Earth days, and Mars orbits the Sun in $686\frac{49}{50}$ Earth days. Express each mixed number as a decimal. (Example 6)

_____

10. **Financial Literacy** Last week, the cost of a tank of gas increased by $1.64. Express this increase as a mixed number in simplest form. (Example 4)

_____

11. **MP Select Tools and Techniques** The table shows the ingredients in an Italian sandwich.

Ingredient	Amount (lb)
meat	0.35
vegetables	0.15
secret sauce	0.05
bread	0.05

a. What fraction of a pound is each ingredient?

_____

b. How much more meat is in the sandwich than vegetables? Express the amount as a fraction in simplest form.

_____

_____

c. What is the total weight of the Italian sandwich? Express the amount as a fraction in simplest form. _____

_____

12. Paloma can run the 100-meter dash in $16\frac{1}{5}$ seconds. Savannah's best time is 19.8 seconds. How much faster is Paloma than Savannah in the 100-meter dash? _____

13. The average length of a ladybug can range from 0.08 to 0.4 inch. Find two lengths that are within the given span.

Express them as fractions in simplest form. _____

_____

_____

14. Find the Error Mei is writing 4.28 as a mixed number. Determine her mistake and correct it.

_____

_____

_____

_____

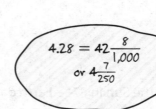

$$4.28 = 42\frac{8}{1,000}$$
$$\text{or } 4\frac{7}{250}$$

 H.O.T. Problems Higher-Order Thinking

15. Evaluate Decide whether the following statement is *always*, *sometimes*, or *never* true. Explain your reasoning.

> *Any decimal that ends with a digit in the thousandths place can be expressed as a fraction with a denominator that is divisible by both 2 and 5.*

_____

_____

_____

16. Create Name a fraction with a decimal value between $\frac{1}{2}$ and $\frac{3}{4}$. Express both the fraction and the equivalent decimal.

_____

_____

17. Analyze Alan bought 20 yards of fencing. He used 5.9 yards to surround one flower garden and 10.3 yards to surround another garden. Express the amount remaining as a fraction in simplest form.

_____

Multi-Step Problem Solving

18. The frequency table shows the favorite lunch of some sixth graders. What decimal represents the part of these students that chose pizza or burgers?

Food	Tally	Frequency
Tacos	IIII	3
Burgers	NN I	6
Chicken	NN	5
Pizza	NN NN I	11

Use a problem-solving model to solve this problem.

1 Analyze

Read the problem. Circle the information you know. Underline what the problem is asking you to find.

Read to Succeed!
Use a pencil to write your answer in the boxes at the top of the grid and to fill in the correct bubble(s) of each digit in your answer below.

2 Plan

What will you need to do to solve the problem? Write your plan in steps.

Step 1 Determine the total number of students surveyed.

Step 2 Determine the number of students that chose _____ or _____.

Step 3 _____ to find the decimal.

3 Solve

Use your plan to solve the problem. Show your steps.

There were 3 + 6 + 5 + 11 or _____ students surveyed.

There were 6 + 11 or _____ students that chose pizza or burgers.

_____ ÷ _____ = _____

So, _____ of the students surveyed chose pizza or burgers. Complete the grid.

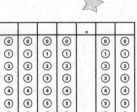

4 Justify and Evaluate

How do you know your solution is accurate?

_____

_____

 **N** = Number and Operations   **MD** = Measurement and Data   **MP** = Mathematical Processes

More Multi-Step Problem Solving

Use a problem-solving model to solve each problem.

19. The graph shows how Bianca spends her weekly allowance. What decimal represents the part of Bianca's allowance that she spends on entertainment and clothes?

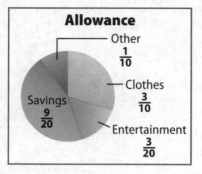

Allowance

Other $\frac{1}{10}$

Clothes $\frac{3}{10}$

Savings $\frac{9}{20}$

Entertainment $\frac{3}{20}$

20. Renee's goal is to run for at least $\frac{1}{4}$ mile more than she ran the previous day. On Day 1, she ran 0.75 mile. The table shows the distances she ran for the next five days. On which of these days did she NOT reach her goal?

Day	Distance (mi)
2	$1\frac{1}{10}$
3	1.35
4	$1\frac{1}{2}$
5	$1\frac{4}{5}$
6	2.05

21. The table shows the number of free throws that Raj successfully made and the number of his attempts over four days.

Day	Shots Made	Attempts
Monday	21	30
Tuesday	18	25
Wednesday	20	32
Thursday	18	24

On which day was the fraction of shots made to attempts the greatest? Express the fraction as a decimal. P N MP

22. Write a fraction that is between 0.1 and $\frac{1}{5}$, has a whole-number numerator, and has a denominator of 100. Then express an equivalent decimal form for this fraction. P N MP

INQUIRY HOW can you use multiple representations to model and compare positive and negative rational numbers?

Marcus and Silvio are at the beach. Marcus builds a sandcastle 0.6 meter high. Silvio digs a hole in the sand 0.8 meter deep.

Texas Essential Knowledge and Skills

Targeted TEKS
6.2(C) Locate, compare, and order integers and rational numbers using a number line.

Mathematical Processes
6.1(C), 6.1(D), 6.1(E), 6.1(F), 6.1(G)

Hands-On Activity 1

Just as you can locate integers on a number line, you can locate positive and negative fractions and decimals. Recall that positive numbers are to the right of, or above, zero on the number line and negative numbers are to the left of, or below, zero.

Step 1 Complete the number line from −1 to 1, with increments of 0.2.

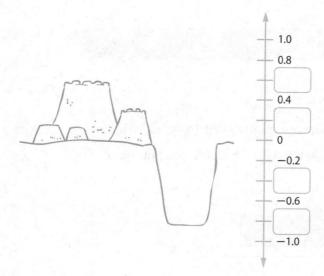

Step 2 The sandcastle is above sea level. Its height is *greater than zero* on the number line, so draw a dot at ☐ to represent the sandcastle.

Step 3 The hole is below sea level. Its depth is *less than zero* on the number line. So draw a dot at ☐ to represent the hole.

Investigate

MP Select Tools and Techniques Work with a partner. Locate each number on a number line.

1. −2.4

Show your work.

2. 0.1

3. −4.5

4. −6.8

Hands-On Activity 2

Tools

Locate $-\dfrac{3}{4}$ on a number line.

Step 1 Model $-\dfrac{3}{4}$ using fraction tiles. Draw a number line from −1 to 0.

Since the denominator of the fraction is ☐, divide your number line into ☐ equal parts.

Step 2 Each mark on the number line represents $\dfrac{\square}{\square}$. Label the number line with $-\dfrac{3}{4}$, $-\dfrac{2}{4}$, and $-\dfrac{1}{4}$.

Step 3 Draw a dot to graph $-\dfrac{3}{4}$ on the number line above.

Investigate

MP **Select Tools and Techniques** Work with a partner. Locate each number on a number line.

5. $-\dfrac{4}{5}$

Show your work.

6. -5.75

7. $\dfrac{7}{10}$

8. $-\dfrac{3}{8}$

9. 8.75

10. $-\dfrac{3}{10}$

11. $-\dfrac{5}{12}$

Analyze and Reflect

Work with a partner to complete the table. The first one is done for you.

	Number	Positive or Negative	Greater Than or Less Than Zero	Left or Right of 0 on the Number Line
	-3.5	negative	$<$	left
12.	$+\frac{4}{5}$			
13.	$-\frac{1}{3}$			
14.	$+0.3$			

15. **MP Analyze Relationships** Which number is greater, 0.3 or -0.7? Explain.

_____

_____

16. **MP Justify Arguments** Jacyln thinks that $-\frac{1}{2}$ is greater than $\frac{1}{4}$ because it is farther from zero on the number line. Is her thinking correct? Explain.

_____

_____

_____

Create

17. **MP Use Multiple Representations** On the number line below, locate whole numbers by placing a dot. Locate integers with an x.

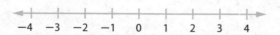

$$\begin{array}{ccccccccc} -4 & -3 & -2 & -1 & 0 & 1 & 2 & 3 & 4 \end{array}$$

a. Which numbers are labeled with only an x? _____

b. Which numbers are labeled with both a dot and an x? _____

c. What do you notice about the numbers labeled with both a dot and an x?

_____

18. **INQUIRY** How can you use multiple representations to model and compare positive and negative rational numbers?

_____

_____

Classify Rational Numbers

 Launch the Lesson: Vocabulary

 Watch

Recall that any number that can be expressed as a fraction is called a rational number. Every rational number can be expressed as either a **terminating decimal** or a **repeating decimal**.

Draw lines from each word to its matching statement.

terminating decimal

repeating decimal

the decimal form of a rational number; 0.33333...

the decimal form of a rational number which has a repeating digit of zero; 0.625

Texas Essential Knowledge and Skills

Targeted TEKS
6.2(A) Classify whole numbers, integers, and rational numbers using a visual representation such as a Venn diagram to describe relationships between sets of numbers. *Also addresses 6.2(E).*

Mathematical Processes
6.1(A), 6.1(B), 6.1(C), 6.1(D), 6.1(F), 6.1(G)

Vocabulary Vocab

terminating decimal
repeating decimal
bar notation

Essential Question

HOW are rational numbers used in real-world situations?

 Real-World Investigation

Jude is buying fruit snacks for party favors. He asks the cashier for a half pound of fruit snacks.

1. Express one half as a fraction.

_____

2. Identify the decimal that represents half a pound.

_____

3. Suppose Jude wanted to buy one third of a pound. What decimal would the scale show?

_____

Which MP **Mathematical Processes** did you use?
Shade the circle(s) that applies.

Ⓐ Apply Math to the Real World.
Ⓑ Use a Problem-Solving Model.
Ⓒ Select Tools and Techniques.
Ⓓ Use Multiple Representations.

Ⓔ Organize Ideas.
Ⓕ Analyze Relationships.
Ⓖ Justify Arguments.

Key Concept ▶ Rational Numbers

Words Rational numbers can be expressed as fractions.

Algebra $\frac{a}{b}$, where a and b are integers and $b \neq 0$.

Model

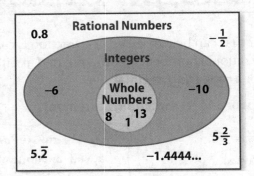

Rational Numbers

0.8 $-\frac{1}{2}$

Integers

-6 Whole Numbers -10

8   13
1

$5\frac{2}{3}$

$5.\overline{2}$ $-1.4444...$

Fractions, terminating and repeating decimals, percents, and integers are all rational numbers. Every rational number can be expressed as a decimal by dividing the numerator by the denominator.

Rational Number	Repeating Decimal	Terminating Decimal
$\frac{3}{10}$	$0.300...$	0.3
$-\frac{4}{5}$	$-0.800...$	-0.8
$\frac{5}{6}$	$0.833...$	does not terminate

To indicate the number pattern that repeats indefinitely, use bar notation. **Bar notation** is a bar placed over the digits that repeat.

$0.545454... = 0.\overline{54}$ $-0.583333... = -0.58\overline{3}$

Tutor

Example

1. **Express $\frac{5}{12}$ as a decimal.**

$$
\begin{array}{r}
0.4166 \\
12\overline{)5.000} \\
-48 \\
\hline
20 \\
-12 \\
\hline
80 \\
-72 \\
\hline
80 \\
-72 \\
\hline
8
\end{array}
$$

Divide 5 by 12.

The remainder will never be zero.

So, $\frac{5}{12} = 0.4166...$ or $0.41\overline{6}$.

Got It? Do this problem to find out.

Express the fraction as a decimal. Use bar notation if necessary.

a. $\frac{1}{6}$

Classify Rational Numbers

You can use a visual representation, such as a Venn diagram, to classify numbers. The Venn diagram on page 70 shows that all whole numbers are integers and rational numbers, and all integers are rational numbers.

Examples

Tutor

For each number, place it in the Venn Diagram and then classify it. Name all sets to which the number belongs.

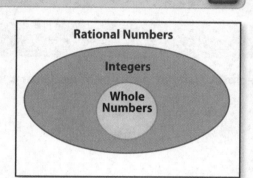

2. −7 The number is an integer and a rational number. So, place −7 inside the *Integers* circle, but not inside the *Whole Numbers* circle.

3. 5 The number 5 is a whole number, a positive integer, and a rational number. So, place 5 inside the *Whole Numbers* circle.

4. $\frac{3}{7}$ Since all fractions are rational numbers, the number is a rational number. So, place $\frac{3}{7}$ inside *Rational Numbers*, but not inside the *Integers* or *Whole Numbers* circles.

5. $-0.\overline{36}$ The decimal repeats. It is a rational number. So, place $-0.\overline{36}$ inside *Rational Numbers*, but not inside the *Integers* or *Whole Numbers* circles.

Got It? Do these problems to find out.

Classify each number. Name all sets to which the number belongs. Place the number in the appropriate section in the Venn Diagram above.

b. −4.8   c. −31   d. $\frac{2}{9}$

Negative Fractions
When expressing negative fractions as decimals, divide as with positive fractions. Write the negative sign in front of the decimal.

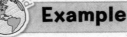

Example

6. Frankie made $\frac{34}{44}$ free throws this season. To the nearest thousandth, what is his free-throw average?

Using a calculator, divide 34 by 44.

34 ÷ 44 [ENTER] 0.77272727

To the nearest thousandth, his free-throw average is 0.773.

Got It? Do this problem to find out.

e. Of the students surveyed, $\frac{4}{9}$ said they prefer exercising in the morning rather than in the evening. Express this fraction as a decimal. Use bar notation if necessary.

Show your work.

e. _____

Guided Practice

Express each fraction as a decimal. Use bar notation if necessary. (Example 1)

1. $\frac{7}{9} =$ _____

2. $-\frac{1}{33} =$ _____

3. $-2\frac{5}{6} =$ _____

Classify each number. Name all sets to which the number belongs. (Examples 2–5)

4. $-8 =$ _____

5. $-\frac{4}{5} =$ _____

6. $6.\overline{3} =$ _____

7. Dana bought $\frac{2}{3}$ yard of fabric to make a new purse. Express the amount of fabric she bought as a decimal. (Example 6)

_____

8. 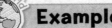 **Building on the Essential Question** How are repeating decimals used in real-world situations?

_____

_____

_____

Rate Yourself!

Are you ready to move on? Shade the section that applies.

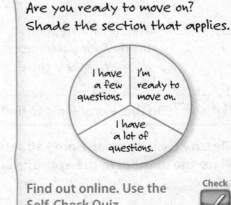

I have a few questions.

I'm ready to move on.

I have a lot of questions.

Find out online. Use the Self-Check Quiz.

Check

Independent Practice

6.2(A), 6.2(E)
6.1(F), 6.1(G)
TEKS

Express each fraction as a decimal. Use bar notation if necessary. (Example 1)

Show your work.

1. $\frac{7}{15} =$ _____

2. $\frac{8}{18} =$ _____

3. $-\frac{8}{12} =$ _____

Classify each number. Name all sets to which the number belongs. Place each number in the Venn diagram. (Examples 2–5)

4. $-\frac{6}{7}$ _____

5. 3 _____

6. −2 _____

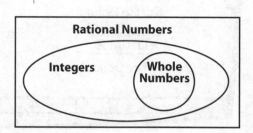

Rational Numbers

Integers   Whole Numbers

7. Sarafina had 34 out of 99 hits when she was at bat during the softball season. What was her batting average? (Example 6)

_____

8. Shiv and his friends ate $3\frac{1}{6}$ pizzas. Express this amount as a decimal. (Example 6)

_____

MP Analyze Relationships Determine whether each statement is *true* or *false*. If false, give a counterexample.

9. All rational numbers are integers. _____

10. All whole numbers are integers. _____

11. No rational number is a whole number. _____

_____

Evaluate each expression.

12. $|-2.3| =$ _____

13. $\left|\frac{4}{13}\right| =$ _____

14. $\left|-8\frac{7}{11}\right| =$ _____

15. **STEM** There are over 2,700 species of snakes in the world. Over 600 species are venomous. Express the fraction of species that are *not* venomous as a decimal. _____

16. **MP Justify Arguments** The ratio of the circumference of a circle to its diameter is represented by the number π. The number π is a decimal that does not repeat. The fraction $\frac{22}{7}$ is sometimes used as an estimate of π. Is $\frac{22}{7}$ a repeating decimal? Explain.

_____

_____

17. **MP Analyze Relationships** Refer to the graphic novel frame below for Exercises a–b.

a. How many total photos were taken? _____

b. What fraction of the photos were taken after school? Express this fraction as a decimal. Round to the nearest thousandth. _____

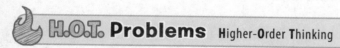 **H.O.T. Problems** Higher-Order Thinking

18. Create Name a number that is a rational number, but not an integer. Justify your response.

_____

_____

19. Evaluate Predict whether or not the decimal equivalent to $\frac{17}{36}$ is terminating. Explain your reasoning. Check your prediction with a calculator. _____

_____

20. Evaluate Which fraction does *not* belong with the other three? Explain.

$\frac{1}{12}$ $\frac{2}{12}$ $\frac{3}{12}$ $\frac{4}{12}$

21. Evaluate Determine the decimal equivalents for $\frac{1}{11}$, $\frac{2}{11}$, and $\frac{3}{11}$. Use the pattern to mentally determine the decimal equivalents for $\frac{7}{11}$ and $\frac{8}{11}$.

_____

_____

Multi-Step Problem Solving

22. There are 84 chairs that need to be set up in the school's auditorium. Students were asked to write an expression to show how to find the number of chairs needed in each of 12 rows. The table shows samples of expressions given by students. Which sample(s) result in the correct solution?

Sample	Expression
A	$12 \div 84$
B	$84 \div 12$
C	$\frac{12}{84}$
D	$\frac{84}{12}$

Ⓐ Sample A

Ⓑ Sample B

Ⓒ Samples A and C

Ⓓ Samples B and D

Use a problem-solving model to solve this problem.

1 Analyze

Read the problem. Circle the information you know. Underline what the problem is asking you to find.

2 Plan

What will you need to do to solve the problem? Write your plan in steps.

Step 1 Determine the number of chairs needed in each row.

Step 2 Determine whether each sample's expression results in the correct solution.

> **Read to Succeed!**
> Make sure to read all choices given when answering multiple choice questions.

3 Solve

Use your plan to solve the problem. Show your steps.

There are $84 \div$ _____, or _____ chairs needed in each row.

Sample A $12 \div 84 \approx$ _____   **Sample C** $\frac{12}{84} \approx$ _____

Sample B $84 \div 12 =$ _____   **Sample D** $\frac{84}{12} =$ _____

Samples _____ and _____ result in the correct solution. So, choice _____ is correct. Fill in that answer choice.

4 Justify and Evaluate

How do you know your solution is accurate?

_____

_____

Ⓝ = Number and Operations   Ⓟ = Proportionality   MP = Mathematical Processes

More Multi-Step Problem Solving

Use a problem-solving model to solve each problem.

23. Selina has 8 cups of sugar to use for baking pies. She would like to bake 12 pies. She knows she can divide to find how much sugar to use for each pie. Which expression is equivalent to 8 ÷ 12? Ⓝ Ⓟ ⓂⓅ

Ⓐ 2×3

Ⓑ 3×2

Ⓒ $\dfrac{2}{3}$

Ⓓ $\dfrac{3}{2}$

24. Alivia needs to classify the numbers in the table using the Venn diagram shown.

Numbers
$|-6|, \dfrac{3}{4}, 1.55, 11 \div 6, -2, 0.\overline{7}, \dfrac{2}{3}, 6 \div 2$

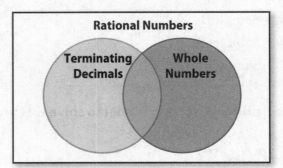

She decides to first color-code the numbers by highlighting the numbers that represent *terminating* decimals in yellow and *repeating* decimals in red. How many numbers should Alivia highlight in red? Ⓝ Ⓟ ⓂⓅ

_____

25. The table shows the perimeters of different equilateral triangles. How many of the triangles have side lengths that are terminating decimals? Ⓝ ⓂⓅ

Perimeter (in.)
11
$15.\overline{6}$
18
21
$21.\overline{33}$
23.3

_____

26. Which number is greater, $-\dfrac{1}{3}$ or -0.3? Use the number line to help explain your answer. Ⓝ Ⓟ ⓂⓅ

_____

_____

_____

_____

Ⓝ = Number and Operations ⠀⠀ Ⓟ = Proportionality ⠀⠀ ⓂⓅ = Mathematical Processes

Compare and Order Rational Numbers

Launch the Lesson: Real World

The lengths of several common types of insects are shown in the table. How can we compare these lengths?

Insect	Length (in.)
Green June beetle	$\frac{3}{4}$
Cricket	$\frac{1}{1}$
Fire ant	$\frac{1}{3}$
Firefly	$\frac{3}{4}$
Housefly	$\frac{1}{4}$
Japanese beetle	$\frac{1}{2}$
Mosquito	$\frac{5}{8}$

1. Which of the insects is the longest?

_____

2. Draw a model to represent the lengths of a fire ant and a housefly. Which is longer, the fire ant or housefly?

_____

3. How many of the insects are longer than 0.5 inch? Explain how you determined this.

_____

_____

_____

4. Order the lengths of a housefly, a Green June beetle, and a fire ant from the shortest to longest.

Texas Essential Knowledge and Skills

Targeted TEKS
6.2(D) Order a set of rational numbers arising from mathematical and real-world contexts. *Also addresses 6.2(C).*

Mathematical Processes
6.1(A), 6.1(B)

Essential Question

HOW are rational numbers used in real-world situations?

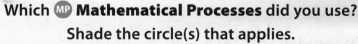

Which MP Mathematical Processes did you use?
Shade the circle(s) that applies.

Ⓐ Apply Math to the Real World.   Ⓔ Organize Ideas.

Ⓑ Use a Problem-Solving Model.   Ⓕ Analyze Relationships.

Ⓒ Select Tools and Techniques.   Ⓖ Justify Arguments.

Ⓓ Use Multiple Representations.

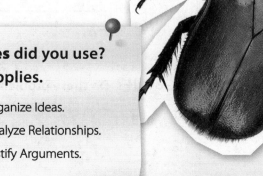

Compare Decimals and Fractions

Positive and negative rational numbers can be represented on a number line. You can use a number line to help you compare and order rational numbers.

Tutor

Examples

Fill in each ⬭ with $<$, $>$, or $=$ to make a true statement.

1. -1.2 ⬭ 0.8

Locate the decimals on a number line.

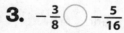

$$-1.4\ -1.2\ -1\ -0.8\ -0.6\ -0.4\ -0.2\ \ 0\ \ 0.2\ \ 0.4\ \ 0.6\ \ 0.8\ \ 1\ \ 1.2\ \ 1.4$$

Since -1.2 is to the left of 0.8, $-1.2 < 0.8$.

2. -1.40 ⬭ -1.25

Locate the decimals on a number line.

Since -1.40 is below -1.25, $-1.40 < -1.25$.

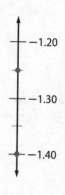

-1.20

-1.30

-1.40

Least Common Multiple (LCM)

Find the LCM of 8 and 16.

8: 8, 16, 24

16: 16, 32, 48

The LCM is 16.

3. $-\dfrac{3}{8}$ ⬭ $-\dfrac{5}{16}$

Rename the fractions using the least common denominator.

$$-\frac{3}{8} = -\frac{3 \times 2}{8 \times 2} = -\frac{6}{16} \qquad\qquad -\frac{5}{16} = -\frac{5 \times 1}{16 \times 1} = -\frac{5}{16}$$

Since $-6 < -5$, $-\dfrac{6}{16} < -\dfrac{5}{16}$ and $-\dfrac{3}{8} < -\dfrac{5}{16}$.

Check

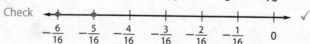

$$-\frac{6}{16}\quad -\frac{5}{16}\quad -\frac{4}{16}\quad -\frac{3}{16}\quad -\frac{2}{16}\quad -\frac{1}{16}\quad 0$$

Got It? Do these problems to find out.

a. 3.1 ⬭ -3.7

b. -4.5 ⬭ -4.49

c. $\dfrac{9}{16}$ ⬭ $\dfrac{12}{16}$

d. $-\dfrac{7}{10}$ ⬭ $-\dfrac{4}{5}$

Compare and Order Rational Numbers

To compare and order rational numbers, first express them in the same form.

Examples

 Tutor

Fill in each ◯ with <, >, or = to make a true statement.

4. -0.51 ◯ $-\dfrac{8}{15}$

Rename $-\dfrac{8}{15}$ as a decimal. Then locate both decimals on a number line.

$-\dfrac{8}{15} = -0.5\overline{3}$

$-0.5\overline{3}$ -0.51

-0.6 -0.55 -0.5 -0.45 -0.4

Since -0.51 is to the right of $-0.5\overline{3}$ on the number line, $-0.51 > -\dfrac{8}{15}$.

STOP and Reflect

How could you represent that -8.3 feet is deeper than -5.7 feet? Explain.

5. Order the set $\left\{-2.46, -2\dfrac{22}{25}, -2\dfrac{1}{10}\right\}$ from least to greatest.

Express $-2\dfrac{22}{25}$ and $-2\dfrac{1}{10}$ as decimals to the hundredths place.

$-2\dfrac{22}{25} =$ ☐ $-2\dfrac{1}{10} =$ ☐

-2.88 -2.46 -2.10

-3.00 -2.75 -2.50 -2.25 -2.00

Locate the decimals on the number line.

From least to greatest, the order is _____, _____, and _____.

Got It? Do these problems to find out.

Fill in each ◯ with <, >, or = to make a true statement.

e. $-3\dfrac{5}{8}$ ◯ -3.625

f. $\dfrac{3}{7}$ ◯ 0.413

g. Order the set $\left\{-7\dfrac{13}{20}, -7.78, -7\dfrac{17}{100}\right\}$ from greatest to least.

 Show your work.

g. _____

Example

Real World   Tutor

6. The table shows the melting points of various elements. As the temperature rises above the melting point, the element changes from a solid to a liquid. Order the melting points from least to greatest.

Element	Melting Point (°C)
Hydrogen	-259.14
Iron	$1{,}535$
Oxygen	$-218\frac{2}{5}$
Phosphorus	$44\frac{1}{10}$

Express each number as a decimal.

Hydrogen: -259.14 Oxygen: $-218\frac{2}{5} = -218.4$

Iron: $1{,}535$ Phosphorus: $44\frac{1}{10} = 44.1$

From least to greatest, the melting points are -259.14, $-218\frac{2}{5}$, $44\frac{1}{10}$, $1{,}535$.

Guided Practice

Fill in each ◯ with $<$, $>$, or $=$ to make a true statement. (Examples 1–4)

Show your work.

1. 9.7 ◯ -10.3

2. $\frac{5}{8}$ ◯ $-\frac{3}{8}$

3. -6.7 ◯ $-6\frac{7}{10}$

4. $-\frac{5}{6}$ ◯ -0.94

Order the following sets of numbers from least to greatest. (Example 5)

5. $\left\{-3\frac{1}{3},\ 3.3,\ -3\frac{3}{4},\ 3.5\right\}$ _____

6. $\left\{2.\overline{1},\ -2.1,\ 2\frac{1}{11},\ -2\right\}$ _____

7. **Financial Literacy** Steve recorded these amounts in his checkbook: $-\$6.50$, $\$7.00$, $-\$6.75$, and $\$7.25$. Order these amounts from least to greatest. (Example 6)

_____

8. **?** **Building on the Essential Question** How can a number line help in ordering rational numbers?

_____

_____

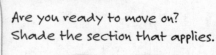

Rate Yourself!

Are you ready to move on?
Shade the section that applies.

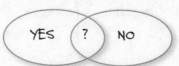

YES   ?   NO

Find out online. Use the Self-Check Quiz.

Check

FOLDABLES Time to update your Foldable!

Name _____ My Homework _____

Independent Practice

  6.2(D), 6.2(C), 6.1(D), 6.1(F) TEKS

Fill in each ⬭ with <, >, or = to make a true statement. (Examples 1–4)

1. $\frac{5}{4}$ ◯ $-\frac{1}{4}$

Show your work.

2. $-6\frac{1}{3}$ ◯ -6.375

3. $-\frac{3}{5}$ ◯ -0.6

4. $-9\frac{2}{7}$ ◯ -9.3

Order each set of numbers from least to greatest. (Example 5)

5. $\left\{2.8, -2\frac{3}{4}, 3\frac{1}{8}, -2.\overline{2}\right\}$ _____

6. $\left\{\frac{2}{3}, -0.6, 0.65, \frac{4}{5}\right\}$ _____

7. Financial Literacy The elevations of four walking paths are $-4\frac{1}{2}$ meters, 5.6 meters, $-2\frac{3}{8}$ meters, and 1.35 meters. Order the elevations from least to greatest. (Example 6)

_____

8. (MP) **Use Multiple Representations** Consider the inequality $-3.5 < -1.5$.

a. Words Write a real-world problem that could be represented by the inequality.

_____

_____

b. Number Line Locate -3.5 and -1.5 on the number line.

c. Symbols Use the symbol > to compare -3.5 and -1.5.

_____

9. The table shows the water levels of a river under a bridge for several months. The lower the number, the lower the water level from under the bridge. Order the water levels from least to greatest.

_____

Month	Water Level Below Bridge (ft)
April	−4.56
May	−3.11
June	−0.23
July	−1.98

10. 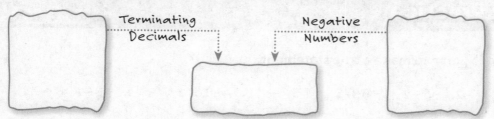 **Analyze Relationships** Fill in the diagram with rational numbers.

Terminating Decimals

Negative Numbers

 H.O.T. Problems Higher-Order Thinking

11. **Evaluate** Determine whether the following statement is *always, sometimes,* or *never* true. Give examples to justify your answer.

   If x and y are both greater than zero and x > y, then −x < −y.

_____

_____

12. **Analyze** Determine whether the fractions $-\frac{4}{5}$, $-\frac{4}{6}$, $-\frac{4}{7}$, and $-\frac{4}{8}$ are arranged in order from least to greatest. Explain.

_____

_____

_____

13. **Evaluate** Explain why −0.33 is greater than −0.$\overline{33}$.

_____

_____

_____

14. **Analyze** Compare the set $\left\{-0.\overline{7}, -0.\overline{6}, -\frac{7}{9}, -\frac{2}{3}\right\}$. Explain your answer.

_____

_____

15. **Create** Write a real-world problem in which you must order a set of four rational numbers.

_____

_____

_____

Multi-Step Problem Solving

16. The table shows the difference between the actual amount of rainfall, in inches, that a city received over four weeks and the average amount that it usually receives during those weeks. Which shows the weeks in order of the differences from least to greatest?

Week	Difference (in.)
1	$\frac{1}{3}$
2	-1.6
3	0.3
4	$-1\frac{1}{2}$

Ⓐ 3, 1, 4, 2

Ⓑ 2, 4, 3, 1

Ⓒ 1, 3, 4, 2

Ⓓ 2, 4, 1, 3

Use a problem-solving model to solve this problem.

1 Analyze

Read the problem. Circle the information you know. Underline what the problem is asking you to find.

2 Plan

What will you need to do to solve the problem? Write your plan in steps.

| **Step 1** | Compare the negative rational numbers. |

| **Step 2** | Compare the positive rational numbers. |

| **Step 3** | Order the rational numbers. |

Read to Succeed!

When ordering from least to greatest, remember negative numbers are less than positive numbers.

3 Solve

Use your plan to solve the problem. Show your steps.

$-1.6 \bigcirc -1\frac{1}{2}$ and $\frac{1}{3} \bigcirc 0.3$

So, the correct order of weeks is 2, 4, 3, 1. Choice _____ is correct. Fill in that answer choice.

4 Justify and Evaluate

How do you know your solution is accurate?

_____

_____

_____

 **N** = Number and Operations   **MP** = Mathematical Processes

More Multi-Step Problem Solving

Use a problem-solving model to solve each problem.

17. In last year's diving competition, Stefani's average score per dive was 9.55 points. The table shows the difference between her average score and her actual scores for her first four dives from this year's competition. Which of the following lists the dives in order of the differences from greatest to least? N P MP

Dive	Difference (points)
1	$\frac{1}{4}$
2	-0.35
3	$-\frac{3}{10}$
4	0.4

- Ⓐ 4, 1, 3, 2
- Ⓑ 1, 3, 2, 4
- Ⓒ 4, 1, 2, 3
- Ⓓ 2, 3, 1, 4

18. The table shows the heights, in feet, of five classmates. How many of these classmates are taller than $5\frac{1}{2}$ feet? N P MP

Student	Height (ft)
Mario	5.6
Phong	$5\frac{1}{3}$
Travis	$5\frac{5}{6}$
Zack	5.45
Tavon	$5\frac{3}{5}$

19. The table shows the dimensions, in centimeters, of four rectangles. How many centimeters wider is the rectangle with the greatest perimeter than the rectangle with the least perimeter? N MP

Rectangle	Width (cm)	Length (cm)
A	6.25	8.9
B	6.3	8.73
C	6.5	8.7
D	6.6	8.5

20. Jaquan has lengths of colored string as shown in the table. He finds a piece of yellow string that is 0.2 yard shorter than the blue string. He lays all four pieces of string end to end from left to right in order of length, beginning with the shortest piece. Between which two colors is the yellow string? N P MP

Color	Length (yd)
Red	$3\frac{2}{5}$
Blue	$3\frac{5}{8}$
Green	3.5

N = Number and Operations   P = Proportionality   MP = Mathematical Processes

The Coordinate Plane

 Launch the Lesson: Real World ▶ Watch

Texas Essential Knowledge and Skills

Targeted TEKS
6.11 Graph points in all four quadrants using ordered pairs of rational numbers.

Mathematical Processes
6.1(A), 6.1(B)

The map shows the layout of a small town. The locations of buildings are described in respect to the town hall. Each unit on the grid represents one block. How can we use numbers and directions to describe these locations?

1. Describe the location of the barber shop in relation to the town hall.

_____

_____

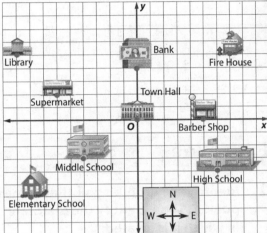

Vocab

Vocabulary
quadrants

Essential Question
HOW are rational numbers used in real-world situations?

2. What building is located 7 blocks east and 5 blocks north of the town hall?

_____

3. Violeta is at the library. Describe how many blocks and in what direction she should travel

to get to the supermarket. _____

4. How can we use numbers and directions to describe locations on

a map? _____

_____

5. **Create** Determine a question using the map. _____

_____

Which MP **Mathematical Processes did you use?**
Shade the circle(s) that applies.

Ⓐ Apply Math to the Real World.
Ⓑ Use a Problem-Solving Model.
Ⓒ Select Tools and Techniques.
Ⓓ Use Multiple Representations.
Ⓔ Organize Ideas.
Ⓕ Analyze Relationships.
Ⓖ Justify Arguments.

Identify Points and Ordered Pairs

A coordinate plane is formed when the *x*-axis and *y*-axis intersect at their zero points. The axes separate the coordinate plane into four regions called **quadrants**.

You can use the location on the plane or use the *x*-coordinates and *y*-coordinates to identify the quadrant in which a point is located.

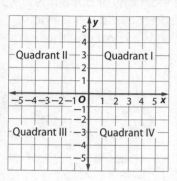

Quadrant	*x*-coordinate	*y*-coordinate	Example
I	positive	positive	(2, 5)
II	negative	positive	(−2, 5)
III	negative	negative	(−2, −5)
IV	positive	negative	(2, −5)

Examples

Tutor

1. **Identify the ordered pair that names point *C*. Then identify the quadrant in which it is located.**

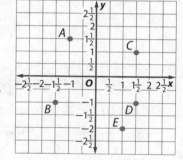

> **Step 1** Start at the origin. Move right on the *x*-axis. The *x*-coordinate of point *C* is $1\frac{1}{2}$.

> **Step 2** Move up the *y*-axis. The *y*-coordinate is 1.

Point *C* is located at $\left(1\frac{1}{2}, 1\right)$. Both coordinates are positive.

So, point *C* is in Quadrant I.

- -

2. **Identify the point located at $\left(-1\frac{1}{2}, -1\right)$. Then identify the quadrant in which it is located.**

> **Step 1** Start at the origin. Move left on the *x*-axis. The *x*-coordinate is $-1\frac{1}{2}$.

> **Step 2** Move down the *y*-axis. The *y*-coordinate is −1. Point *B* is located at $\left(-1\frac{1}{2}, -1\right)$. Both coordinates are negative. So, point *B* is in Quadrant III.

Ordered Pairs

A point located on the *x*-axis will have a *y*-coordinate of 0. A point located on the *y*-axis will have an *x*-coordinate of 0. Points located on an axis are not in any quadrant.

Got It? Do these problems to find out.

Show your work.

a. Identify the ordered pair that names point *A*. Then identify the quadrant in which it is located.

a. _____

b. Identify the point located at (1, −2). Then identify the quadrant in which it is located.

b. _____

Graph Ordered Pairs

To graph an ordered pair, draw a dot at the point that corresponds to the coordinates.

Examples

Tutor

3. Graph point *M* at (−3, 5).

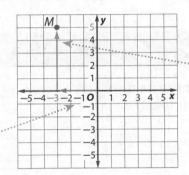

Next, since the y-coordinate is 5, move 5 units up. Draw a dot.

Start at the origin. The x-coordinate is −3. So, move 3 units to the left.

4. Graph point *N* at $\left(-2\frac{1}{2}, -3\frac{1}{2}\right)$.

The x-coordinate $-2\frac{1}{2}$ is between −2 and −3.

Start at the origin and move $2\frac{1}{2}$ units left.

The y-coordinate $-3\frac{1}{2}$ is between −3 and −4.

Next, move $3\frac{1}{2}$ units down. Draw a dot.

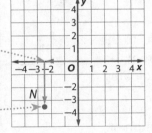

Got It? Do these problems to find out.

Graph and label each point on the coordinate plane.

  c. *P*(−2, 4)   **d.** *Q*(0, −4)   **e.** $R\left(-\frac{1}{2}, -2\frac{1}{2}\right)$

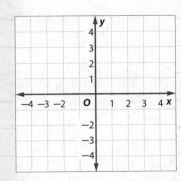

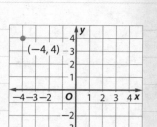

(−4, 4)

Example

5. Kendall is building a square fence. She places a fence post at the location indicated on the grid. Each post is an equal distance to an axis. What are the locations of the three other fence posts?

The point (−4, 4) is 4 units away from the *x*-axis and 4 units away from the *y*-axis. In the first quadrant, the point (4, 4) is 4 units away from each axis. In the third quadrant, (−4, −4) is 4 units away from each axis and in the fourth quadrant, (4, −4) is 4 units away from each axis.

The three other locations are (4, 4), (−4, −4), and (4, −4).

Show your work.

Got It? Do this problem to find out.

f. Kendall is placing a gate in the fourth quadrant. It will be two units long and one endpoint must be connected to a fence post. What are the two possible endpoints of the gate?

f. _____

Guided Practice

Identify the ordered pair that names each point or the name of each point. Then identify the quadrant in which it is located.

(Examples 1 and 2)

1. *T*

_____

2. $\left(-1\frac{1}{2}, 0\right)$

_____

3. $\left(-2, 2\frac{1}{2}\right)$

_____

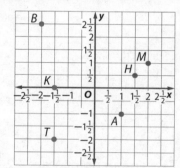

4. Refer to the diagram of a school.

(Examples 3–5)

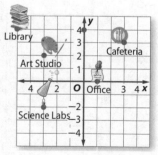

a. The gym is located 2 units to the right and 4 units down from the office. What are the coordinates of this location? _____

b. Graph and label the location of the gym.

5. 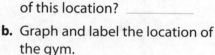 **Building on the Essential Question** How are number lines and the coordinate plane related?

_____

_____

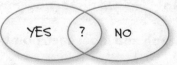
Rate Yourself!

Are you ready to move on?
Shade the section that applies.

YES   ?   NO

Find out online. Use the Self-Check Quiz.

Check

Independent Practice

Identify the ordered pair that names each point. Then identify the quadrant in which it is located. (Example 1)

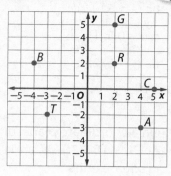

1. R

_____

2. G

_____

3. B

_____

4. T

_____

5. C

_____

6. A

_____

Identify the name of each point. Then identify the quadrant in which it is located. (Example 2)

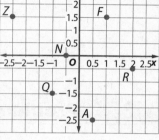

7. (−2.5, 1.5)

_____

8. (1, 1.5)

_____

9. (0.5, −2.5)

_____

10. (2, −0.5)

_____

11. (−0.5, 0)

_____

12. (−1, −1.5)

_____

Graph and label each point on the coordinate plane to the right. (Examples 3 and 4)

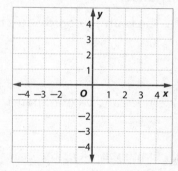

13. $K(-3.25, 3)$

14. $N\left(0, -1\frac{1}{2}\right)$

15. $F(-4.5, 0)$

16. $A\left(-3\frac{1}{2}, -3\right)$

17. **MP Analyze Relationships** Explain why the point (−3, 2) is different from the point (2, −3).

_____

_____

_____

18. **MP Justify Arguments** If you interchange the coordinates of any point in Quadrant II, in which quadrant would the new point be located? Justify your response.

_____

_____

_____

_____

19. Are the following coordinates located within the circle graphed?

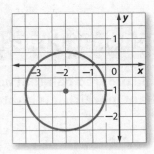

    a. (−1, 1.5) _____

    b. (−1.5, −2) _____

    c. (−0.5, 1) _____

    d. (−1.5, 2) _____

20. On a coordinate plane, draw triangle *ABC* with vertices *A*(−1, −1), *B*(3, −1), and *C*(−1, 2). Determine the area of the triangle in square units.

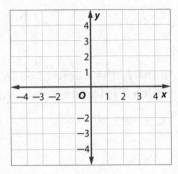

_____

 Problems Higher-Order Thinking

Evaluate Without graphing, identify the quadrant(s) for which each of the following statements is true for any point (*x, y*). Justify your response.

21. The *x*- and *y*-coordinates have the same sign.

_____

_____

22. The *x*- and *y*-coordinates have opposite signs. _____

_____

23. Evaluate Does the order of the numbers in an ordered pair matter when naming a point? Can that point be represented by more than one ordered pair?

_____

_____

_____

24. Create Three vertices of a quadrilateral are (−1 −1), (1, 2), and (5, −1). What are the coordinates of two vertices that will form two different

parallelograms? _____

25. Create A parallelogram is graphed on a coordinate plane so that two points are in the first quadrant and two points are in the third quadrant. What are the possible coordinates of the vertices of the parallelogram?

_____

Multi-Step Problem Solving

26. The table shows the locations for several different places around town. The grid shows a map of the town, and each square on the grid represents one city block. Ben needs to go to the dry cleaner, which is 5 blocks north of the library. Where on the grid must he go? **MD** **MP**

Place	Location
Bank	(5, −4)
Grocery	(−3, 0)
Library	(0, −3)
Post Office	(−4, 5)

Ⓐ (0, −8)

Ⓑ (5, −3)

Ⓒ (0, 2)

Ⓓ (0, 5)

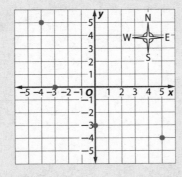

Use a problem-solving model to solve this problem.

1 Analyze

**Read the problem. Circle the information you know.
Underline what the problem is asking you to find.**

2 Plan

What will you need to do to solve the problem? Write your plan in steps.

Step 1 | Determine the dot on the grid that corresponds to the _____.

Step 2 | Determine the ordered pair of the location ___ blocks _____ of the library.

3 Solve

Use your plan to solve the problem. Show your steps.

The library is located at (____, ____). Five blocks north would be

the ordered pair (____, ____). Choice ___ is correct. Fill in that answer

choice.

Read to Succeed!

The x-coordinate of an ordered pair tells you left or right and the y-coordinate tells you up or down.

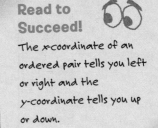

4 Justify and Evaluate

How do you know your solution is accurate?

_____

_____

MD = Measurement and Data   **MP** = Mathematical Processes

More Multi-Step Problem Solving

Use a problem-solving model to solve each problem.

27. Rosa is currently at $(4, -2)$ on the map. To which place in the table is she the closest? **MD MP**

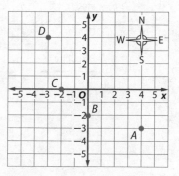

Place	Location
Stadium	A
Playground	B
Mall	C
Hospital	D

- Ⓐ Stadium
- Ⓑ Playground
- Ⓒ Mall
- Ⓓ Hospital

28. Josie posts stakes at the following locations. She ties rope to the stakes to section off a rectangle. Each unit represents 1 foot. What is the perimeter of the rectangle in feet? **MD MP**

Stake	Location
Stake 1	$(2, 0)$
Stake 2	$(2, -4)$
Stake 3	$(-1, 0)$
Stake 4	$(-1, -4)$

29. Eduardo drives from A to B. Each unit on the map represents 10 miles. How many miles does he drive? **MD N MP**

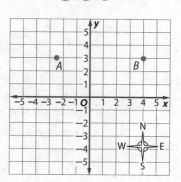

30. Catalina plots point C at $\left(4, -1\frac{1}{2}\right)$. She also plots the point with the opposite y-coordinate and labels the point as D. What is the distance from C to D? **MD N MP**

N = Number and Operations   **MD** = Measurement and Data   **MP** = Mathematical Processes

Scientific Illustrator

If you are artistic and have a strong interest in science, you should think about a career as a scientific illustrator. Scientific illustrators combine their artistic abilities with their scientific backgrounds to draw scientifically accurate images. Karen Carr, a wildlife and natural history artist, has artwork in scientific publications, museums, and zoos. To draw animals that are extinct, she examines fossils, talks to scientists, and uses measurements and proportions from scientific literature.

Mathematical Process
6.1(A) Apply mathematics to problems arising in everyday life, society, and the workplace.
Targeted TEKS 6.2(D)

Is This the Career for You?

Are you interested in a career as a scientific illustrator? Take some of the following courses in high school.

◆ Algebra
◆ Biology
◆ Geometry
◆ Life/Figure Drawing
◆ Physics

Find out how math relates to a career in Art.

College & Career
READINESS

Explore college and careers at ccr.mcgraw-hill.com

93

You be the Scientfic Illustrator!

Use the information in the table to solve each problem. Write in simplest form.

1. Write the length and height of an Argentinosaurus as decimals. Use bar notation if necessary.

   _____

2. How much taller was a Velociraptor than a Microraptor? Write your answer as a decimal. _____

3. Which is greater, the height of the Argentinosaurus or the length of the Camptosaurus? _____

4. How much longer was a Camptosaurus than a Velociraptor? Locate your answer on the number line.

5. Compare the heights of all four dinosaurs. Order them from least to greatest.

   _____

6. What is the difference between the tallest dinosaur and the shortest? Write your answer as a decimal. _____

Dinosaur Measurements		
Dinosaur	**Length (ft)**	**Height (ft)**
Argentinosaurus	$114\frac{5}{6}$	$24\frac{1}{10}$
Camptosaurus	$16\frac{2}{5}$	$11\frac{4}{5}$
Microraptor	$2\frac{5}{8}$	$\frac{24}{25}$
Velociraptor	$5\frac{9}{10}$	$3\frac{7}{25}$

 Career Project

It's time to update your career portfolio! Investigate the education and training requirements for a career as a scientific illustrator. Prepare a brief oral presentation and present it to your classmates. As others are presenting, listen carefully to their presentations. At the end, ask any clarifying questions.

_____

_____

_____

What are some short-term goals you need to achieve to become a scientific illustrator?

• _____

• _____

• _____

• _____

Chapter Review

Vocabulary Check

Work with a partner to complete the puzzle by unscrambling the letters below to reveal words from the vocabulary list at the beginning of the chapter. Seek clarification of each vocabulary term as needed.

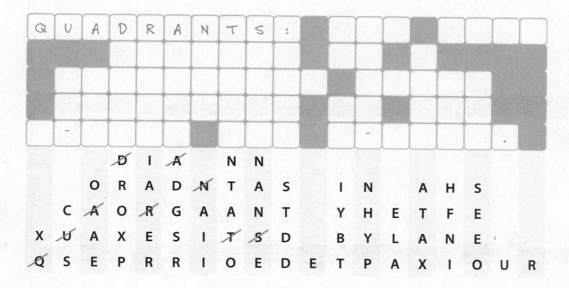

| Q | U | A | D | R | A | N | T | S | : | | | | | | | | |

Complete each sentence using the vocabulary list at the beginning of the chapter.

1. A _____ is a number that can be written as a fraction.

2. A number that is less than zero is a _____.

3. A number that is greater than zero is a _____.

4. The _____ of a number is the distance between the number and zero on a number line.

5. The division of a _____ ends.

6. A decimal whose digits repeat in groups of one or more is a _____.

Use Your FOLDABLES

 Collaborate

Use your Foldable to help review the chapter. Share your Foldable with a partner and take turns summarizing what you learned in this chapter, while the other partner listens carefully. Seek clarification of any concepts, as needed. **TEKS** 6.1(E)

Tape here

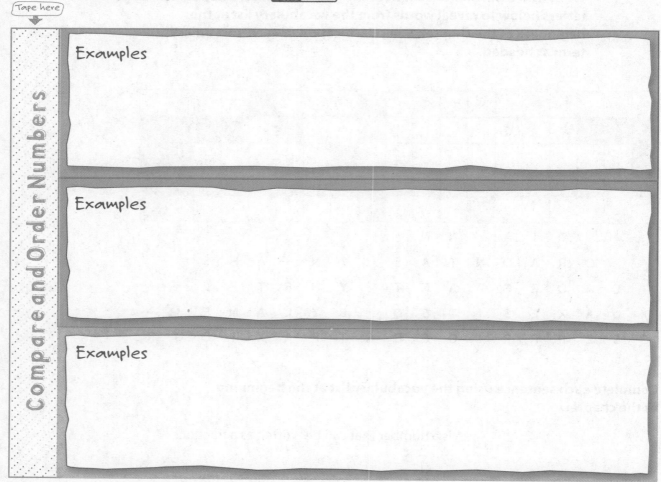

Compare and Order Numbers

Examples

Examples

Examples

Got it?

Circle the correct term or number to complete each sentence. **TEKS** 6.1(G)

1. The opposite of −4 is (−4, 4).

2. The distance of a number from 0 is its (opposite, absolute value).

3. The value listed first in an ordered pair is the (*x*-coordinate, *y*-coordinate).

4. The absolute value of 17 is (−17, 17).

5. (1.$\overline{25}$, 6.543) is a terminating decimal.

6. The table shows the number of at bats and the number of hits for the top three batters on a baseball team. If the batting averages are written as a decimal rounded to the nearest thousandth, what is the ranking of the players based on their batting averages? Show the steps you used and justify your solution. **N** **MP**

	Game 1		Game 2		Game 3	
Player	At Bats	Hits	At Bats	Hits	At Bats	Hits
Smith	4	2	3	2	5	4
Rogers	4	3	4	3	5	3
Kay	3	3	3	2	5	2

1 Analyze

2 Plan

3 Solve

4 Justify and Evaluate

_____

_____

Got it?

7. The table shows the amount of time Katie spent practicing gymnastics this week. Is 10 hours a reasonable estimate for the amount of time she spent practicing this week? Show the steps you used and justify your solution. **N** **MP**

_____

_____

_____

_____

Practice Time	
Day	Time (h)
Monday	1.5
Tuesday	$2\frac{2}{3}$
Wednesday	$1\frac{1}{4}$
Thursday	2.4
Friday	$1\frac{3}{4}$

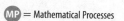 **N** = Number and Operations   **MP** = Mathematical Processes

Reflect

 Answering the Essential Question

 Use what you learned about integers and the coordinate plane to complete the graphic organizer. **TEKS** 6.1(D), 6.1(F), 6.1(G)

 Essential Question

HOW are rational numbers used in real-world situations?

Vocabulary	Definition
integer	
rational number	

Describe a real-world situation that can be represented by $-\frac{1}{2}$.

Describe a real-world situation that can be represented by -16.

 Answer the Essential Question. HOW are rational numbers used in real-world situations? Verbally share your response with a partner, seeking and providing clarification as needed.

Chapter 2

Multiply and Divide Rational Numbers

Texas Essential Knowledge and Skills

Targeted TEKS

6.3 The student applies mathematical process standards to represent addition, subtraction, multiplication, and division while solving problems and justifying solutions.

Mathematical Processes

6.1, 6.1(A), 6.1(B), 6.1(C), 6.1(D), 6.1(E), 6.1(F), 6.1(G)

Essential Question

WHAT does it mean to multiply and divide fractions and decimals?

Math in the Real World

Wild Basin Wilderness Preserve, near Austin, Texas, is home to 2.5 miles of hiking trails. The table shows several trails available. How many times longer is Yaupon Trail than Triknee Trail?

Trail	Distance (mi)
Arroyo Vista	0.5
Laurel	0.1
Triknee	0.15
Woodland	0.12
Yaupon	0.6

Go Online!

www.connectED.mcgraw-hill.com

Watch	Worksheets	Vocab	Tutor	Tools	Check

What Tools Do You Need?

Vocabulary

Commutative Property   reciprocals

Writing Math

Explain Your Answer When you explain your answer, you give reasons why your answer is correct.

Sal wants to buy 5 packages of the limited edition cards. Is $20 enough for 5 packages, or does Sal need to bring $25 to the store to buy them? Explain your answer.

Football Card Prices	
Package	**Price ($)**
All-Star	3.75
Limited Edition	4.59
Deluxe	5.99

Step 1 Estimate.

$5 \times \$4 =$ _____   Round down.

$5 \times \$5 =$ _____   Round up.

Step 2 Answer the question.

Sal should bring _____ to the store.

Step 3 Explain why. Write your explanation in complete sentences.

Using the estimate, Sal knows that the actual cost is between _____

and _____. So _____ is not enough. Explain your answer to a classmate.

Practice explaining your answer.

1. Marta plans to buy 2 baseballs and 1 baseball glove. Is $50 enough to bring to the store or does Marta need to bring

   $55? Explain your answer. _____

   _____

   _____

THE SPORTS COVE
Baseball............6.50
Baseball
glove..............37.99
Baseball
cap.................13.79

Review 5.3(A), 5.3(K)

Quick Review

Example 1

Estimate $4\frac{5}{6} + 1\frac{1}{8}$.

Think: $\frac{5}{6} > \frac{1}{2}$.
So, $4\frac{5}{6}$ rounds to 5.

$\cdots\triangleright 4\frac{5}{6} + 1\frac{1}{8} \triangleleft\cdots$

Think: $\frac{1}{8} < \frac{1}{2}$.
So, $1\frac{1}{8}$ rounds to 1.

$$5 + 1 = 6$$

So, $4\frac{5}{6} + 1\frac{1}{8}$ is about 6.

Example 2

Add $5\frac{9}{10} + 3\frac{3}{4}$. Write in simplest form.

$$5\frac{9}{10} \longrightarrow 5\frac{18}{20}$$

Rename the fractions using the LCD, 20.

$$+ 3\frac{3}{4} \longrightarrow 3\frac{15}{20}$$
$$8\frac{33}{20} \text{ or } 9\frac{13}{20}$$

So, $5\frac{9}{10} + 3\frac{3}{4}$ is equal to $9\frac{13}{20}$.

Quick Check

Check

Estimate with Fractions Estimate each sum or difference.

1. $6\frac{7}{8} + 5\frac{1}{4} \approx$ _____

2. $3\frac{1}{7} + 8\frac{1}{9} \approx$ _____

3. $12\frac{1}{5} - 5\frac{5}{6} \approx$ _____

 Show your work.

Add and Subtract Fractions Add or subtract. Write in simplest form.

4. $\frac{9}{10} + \frac{3}{5} =$ _____

5. $7\frac{2}{3} - 3\frac{1}{7} =$ _____

6. $9\frac{7}{8} - 2\frac{5}{6} =$ _____

7. Suppose a plant grew $4\frac{1}{2}$ inches one week and $2\frac{3}{8}$ inches the next week. How many inches did it grow during both weeks?

_____

How Did You Do?

Which problems did you answer correctly in the Quick Check?
Shade those exercise numbers below.

 ① ② ③ ④ ⑤ ⑥ ⑦

Use this Foldable throughout this chapter to help you learn about multiplying and dividing rational numbers.

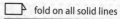 cut on all dashed lines fold on all solid lines tape to page 190

Multiply and Divide Rational Numbers

multiply	divide

Example

Example

decimal × decimal

decimal ÷ decimal

Example

Example

fraction × fraction

fraction ÷ fraction

FOLDABLES® Use this Foldable throughout this chapter to help you learn about multiplying and dividing rational numbers.

✂ cut on all dashed lines ☐ fold on all solid lines ▨ tape to page 190

page 190   Tab 3

How do I divide a decimal by a decimal?

How do I multiply a decimal by a decimal?

page 190   Tab 2

How do I divide a fraction by a fraction?

How do I multiply a fraction by a fraction?

page 190   Tab 1

How do I divide a mixed number by a fraction?

How do I multiply a fraction by a mixed number?

Multiply Decimals by Decimals

 Launch the Lesson: Real World

The table shows the weight of a 1-pound object on each planet. A 0.5-pound object weighs one half as much as a 1-pound object. Let's investigate multiplication of decimals.

Planet	Weight (Pounds)
Mercury	0.3
Venus	0.9
Earth	1
Mars	0.3
Jupiter	2.3
Saturn	1
Uranus	0.8
Neptune	1.1

Texas Essential Knowledge and Skills

Targeted TEKS
6.3(E) Multiply and divide positive rational numbers fluently.

Mathematical Processes
6.1(A), 6.1(B), 6.1(C), 6.1(G)

Essential Question
WHAT does it mean to multiply and divide fractions and decimals?

1. If a cheeseburger weighs a half pound on Earth, what will it weigh on Jupiter? _____

2. Write a multiplication expression to represent this situation. _____

3. What would a barbell that weighs 5 pounds on Earth weigh on Jupiter? _____

4. Write a multiplication expression to represent this situation. _____

5. **Analyze** Use the results from Exercises 1 and 2 to find 0.05×2.3. Explain your answer. _____

Which MP Mathematical Processes did you use?
Shade the circle(s) that applies.

Ⓐ Apply Math to the Real World.

Ⓑ Use a Problem-Solving Model.

Ⓒ Select Tools and Techniques.

Ⓓ Use Multiple Representations.

Ⓔ Organize Ideas.

Ⓕ Analyze Relationships.

Ⓖ Justify Arguments.

Multiply Decimals

You can use models to multiply decimals.

To find 0.7 × 0.6, use a 10-by-10 grid to shade a rectangle that is 7 tenths unit wide and 6 tenths unit long. The model shows that there are *forty-two hundredths* in the shaded region.

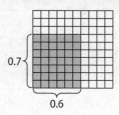

So, 0.7 × 0.6 = 0.42.

Whole Numbers	Decimals
7 × 6 = 42	0.7 × 0.6 = 0.42

To multiply decimals, you can multiply as with whole numbers first. To place the decimal point in the product, find the sum of the number of decimal places in each factor. The product has the same number of decimal places.

Tutor

Examples

1. **Determine 0.8 × 0.9.**

$$
\begin{array}{r}
0.8 \\
\times\ 0.9 \\
\hline
0.72
\end{array}
$$

0.8 ← 1 decimal place
× 0.9 ← 1 decimal place
0.72 ← 1 + 1, or 2 decimal places

The product is 0.72.

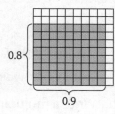

2. **Determine 0.112 × 7.2.**

Multiply as with whole numbers.

| 0. | 1 | 1 | 2 | ← 3 decimal places |
| × | | 7. | 2 | ← 1 decimal place |

+ ☐ ☐ ☐

☐ ☐ ☐ ☐ ☐ ← 3 + 1, or 4 decimal places

The product is _____.

Got It? Do these problems to find out.

a. 5 × 2.8   **b.** 4.12 × 0.05   **c.** 0.014 × 3

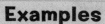

STOP and Reflect

How is the product of 4.2 × 6.7 similar to the product of 42 × 67? How are they different? Explain below.

Show your work.

a. _____

b. _____

c. _____

Annex Zeros

Sometimes you need to annex a zero when multiplying decimals. The model shows 0.3 × 0.3. The product is *nine hundredths*, or 0.09.

So, 0.3 × 0.3 = 0.09.

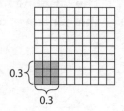

Whole Numbers	Decimals
3 × 3 = 9	0.3 × 0.3 = 0.09

If there are not enough decimal places in the product, annex zeros to the left.

Examples

 Tutor

3. **Determine 0.2 × 0.4.**

$$
\begin{array}{r}
0.2 \\
\times \quad 0.4 \\
\hline
0.08
\end{array}
$$

← 1 decimal place
← 1 decimal place
← Annex zeros to make 2 decimal places.

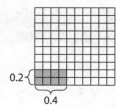

4. **Determine 0.45 × 0.053.**

The product will have ☐ decimal places. Annex zeros, if needed.

$$
\begin{array}{cccc}
 & 0. & 4 & 5 \\
\times \quad 0. & 0 & 5 & 3 \\
\hline
\end{array}
$$

		☐	☐	☐
+	☐	☐	☐	
☐	☐	☐	☐	☐	☐

Got It? Do these problems to find out.

d. 0.04 × 0.32   **e.** 0.26 × 0.205   **f.** 1.33 × 0.06

Show your work.

d. _____

e. _____

f. _____

Example

5. A certain car can travel 28.45 miles with one gallon of gasoline. The gasoline tank can hold 11.5 gallons. How many miles can this car travel on a full tank of gas? Justify your answer.

Estimate 28.45×11.5 ⟶ 30×12 or 360

```
      28.45      ← two decimal places
    × 11.5       ← one decimal place
    14225
     2845
+    2845
   327.175       ← The product has three decimal places.
```

The car could travel 327.175 miles. Since $327.175 \approx 360$, the answer is reasonable.

Guided Practice

Multiply. (Examples 1–4)

1. $0.6 \times 5 =$ _____

2. $27.43 \times 1.089 =$ _____

3. $0.98 \times 7 =$ _____

 Show your work.

4. $2.7 \times 1.35 =$ _____

5. $0.03 \times 0.09 =$ _____

6. $0.04 \times 2.12 =$ _____

7. **MP Justify Arguments** A mile is equal to approximately 1.609 kilometers. How many kilometers is 2.5 miles?

Justify your answer. (Example 5) _____

_____

8. **? Building on the Essential Question** Why is estimating not as helpful when multiplying very small numbers such as 0.007 and 0.053? _____

_____

_____

Rate Yourself!

Are you ready to move on? Shade the section that applies.

I have a few questions. | I'm ready to move on.

I have a lot of questions.

Find out online. Use the Self-Check Quiz.

Check

Independent Practice

6.3(E), 6.1(C), 6.1(G) TEKS

Multiply. (Examples 1–4)

1. $0.7 \times 4 =$ _____

2. $4 \times 3.7 =$ _____

3. $0.52 \times 2.1 =$ _____

4. $6.2 \times 0.03 =$ _____

5. $14.7 \times 11.361 =$ _____

6. $0.28 \times 0.08 =$ _____

7. **STEM** A giraffe can run up to 46.93 feet per second. How far could a giraffe run in 1.8 seconds? Justify your answer. (Example 5)

_____

_____

8. **MP Justify Arguments** A nutrition label indicates that one serving of apple crisp oatmeal has 2.5 grams of fat. How many grams of fat are there in 3.75 servings? Justify your answer. (Example 5)

_____

_____

9. **Financial Literacy** Pears cost $0.92 per pound and apples cost $1.10 per pound. Mr. Bonilla bought 3.75 pounds of pears and 2.1 pounds of apples. How much did he pay for the pears and apples? Explain your answer.

_____

_____

Multiply.

10. $25.04 \times 3.005 =$ _____

11. $1.03 \times 1.005 =$ _____

12. $5.12 \times 4.001 =$ _____

13. About how many more miles would a satellite travel
    if it circled the equator 2.5 times than if it circled

    around the poles 2.5 times? _____

	Approximate Distance (mi)
around Earth at the equator	24,889.78
around Earth through the poles	24,805.94

14. The distance around Jupiter at the equator is about 17.6 times greater than
    the distance around Earth at the equator. About how many more miles would
    a satellite travel if it circled Jupiter's equator than if it circled Earth's equator?

    Round to the nearest tenth. _____

 H.O.T. **Problems** Higher-Order Thinking

15. **Create** Write a multiplication problem in which the product is between 0.05

    and 0.75. _____

16. **Analyze** Place the decimal point in the product of the following problem to
    make it correct. Explain your reasoning.

    $$3.9853 \times 8.032856 = 32013341\dots$$

    _____

    _____

17. **Evaluate** Determine whether the following statement is *always, sometimes,*
    or *never* true. Give examples to justify your answer.

    The product of two decimals less than 1
    is less than either of the factors.

    _____

    _____

18. **Analyze** Is the product of 0.4 × 1.8 greater than or less than 0.4?
    Explain your reasoning.

    _____

19. **Evaluate** Evaluate the expression 0.3(3 − 0.5). _____

20. **Create** Write a word problem in which you multiply two decimals.
    The product should be between 0 and 1.

    _____

    _____

Multi-Step Problem Solving

21. The table shows the cost of produce per pound at a farmer's market. Mr. Gonzalez bought 0.75 pound of pears and 3.5 pounds of plums. What was his change from $10?

Ⓐ $4.05

Ⓑ $5.95

Ⓒ $6.33

Ⓓ $10.50

Produce	Cost per Pound
Pears	$0.98
Oranges	$1.29
Carrots	$1.18
Plums	$1.49

Use a problem-solving model to solve this problem.

1 Analyze

Read the problem. Circle the information you know.
Underline what the problem is asking you to find.

2 Plan

What will you need to do to solve the problem? Write your plan in steps.

Step 1 Determine the total amount spent on pears and the total amount spent on plums.

Step 2 Subtract the amounts spent on pears and plums from $10.00.

3 Solve

Use your plan to solve the problem. Show your steps.

Pears: 0.75 × $_____ = $_____

Plums: 3.5 × $_____ = $_____

Total spent: $_____ + $_____ = $_____

$10.00 − $_____ = $_____

So, Mr. Gonzalez would receive $_____ in change. The correct answer is _____.

Read to Succeed!

When rounding, wait to round until the end of the problem.

4 Justify and Evaluate

How do you know your solution is accurate?

_____

_____

_____

Ⓝ = Number and Operations   ⓂⓅ = Mathematical Processes

More Multi-Step Problem Solving

Use a problem-solving model to solve each problem.

22. The table shows the cost per yard of different types of fabric. Sierra bought 2.5 yards of nylon and 4.5 yards of cotton. What is the change from $5? Round to the nearest cent.

Fabric	Cost per Yard
Cotton	$0.50
Linen	$0.25
Rayon	$0.125
Nylon	$0.75

- Ⓐ $0.87
- Ⓑ $2.00
- Ⓒ $2.25
- Ⓓ $4.13

23. The rectangle represents Demarco's garden. For each square foot, he needs to use 2 scoops of fertilizer. How many scoops does he use? N EE MP

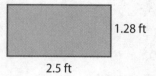

1.28 ft

2.5 ft

24. Abigail runs at a constant rate of 7.057 miles per hour. Jamal runs at a constant rate of 6.4 miles per hour. At these rates, how much farther did Abigail run than Jamal after the first 0.5 hour? Round your answer to the nearest hundredth. (*Hint*: Distance = rate × time) N P EE MP

25. A name brand cereal is on sale and costs $4.50 for an 18.2-oz box. The grocery store version of the cereal costs $4.03 for a 13.1-oz box. Which cereal costs less per ounce? N P MD MP

N = Number and Operations   P = Proportionality   EE = Expressions, Equations, and Relationships   MD = Measurement and Data   MP = Mathematical Processes

112   Chapter 2 Multiply and Divide Rational Numbers

Multiply by Powers of Ten

Texas Essential Knowledge and Skills

Targeted TEKS
6.3(E) Multiply and divide positive rational numbers fluently.

Mathematical Processes
6.1(C), 6.1(E), 6.1(F), 6.1(G)

INQUIRY HOW can I analyze relationships to multiply by powers of 10?

Each planet in our solar system orbits around the Sun at a different distance from the Sun. Mercury orbits at an average distance of 28.6 million miles. One million is 1,000,000. What is 28.6 × 1,000,000?

What do you know? _____

What do you need to know? _____

Hands-On Activity

Numbers like 10, 100, and 1,000 are called *powers of 10* because they can be obtained by raising 10 to a power.

Step 1 Look for a pattern. Complete the table.

Decimal		Power of 10		Product
28.6	×	0.1	=	2.86
28.6	×	1	=	28.6
28.6	×	10	=	286
28.6	×	100	=	2,860
28.6	×	1,000	=	28,600

Move the decimal point the _____ number of places as the number of zeros in the power of 10.

Move the decimal point to the _____ when multiplying by a power of 10 that is less than 1.

Move the decimal point to the _____ when multiplying by a power of 10 that is greater than 1.

Step 2 Determine how many zeros are in 1,000,000 and move the decimal point in 28.6 the appropriate number of places.

There are ☐ zeros in 1,000,000.

28.6 million = 28.6 × 1,000,000
            = 28.600000   Move the decimal point ☐
            = 28,600,000   places to the right.

Investigate

MP **Select Tools and Techniques** Work with a partner to complete the tables.

Decimal		Power of 10		Product
12.4	×	0.1	=	1.24
1. 12.4	×	0.01	=	
2. 12.4	×	0.001	=	
3. 12.4	×	0.0001	=	

Decimal		Power of 10		Product
1.24	×	1	=	1.24
4. 1.24	×	10	=	
5. 1.24	×	100	=	
6. 1.24	×	1,000	=	
7. 1.24	×	10,000	=	

Analyze and Reflect

8. **MP** **Analyze Relationships** Suppose you plan to purchase 10 items that each cost $4.95. Explain how to use mental math to find the cost of the 10 items.

_____

9. **MP** **Justify Arguments** The product of 13.6 and a power of 10 is 13,600. What is the power of 10? Explain. _____

_____

Create

10. **Create** Write a rule you can use to find the product of a number and power of 10 without using paper and pencil or a calculator. _____

_____

_____

11. **INQUIRY** HOW can I analyze relationships to multiply by powers of 10?

_____

_____

Divide Decimals by Decimals

 Launch the Lesson: Real World

Texas Essential Knowledge and Skills

Targeted TEKS
6.3(E) Multiply and divide positive rational numbers fluently.

Mathematical Processes
6.1(A), 6.1(B), 6.1(D), 6.1(G)

An art studio has 3.6 gallons of acrylic paint. They separate it into 9 containers. How many gallons of paint are in each container?

Essential Question

WHAT does it mean to multiply and divide fractions and decimals?

1. **Analyze** Study the table that shows how each division problem compares to the problem 3.6 ÷ 9.

   What is true about the quotients?

Division Problem	Quotient
0.0036 ÷ 0.009	0.4
0.036 ÷ 0.09	0.4
0.36 ÷ 0.9	0.4
3.6 ÷ 9	0.4

2. Describe the pattern among the dividends and divisors as you move down the table.

3. **Create** Complete a similar table to show the quotients for the division problems based on the division problem 4.8 ÷ 6.

Division Problem	Quotient
0.0048 ÷ 0.006	
4.8 ÷ 6	

4. Predict the quotient of 0.49 ÷ 0.7. Justify your response.

Which MP **Mathematical Processes** did you use?
Shade the circle(s) that applies.

Ⓐ Apply Math to the Real World.
Ⓑ Use a Problem-Solving Model.
Ⓒ Select Tools and Techniques.
Ⓓ Use Multiple Representations.
Ⓔ Organize Ideas.
Ⓕ Analyze Relationships.
Ⓖ Justify Arguments.

Divide by Decimals

When dividing by decimals, multiply both the divisor and the dividend by the same power of 10 so that the divisor is a whole number. Then divide as with whole numbers.

Tutor

Examples

1. **Determine 1.71 ÷ 0.9.**   Estimate $2 \div 1 = 2$

Multiply by 10 to make a whole number.

$$0.9\overline{)1.71} \longrightarrow 9\overline{)17.1}$$

Multiply by the same number, 10.

$$
\begin{array}{r}
1.9 \\
9\overline{)17.1} \\
-9 \\
\hline
81 \\
-81 \\
\hline
0
\end{array}
$$

Place the decimal point.
Divide as with whole numbers.

1.71 divided by 0.9 is 1.9.   Compared to the estimate, the quotient is reasonable.

Check $1.9 \times 0.9 = 1.71$ ✓

2. **Determine 2.64 ÷ 0.6.**   Estimate ☐ ÷ ☐ = ☐

$$0.6\overline{)2.64}$$

Multiply 0.6 by ☐ to make a whole number.

Multiply the dividend, ☐ , by the same power of 10.

☐
$$0.6\overline{)2.64}$$ Place the decimal point in the quotient.

☐   Divide as with whole numbers.

☐

☐

2.64 divided by 0.6 is ☐ .

Compared to the estimate, is the quotient reasonable? _____

Show your work.

a. _____

b. _____

c. _____

Got It? Do these problems to find out.

a. $54.4 \div 1.7$ **b.** $8.424 \div 0.36$ **c.** $0.0063 \div 0.007$

Zeros in the Quotient and Dividend

Line up the numbers by place value as you divide. Annex zeros in the quotient in order to keep digits with the correct place value. Annex zeros in the dividend to continue dividing after the decimal point.

Examples

Tutor

3. **Determine 52 ÷ 0.4.**

$$0.4\overline{)52.0}$$

Multiply each by 10.

```
   130.
4)520.
 - 4
   12
 - 12
   00
```

Place the decimal point.

Write a zero in the ones place of the quotient because 0 ÷ 4 = 0.

So, 52 ÷ 0.4 = 130.

- -

4. **Determine 0.009 ÷ 0.18.**

$$0.18\overline{)0.009}$$

Multiply each by 100.

```
    0.05
18)0.90
 - 0
   09
 - 00
   90
 - 90
    0
```

Place the decimal point.

9 tenths divided by 18 is 0, so write a 0 in the tenths place.

Annex a 0 in the dividend and continue to divide.

So, 0.009 ÷ 0.18 is 0.05.

> **Checking Answers**
> You can always check your answer to a division problem by multiplying the quotient by the divisor.

- -

5. **Determine 11.2 ÷ 0.07.**

Multiply 0.07 and 11.2 by [ ].

$$0.07\overline{)11.20}$$

Place the decimal point in the quotient.
Divide as with whole numbers.

Show your work.

d. _____

e. _____

Got It? Do these problems to find out.

d. 5.6 ÷ 0.014   **e.** 6.24 ÷ 200   **f.** 0.4 ÷ 25

f. _____

 Example

Tutor

6. **How many times as many Internet users are there in Japan than in Spain? Round to the nearest tenth.**

Internet Users in 2012 (millions)	
China	513.1
United States	245.2
Japan	101.2
France	50.3
Spain	30.7

Find 101.2 ÷ 30.7.

$$
\begin{array}{r}
3.29 \\
30.7\overline{)101.2} \rightarrow 307\overline{)1012.00} \\
-921 \\
\hline
910 \\
-614 \\
\hline
2960 \\
-2763 \\
\hline
197
\end{array}
$$

To the nearest tenth, 101.2 ÷ 30.7 = 3.3. So, there are about 3.3 times as many Internet users in Japan than in Spain.

Guided Practice

Divide. (Examples 1–5)

1. 3.69 ÷ 0.3 = _____

Show your work.

2. 0.0338 ÷ 1.3 = _____

3. 2.943 ÷ 2.7 = _____

4. Alicia bought 5.75 yards of fleece fabric to make blankets for a charity. She needs 1.85 yards of fabric for each blanket. How many blankets can Alicia make with the fabric she bought? (Example 6)

_____

5. 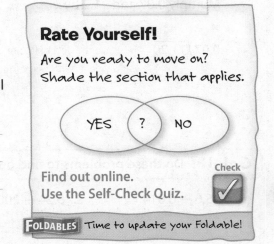 **Building on the Essential Question** When is it helpful to round the quotient to the nearest hundredth?

_____

_____

_____

Rate Yourself!

Are you ready to move on?
Shade the section that applies.

YES   ?   NO

Find out online.
Use the Self-Check Quiz.

Check ✓

FOLDABLES Time to update your Foldable!

Independent Practice

Divide. (Examples 1–5)

1. $1.44 \div 0.4 =$ _____

Show your work.

2. $16.24 \div 14 =$ _____

3. $0.6 \div 0.0024 =$ _____

4. $96.6 \div 0.42 =$ _____

5. $13.5 \div 0.03 =$ _____

6. $0.12 \div 15 =$ _____

7. The average person's *stride length*, the distance covered by one step, is approximately 2.5 feet long. How many steps would the average person take to travel 50 feet? (Example 6)

_____

8. **STEM** Alaska has a coastline of about 6.64 thousand miles. Florida has about 1.35 thousand miles of coastline. How many times more miles of coastline does Alaska have than Florida? Round to the nearest tenth if necessary. Justify your procedure.

_____

9. **MP** **Apply Math to the Real World** Refer to the graphic novel frame below for Exercises a–b.

I hope 5 bags is enough.

a. If each bag holds 3.75 pounds and they use 0.75 pound of birdseed each day, for how many days will one bag last? _____

_____

b. Suppose they spent $74.95 for 5 bags. How much does one bag cost?

_____

10. A necklace is being made with beads that are each 1.25 centimeters in diameter. The necklace is 30 centimeters long. Each bead costs $0.15. How much will be spent on beads for the necklace? _____

11. (MP) **Select Tools and Techniques** Use the table that shows popular sports car colors in North America.

Popular Sports Car Colors	
Color	**Portion of Responses**
Silver	0.2
Blue	0.16
Black	0.14
Red	0.09
Other	0.41

  a. How many times more respondents chose silver than red? Round to the nearest tenth if necessary.

  _____

  b. How many times more respondents chose either silver or black than red? Round to the nearest tenth if necessary.

  _____

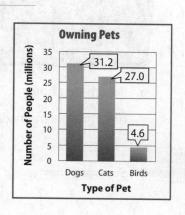

H.O.T. Problems Higher-Order Thinking

12. Evaluate Determine two positive decimals a and b that make the following statement true. Then determine two positive decimals a and b that make the statement false.

If $a < 1$ and $b < 1$, then $a \div b < 1$.

_____

_____

_____

13. Analyze Identify the problem that does not belong with the other three. Explain your reasoning.

$49 \div 7$	$4.9 \div 7$	$0.49 \div 0.7$	$0.049 \div 0.07$

_____

_____

14. Analyze Rodrigo researched the number of pets owned in the U.S. and displayed his results in the bar graph shown. In his research, he found that $7,737.6 million was spent annually on veterinary visits for dogs and $5,913 million was spent annually on visits for cats. How much more was spent, on average, by each person for dogs than for cats?

_____

Multi-Step Problem Solving

15. Cheyenne buys the amounts of fruit shown in the table. She uses 1.05 pounds of grapes in a salad. How many times more pounds of grapes does she have now than apples? Round to the nearest hundredth.

Fruit	Pounds
Cherries	3.2
Grapes	4.8
Bananas	3.8
Apples	2.25

Ⓐ 1.47   Ⓒ 1.67

Ⓑ 1.50   Ⓓ 2.13

Use a problem-solving model to solve this problem.

1 Analyze

Read the problem. Circle the information you know. Underline what the problem is asking you to find.

2 Plan

What will you need to do to solve the problem? Write your plan in steps.

Step 1 _____ to find the number of pounds of grapes she has after making the salad.

Step 2 _____ to find how many times more pounds of grapes she has than apples.

3 Solve

Use your plan to solve the problem. Show your steps.

She has 4.8 — 1.05 or _____ pounds of grapes left.

She has _____ ÷ 2.25 or _____ times more pounds of grapes than apples.

Since 1.6̄6̄ is about _____, the correct choice is _____. Fill in that answer choice.

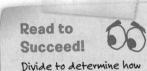
Read to Succeed!
Divide to determine how many times greater one quantity is of another.

4 Justify and Evaluate

How do you know your solution is reasonable?

_____

_____

_____

More Multi-Step Problem Solving

Use a problem-solving model to solve each problem.

16. The lengths of two wires are shown below. A project uses 32.6 centimeters of the red wire. How many times longer is the red wire than the blue wire after part of the red wire is used? (Wires not drawn to scale.)

125.92 cm

221.48 cm

(A) 1.5

(B) 2.4

(C) 3.9

(D) 6.8

17. Mika has $9.50. She buys as many bumper stickers as she can afford. Then she earns $2.50 for her allowance. How much money, in dollars, does she have now? Ⓝ Ⓟ MP

Item	Cost
Bumper sticker	$1.25
Hat	$6.00
Mug	$5.50

18. Elijah has a red ribbon that is 12.2 inches long. He has a green ribbon that is 3.4 inches longer than the red ribbon. He has a yellow ribbon that is 28.08 inches long. How many times longer is the yellow ribbon than the green ribbon? Ⓝ Ⓟ MP

19. Determine which quotient is greater, without performing the division. Explain your reasoning. Ⓝ Ⓟ MP

$$8.54 \div 5.23 \qquad 8.54 \div 5.32$$

Multiply Fractions and Whole Numbers

 ## Launch the Lesson: Vocabulary

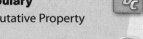 **Texas Essential Knowledge and Skills**

Targeted TEKS
6.3(E) Multiply and divide positive rational numbers fluently.

Mathematical Processes
6.1(A), 6.1(B), 6.1(D), 6.1(G)

A commuter train travels back and forth but does not change the distance traveled. In mathematics, operations that follow the **Commutative Property** can be performed in any order. For example, addition and multiplication are commutative.

Draw a line to "Commutative" if the examples can be done in either order. Draw a line to "Not Commutative" if the order changes the outcome.

Vocab

Vocabulary
Commutative Property

	$12 \div 6; 6 \div 12$
Commutative	tying your left shoe; tying your right shoe
	$5 \times 7; 7 \times 5$
Not Commutative	play a soccer game; change into your team uniform
	$15 + 5; 5 + 15$

Essential Question
WHAT does it mean to multiply and divide fractions and decimals?

 ## Real-World Investigation

Some morning routines can be done in any order. Sometimes, the order matters. Describe a situation when the order you perform two actions is important.

_____

_____

Which **MP** Mathematical Processes did you use?
Shade the circle(s) that applies.

Ⓐ Apply Math to the Real World.   Ⓔ Organize Ideas.

Ⓑ Use a Problem-Solving Model.   Ⓕ Analyze Relationships.

Ⓒ Select Tools and Techniques.   Ⓖ Justify Arguments.

Ⓓ Use Multiple Representations.

Multiply a Whole Number by a Fraction

Words Write the whole number as a fraction. Multiply the numerators and multiply the denominators.

Example

$5 \times \frac{3}{4} = \frac{5}{1} \times \frac{3}{4}$ Write 5 as $\frac{5}{1}$.

$= \frac{5 \times 3}{1 \times 4}$ Multiply.

$= \frac{15}{4}$ or $3\frac{3}{4}$ Simplify.

Example

Tutor

1. **Determine $2 \times \frac{2}{5}$.**

   Method 1 Use an area model.

   Shade $\frac{2}{5}$ of each of the first two columns.

   A total of $\frac{4}{5}$ has been shaded.

   Shade $\frac{4}{5}$ on the third column.

   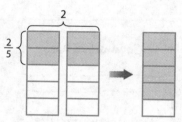

   Method 2 Use an equation.

   Estimate $2 \times \frac{1}{2} = 1$

   $2 \times \frac{2}{5} = \blacksquare$

   $2 \times \frac{2}{5} = \frac{2}{1} \times \frac{2}{5}$ Write 2 as $\frac{2}{1}$.

   $= \frac{2 \times 2}{1 \times 5}$ Multiply.

   $= \frac{4}{5}$ Simplify.

   Using either method, $2 \times \frac{2}{5}$ is $\frac{4}{5}$.

   Check for Reasonableness $\frac{4}{5} \approx 1$ ✔

Show your work.

a. _____

b. _____

c. _____

Got It? Do these problems to find out.

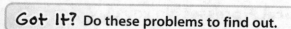

a. $6 \times \frac{2}{3}$ b. $9 \times \frac{1}{3}$ c. $4 \times \frac{1}{8}$

Multiply a Fraction by a Whole Number

When multiplying whole numbers and fractions, the order of the factors does not change the product. So, $4 \times \frac{3}{5} = \frac{3}{5} \times 4$. This is an example of the Commutative Property.

Examples

Tutor

2. Determine $\frac{3}{5} \times 4$.

Method 1 Use an area model.

Shade $\frac{3}{5}$ of each of the 4 columns.

A total of $\frac{12}{5}$ or $2\frac{2}{5}$ has been shaded.

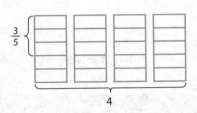

Method 2 Use an equation. Estimate $\frac{1}{2} \times 4 = 2$

$\frac{3}{5} \times 4 = \blacksquare$

$\frac{3}{5} \times 4 = \frac{3}{5} \times \frac{4}{1}$ Write 4 as $\frac{4}{1}$.

$= \frac{3 \times 4}{5 \times 1}$ Multiply.

$= \frac{12}{5}$ Simplify. Compare to the estimate.

$= 2\frac{2}{5}$

Using either method, $\frac{3}{5} \times 4$ is $2\frac{2}{5}$.

3. Determine $\frac{1}{4} \times 5$.

Estimate $\frac{1}{4} \times 4 = 1$

$\frac{1}{4} \times 5 = \frac{1}{4} \times \frac{5}{1}$ Write 5 as $\frac{5}{1}$.

$= \frac{1 \times 5}{4 \times 1}$ Multiply.

$= \frac{5}{4}$ or $1\frac{1}{4}$ Simplify.

Check for Reasonableness $1\frac{1}{4} \approx 1$ ✔

Got It? Do these problems to find out.

   d. $\frac{1}{2} \times 3$ **e.** $\frac{2}{5} \times 4$ **f.** $\frac{3}{4} \times 5$

Renaming

To rename an improper fraction as a mixed number, divide the numerator by the denominator. Write the remainder as a fraction with the divisor as the denominator.

Show your work.

d. _____

e. _____

f. _____

Multi-Step Example

4. A sloth spends $\frac{4}{5}$ of its life asleep. If a sloth lives to be 28 years old, how many years does it spend awake?

Step 1 $1 - \frac{4}{5} = \frac{5}{5} - \frac{4}{5}$ Find the fraction a sloth spends awake.

$= \frac{1}{5}$ A sloth spends $\frac{1}{5}$ of its life awake.

Step 2 $\frac{1}{5} \times 28 = \frac{1}{5} \times \frac{28}{1}$ Find $\frac{1}{5}$ of 28. Write 28 as $\frac{28}{1}$.

$= \frac{1 \times 28}{5 \times 1}$ Multiply.

$= \frac{28}{5}$ or $5\frac{3}{5}$ Simplify.

A sloth spends $5\frac{3}{5}$ years of its life awake.

Guided Practice

Multiply. Express in simplest form. (Examples 1–3)

1. $10 \times \frac{4}{5} =$ _____

Show your work.

2. $2 \times \frac{3}{4} =$ _____

3. $\frac{3}{8} \times 11 =$ _____

4. $\frac{3}{7} \times 9 =$ _____

5. A cat spends $\frac{2}{3}$ of its life asleep. If a cat lives to be 15 years old, how many years did it spend awake? (Example 4) _____

6. **?** **Building on the Essential Question** How is the process used to multiply a fraction and a whole number similar to the process used to multiply two whole numbers?

_____

_____

_____

_____

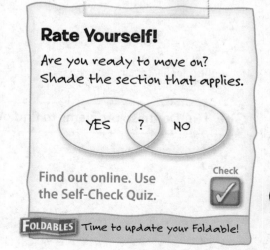

Rate Yourself!

Are you ready to move on?
Shade the section that applies.

YES   ?   NO

Find out online. Use the Self-Check Quiz.

Check ✓

FOLDABLES Time to update your Foldable!

Independent Practice

Multiply. Express in simplest form. (Examples 1–3)

Show your work.

1. $20 \times \frac{3}{4} =$ _____

2. $14 \times \frac{2}{7} =$ _____

3. $10 \times \frac{1}{5} =$ _____

4. $\frac{3}{4} \times 6 =$ _____

5. $\frac{2}{5} \times 11 =$ _____

6. $\frac{1}{4} \times 6 =$ _____

7. **STEM** The male Cuban tree frog is about $\frac{2}{5}$ the size of the female Cuban tree frog. The average size of the female Cuban tree frog is shown at the right. What is the size of the male Cuban tree frog? (Example 4) _____

6 in.

8. The Mississippi River is the second longest river in the United States, second only to the Missouri River. The Mississippi River is about $\frac{23}{25}$ the length of the Missouri River. If the Missouri River is 2,540 miles long, how long is the Mississippi River? (Example 4)

_____

_____

9. One evening, $\frac{2}{3}$ of Mrs. Thorne's students watched a reality television show. Of Mrs. Lombardo's students, $\frac{4}{5}$ watched the same reality show. Which teacher had more students that watched the reality show? Explain.

_____

_____

Teacher	Number of Students
Mrs. Thorne	36
Mrs. Lombardo	30
Mr. Hollern	28

10. **MP** **Use a Problem-Solving Model** The table shows where sixth grade students at Sharonton Middle School attended fifth grade. There are 156 sixth grade students. How many more students attended Sharonton Elementary than Deacon Elementary?

_____

School	Fraction of Students
Sharonton Elementary	$\frac{1}{2}$
Deacon Elementary	$\frac{1}{4}$
Banyon Elementary	$\frac{1}{6}$
New Students	$\frac{1}{12}$

11. 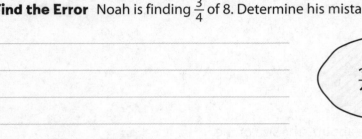 **Use a Problem-Solving Model** Students at Marzo Middle School were recently surveyed. The results reported $\frac{1}{4}$ of sixth grade students, $\frac{3}{10}$ of seventh grade students, and $\frac{2}{7}$ of eighth grade students plan a career in STEM. In which grade do the most students plan to have careers in STEM?

Grade	Total Students
6	152
7	160
8	147

_____

_____

12. Find the Error Noah is finding $\frac{3}{4}$ of 8. Determine his mistake and correct it.

$$\frac{3}{4} \times 8 = \frac{24}{32}$$

_____

_____

_____

_____

🔥 H.O.T. Problems Higher-Order Thinking

13. Create Write a problem involving the multiplication of a fraction and a whole number with a product that is between 8 and 10.

_____

_____

_____

14. Create Use the digits 2, 3, and 5 to create a fraction and a whole number with a product greater than 2.

_____

15. Analyze Jenny made five loaves of banana bread that had $\frac{1}{4}$ cup of oil in each loaf. After she was done baking, she had $\frac{5}{8}$ cup of oil remaining. How much oil did she have before baking?

_____

Multi-Step Problem Solving

16. Sophia is $\frac{3}{4}$ as tall as Mandy. Alexis is $\frac{5}{6}$ as tall as Mandy. What is the difference in height between Sophia and Alexis?

(A) $\frac{1}{12}$ foot

(C) $4\frac{1}{6}$ feet

(B) $\frac{5}{12}$ foot

(D) $3\frac{3}{4}$ feet

Girl	Height (ft)
Sophia	
Mandy	5
Alexis	

Use a problem-solving model to solve this problem.

1 Analyze

Read the problem. Circle the information you know. Underline what the problem is asking you to find.

2 Plan

What will you need to do to solve the problem? Write your plan in steps.

Step 1 Determine the heights of Sophia and Alexis.

Step 2 Subtract to determine the difference between Sophia's height and Alexis's height.

3 Solve

Use your plan to solve the problem. Show your steps.

Sophia: $\frac{3}{4} \times 5 = \dfrac{\boxed{}}{4} = \boxed{} \dfrac{\boxed{}}{4}$ ft tall

Alexis: $\frac{5}{6} \times 5 = \dfrac{\boxed{}}{6} = \boxed{} \dfrac{\boxed{}}{6}$ ft tall

$4\frac{1}{6} - 3\frac{3}{4} = 4\frac{2}{12} - 3\frac{9}{12}$

$\qquad = 3\frac{14}{12} - 3\frac{9}{12}$ or $\frac{5}{12}$

So, Alexis is $\frac{5}{12}$ ft taller than Sophia. The correct answer is _____.

Fill in that answer choice.

> **Read to Succeed!**
> When subtracting mixed numbers, remember to regroup when necessary.
> $4\frac{2}{12} = 3\frac{14}{12}$

4 Justify and Evaluate

How do you know your solution is accurate?

_____

_____

_____

N = Number and Operations   **MP** = Mathematical Processes

More **Multi-Step** Problem Solving

Use a problem-solving model to solve each problem.

17. In June, Arturo spent 20 hours walking dogs in his neighborhood. In July, he spent $\frac{4}{5}$ as much time walking dogs. In August, he spent $\frac{9}{10}$ as much time walking dogs as he did in June. How many more hours did Arturo walk dogs in August than July? N P MP

Ⓐ $\frac{1}{10}$ hour

Ⓑ $\frac{18}{25}$ hour

Ⓒ 2 hours

Ⓓ 16 hours

18. The table shows the number of students in three classes at Hammond Middle School. Of all these students, $\frac{3}{8}$ plan to play in the school band and $\frac{1}{4}$ plan to play sports. How many more students plan to play in the band than play sports? N P MP

Class	Total Students
Ms. Chen	33
Mr. Rice	28
Ms. Lang	35

19. During a read-a-thon, 40 students read as many books as they could in one month. The circle graph below shows the fraction of students that read less than 10 books, 10 to 20 books, and more than 20 books. How many more students read more than 20 books versus less than 10 books? N P MP

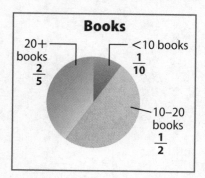

Books

20+ books $\frac{2}{5}$

<10 books $\frac{1}{10}$

10–20 books $\frac{1}{2}$

20. Kisho wants to make ten dozen chocolate chip cookies. He needs $\frac{3}{4}$ cup granulated sugar for the recipe for one dozen cookies. He only has $\frac{1}{4}$ cup of sugar. How many cookies can he make with this amount of sugar? N P MP

Use Models to Multiply Fractions

INQUIRY HOW can I use multiple representations to find a rule for multiplying?

Gardening Ryan has a garden with an area of $\frac{1}{4}$ acre. He is going to plant tomatoes on $\frac{1}{5}$ of his garden. On what portion of an acre will the tomatoes be planted?

What do you know? _____

_____

What do you need to find? _____

_____

Texas Essential Knowledge and Skills

Targeted TEKS
6.3(E) Multiply and divide positive rational numbers fluently. *Also addresses 6.3(B).*

Mathematical Processes
6.1(C), 6.1(D), 6.1(E), 6.1(F), 6.1(G)

Hands-On Activity 1

Determine $\frac{1}{4} \times \frac{1}{5}$ using an area model.

Step 1 Draw a square to represent 1.

Step 2 Divide the square into four columns. Then divide the square into five rows. Shade a rectangle that is $\frac{1}{4}$ unit long by $\frac{1}{5}$ unit wide.

One twentieth of the square is shaded. So, $\frac{1}{4} \times \frac{1}{5} = \frac{\boxed{}}{\boxed{}}$.

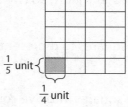

$\frac{1}{5}$ unit

$\frac{1}{4}$ unit

Analyze and Reflect

Collaborate

1. **MP** **Analyze Relationships** Describe how you would change the model to find $\frac{1}{2} \times \frac{1}{10}$. Is the product the same as $\frac{1}{4} \times \frac{1}{5}$? Explain.

_____

_____

_____

Hands-On Activity 2

Determine $\frac{3}{5} \times \frac{1}{3}$ using an area model.

Step 1   Draw a square to represent 1.

Step 2   Divide the square into five columns. Then divide the square into three rows. Shade a rectangle that is $\frac{3}{5}$ unit long by $\frac{1}{3}$ unit wide.

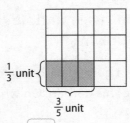

Three-fifteenths, or one-fifth, of the square is shaded. So, $\frac{3}{5} \times \frac{1}{3} = \dfrac{\square}{\square}$.

Analyze and Reflect

2. **MP Analyze Relationships** Compare the product, $\frac{1}{5}$, to the first factor, $\frac{3}{5}$. Explain.

_____

_____

Hands-On Activity 3

Determine $\frac{2}{3} \times \frac{6}{5}$ using an area model.

The second factor is greater than 1, so two squares are needed.

Step 1   Draw two squares to represent 2.

Step 2   Divide the squares into five columns each. Then divide the squares into three rows each. Shade a rectangle that is $\frac{2}{3}$ unit long by $\frac{6}{5}$ unit wide.

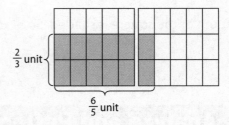

Twelve-fifteenths, or four-fifths, of one square is shaded. So, $\frac{2}{3} \times \frac{6}{5} = \dfrac{\square}{\square}$.

Analyze and Reflect

3. **MP Analyze Relationships** Compare the product, $\frac{4}{5}$, to the first factor, $\frac{2}{3}$. Explain.

_____

_____

Investigate

Work with a partner. Use an area model to determine each product in simplest form.

4. $\frac{1}{2} \times \frac{3}{4}$

5. $\frac{2}{3} \times \frac{3}{5}$

6. $\frac{1}{5} \times \frac{3}{2}$

7. $\frac{1}{6} \times \frac{7}{4}$

8. $\frac{2}{5} \times \frac{1}{2}$

9. $\frac{2}{3} \times \frac{6}{7}$

10. $\frac{3}{8} \times \frac{4}{3}$

11. $\frac{1}{4} \times \frac{7}{5}$

Analyze and Reflect

Work with a partner to complete the table. The first one is done for you.

	Second Factor Greater Than or Less Than One?	Product	Was the First Factor Increased or Decreased?
$\frac{1}{2} \times \frac{3}{4}$	less	$\frac{3}{8}$	decreased
12. $\frac{2}{3} \times \frac{3}{5}$			
13. $\frac{1}{5} \times \frac{3}{2}$			
14. $\frac{1}{6} \times \frac{7}{4}$			
15. $\frac{2}{5} \times \frac{1}{2}$			
16. $\frac{3}{8} \times \frac{4}{3}$			

17. **MP Organize Ideas** When the second factor is less than one, what do you notice about the product?

_____

18. **Connect Models to Rules** Predict whether the products $\frac{2}{3} \times \frac{7}{8}$, $\frac{2}{3} \times 1$ and $\frac{2}{3} \times \frac{3}{2}$ are greater than, less than, or equal to $\frac{2}{3}$. Explain your reasoning with area models.

_____

_____

Create

19. **Connect Models to Rules** Explain the relationship between the numerators of the factors and the numerator of the product, and the relationship between the denominators of the factors and the denominator of the product.

_____

_____

_____

20. **INQUIRY** HOW can I use multiple representations to find a rule for multiplying?

_____

_____

Multiply Fractions

 Launch the Lesson: Real World ▶

A chameleon's body is about $\frac{1}{2}$ the length of its tongue. A certain chameleon has a tongue that is $\frac{2}{3}$ foot long. What is the length of the chameleon's body?

$\frac{2}{3}$ ft $\frac{1}{2}$ size of tongue

Texas Essential Knowledge and Skills TEKS

Targeted TEKS
6.3(E) Multiply and divide positive rational numbers fluently. *Also addresses 6.3(B).*

Mathematical Processes
6.1(A), 6.1(B), 6.1(D), 6.1(G)

Essential Question
WHAT does it mean to multiply and divide fractions and decimals?

Use an area model to show $\frac{1}{2}$ of $\frac{2}{3}$ or $\frac{1}{2} \times \frac{2}{3}$.

1. Divide the rectangle into 2 rows. Then divide it into 3 columns.

2. Shade a rectangle that is $\frac{1}{2}$ unit wide by $\frac{2}{3}$ unit long.

3. Refer to the model. The section that was shaded represents $\frac{1}{2} \times \frac{2}{3}$. What fraction represents $\frac{1}{2} \times \frac{2}{3}$? _____

4. What is the length of a chameleon's body? _____

5. **Analyze** What is the relationship between the numerators and denominators of the factors and the numerator and denominator of the product? _____

_____

_____

Which MP Mathematical Processes did you use?
Shade the circle(s) that applies.

Ⓐ Apply Math to the Real World.   Ⓔ Organize Ideas.

Ⓑ Use a Problem-Solving Model.   Ⓕ Analyze Relationships.

Ⓒ Select Tools and Techniques.   Ⓖ Justify Arguments.

Ⓓ Use Multiple Representations.

Multiply Fractions

Words Multiply the numerators and multiply the denominators.

Models

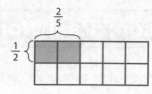

$\frac{2}{5}$

$\frac{1}{2}$

Numbers $\frac{2}{5} \times \frac{1}{2} = \frac{2 \times 1}{5 \times 2}$

Symbols $\frac{a}{b} \times \frac{c}{d} = \frac{a \times c}{b \times d}$, where b and d are not 0.

Work Zone

Tutor

Example

1. **Determine** $\frac{1}{3} \times \frac{1}{4}$. **Write in simplest form.**

   Method 1 Use a model.

   Divide the rectangle into 4 rows. Then divide the rectangle into 3 columns. Shade a section that is $\frac{1}{4}$ unit wide by $\frac{1}{3}$ unit long.

   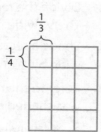

   $\frac{1}{3}$

   $\frac{1}{4}$

   The section that is shaded represents $\frac{1}{4} \times \frac{1}{3}$, or $\frac{1}{12}$.

   Method 2 Use an equation.

   $\frac{1}{3} \times \frac{1}{4} = \blacksquare$

   Show your work.

   $\frac{1}{3} \times \frac{1}{4} = \frac{1 \times 1}{3 \times 4}$ Multiply the numerators.
   Multiply the denominators.

   $= \frac{1}{12}$ Simplify.

   So, $\frac{1}{3} \times \frac{1}{4}$ is $\frac{1}{12}$.

Got It? Do these problems to find out.

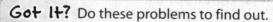

a. $\frac{1}{2} \times \frac{3}{5}$ b. $\frac{1}{3} \times \frac{3}{4}$ c. $\frac{2}{3} \times \frac{5}{6}$

a. _____

b. _____

c. _____

Determine the Size of Products

When multiplying a quantity by a fraction, you can determine whether the quantity will be increased or decreased without computing. By doing so, you can check the reasonableness of your results.

- A quantity is increased if it is multiplied by a fraction greater than one.
- A quantity is decreased if it is multiplied by a fraction less than one.
- A quantity stays the same if it is multiplied by a fraction equal to one.

Examples

Tutor

2. Find $\frac{3}{4} \times \frac{5}{6}$. Does the first factor increase or decrease? Explain.

$$\frac{3}{4} \times \frac{5}{6} = \frac{\overset{1}{3} \times 5}{4 \times \underset{2}{6}}$$ Divide both the numerator and the denominator by 3.

$$= \frac{5}{8}$$ Simplify.

Compare the product to the first factor. The first factor decreases because you found a part of the first factor. $\frac{5}{6} < 1$, so $\frac{3}{4} \times \frac{5}{6} < \frac{3}{4}$.

3. Determine whether $\frac{4}{9} \times 18$ will be less than or greater than $\frac{4}{9}$. Then find the actual product and compare it to your prediction.

Predict $18 > 1$, so the product will be greater than $\frac{4}{9}$.

$$\frac{4}{9} \times 18 = \frac{4}{9} \times \frac{18}{1}$$ Write 18 as a fraction with a denominator of 1.

$$= \frac{4 \times \overset{2}{18}}{\underset{1}{9} \times 1}$$ Divide both the numerator and the denominator by 9.

$$= \frac{8}{1} \text{ or } 8$$ Simplify. Compare to the estimate.

Check The product, 8, is greater than $\frac{4}{9}$. ✔

Got It? Do these problems to find out.

Determine each product. Does the first factor increase or decrease? Explain.

d. $\frac{3}{4} \times \frac{4}{9}$ **e.** $\frac{3}{5} \times 10$

f. Determine whether $\frac{5}{6} \times \frac{9}{10}$ will be less than or greater than $\frac{5}{6}$. Then find the actual product and compare it to your prediction.

g. Determine whether $\frac{7}{10} \times 3$ will be less than or greater than $\frac{7}{10}$. Then find the actual product and compare it to your prediction.

> **Simplify First**
> If the numerators and denominators have a common factor, you can simplify before you multiply.
> $\frac{2}{3} \times \frac{5}{6} = \frac{2 \times 5}{3 \times 6_3} = \frac{5}{9}$

Show your work.

d. _____

e. _____

f. _____

g. _____

Example

 Tutor

4. Frank had $\frac{1}{2}$ of the lawn left to mow. On Saturday, he mowed $\frac{2}{3}$ of what was left. What fraction of the entire lawn did Frank mow on Saturday?

$$\frac{1}{2} \times \frac{2}{3} = \frac{1 \times \overset{1}{\cancel{2}}}{\cancel{2} \times 3}$$ Divide both the numerator and denominator by 2.

$$= \frac{1}{3}$$ Simplify.

So, Frank mowed $\frac{1}{3}$ of the lawn on Saturday.

Guided Practice

Multiply. Write in simplest form. Does the first factor increase or decrease? Explain. (Examples 1–3)

1. $\frac{1}{8} \times \frac{1}{2} =$ _____

2. $\frac{2}{3} \times \frac{4}{5} =$ _____

3. $\frac{4}{5} \times 10 =$ _____

 Show your work.

Determine whether each product will be less than or greater than the first factor. Then determine each product and compare to your prediction.
(Examples 1–3)

4. $\frac{3}{4} \times 12 =$ _____

5. $\frac{3}{10} \times \frac{5}{6} =$ _____

6. $\frac{3}{5} \times \frac{5}{6} =$ _____

7. Rick has $\frac{1}{2}$ of a footlong sub left from yesterday. He ate $\frac{1}{3}$ of the leftover sandwich as a snack. What fraction of the entire sandwich did he eat as a snack? (Example 4)

_____

8. ? **Building on the Essential Question** How can you determine if a factor will increase or decrease when

multiplied by a fraction? _____

_____

_____

Rate Yourself!

Are you ready to move on?
Shade the section that applies.

I have a few questions. | I'm ready to move on.
I have a lot of questions.

Find out online. Use the Self-Check Quiz. Check

Independent Practice

6.3(B), 6.3(E), 6.1(C), 6.1(D)

Multiply. Write in simplest form. Does the first factor increase or decrease? Explain. (Examples 1–3)

1. $\frac{1}{3} \times \frac{2}{5} =$ _____

 Show your work.

2. $\frac{3}{4} \times \frac{5}{8} =$ _____

3. $\frac{2}{3} \times 4 =$ _____

Determine whether each product will be less than or greater than the first factor. Then determine each product and compare to your prediction.
(Examples 1–3)

4. $\frac{5}{6} \times 15 =$ _____

5. $\frac{2}{3} \times \frac{1}{4} =$ _____

6. $\frac{4}{9} \times \frac{3}{8} =$ _____

7. **Financial Literacy** Juanita spent $\frac{3}{4}$ of her allowance at the mall. Of the money spent at the mall, $\frac{1}{2}$ was spent on new earphones. What part of her allowance did Juanita spend on earphones? (Example 4)

_____

8. A paint store has 35 gallons of paint in storage, $\frac{2}{5}$ of which are for outdoor use. The others are for indoor use. If each gallon costs $22, what is the total cost of the indoor paint in storage?

_____

9. Homeroom 101 and Homeroom 102 share a hallway bulletin board. If Homeroom 101 uses $\frac{3}{5}$ of their half to display artwork, what fraction of the bulletin board is used to display Homeroom 101's artwork?

_____

10. **MP Select Tools and Techniques** Mr. Williams' physical education class lasts for $\frac{7}{8}$ -hour.

a. How many minutes are spent warming up and cooling down?

_____

b. How many minutes are *not* spent on instruction? Explain.

_____

_____

Part of $\frac{7}{8}$ -hour Class	
playing game	$\frac{1}{2}$
instruction	$\frac{1}{5}$
warm-up and cool-down	$\frac{3}{10}$

11. **MP** **Use Multiple Representations** Use the bar diagram.

a. **Words** Write a real-world problem represented by the

bar diagram. _____

_____

b. **Models** Draw an area model to represent the situation.

c. **Words** Explain how you would solve your problem.

_____

_____

 H.O.T. Problems Higher-Order Thinking

12. Evaluate State whether each statement is *true* or *false*.
If the statement is *false*, provide a counterexample.

a. The product of two fractions that are each between 0 and 1

is also between 0 and 1. _____

b. The product of a mixed number between 4 and 5 and a fraction

between 0 and 1 is less than 4. _____

c. The product of two mixed numbers that are each between 4 and 5

is between 16 and 25. _____

13. Analyze If the product of two positive fractions a and b is $\frac{15}{56}$, find three pairs

of possible values for a and b. _____

_____

14. Analyze Justify why $\frac{a}{b} \times \frac{b}{c} \times \frac{c}{d} \times \frac{d}{e}$ is equal to $\frac{a}{e}$ when b, c, d, and e are

not zero. _____

_____

15. Create Write a word problem in which you multiply a fraction by a number
greater than 1. Estimate the product, then compare the product to your

estimate. _____

_____

_____

Multi-Step Problem Solving

16. Ella had $\frac{1}{3}$ left of a wall to paint in her bedroom. She painted $\frac{1}{4}$ of what was left to paint as green and $\frac{1}{2}$ of it as yellow. What is the area of the region that Ella has not yet painted?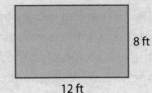

Ⓐ 88 ft^2

Ⓑ 16ft^2

Ⓒ 8 ft^2

Ⓓ 1 ft^2

Use a problem-solving model to solve this problem.

1 Analyze

Read the problem. Circle **the information you know.**
Underline **what the problem is asking you to find.**

2 Plan

What will you need to do to solve the problem? Write your plan in steps.

Step 1 Divide the width into thirds. Divide one of the thirds into fourths. Determine the length of the area not painted.

Step 2 Multiply to find the area.

3 Solve

Use your plan to solve the problem. Show your steps.

1 ft × 8 ft = 8 ft^2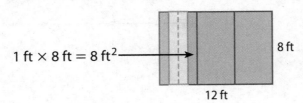

Read to Succeed!
The area of a rectangle is found by using the formula $A = l \cdot w$.

So, Ella has ⬚ square feet left to paint. The correct choice is ⬚.

Fill in that answer choice.

4 Justify and Evaluate

How do you know your solution is accurate?

_____

_____

 N = Number and Operations **EE** = Expressions, Equations, and Relationships **MP** = Mathematical Processes

More Multi-Step Problem Solving

Use a problem-solving model to solve each problem.

17. Denzel earned money after school. He put $\frac{1}{2}$ of this month's earnings into savings. He took the rest to spend at the amusement park. He spent $\frac{1}{5}$ of this amount on popcorn and $\frac{3}{4}$ of it on rides. What fraction of his earnings did he take to the park but not spend on rides or popcorn? **N P MP FL**

Ⓐ $\frac{1}{40}$

Ⓑ $\frac{11}{20}$

Ⓒ $\frac{1}{10}$

Ⓓ $\frac{3}{8}$

18. The table shows how Mura spends her free time on a typical Saturday. If she has 6 hours of free time, how many hours does she spend playing board games or going to the park? **N P MP**

Activity	Fraction of Free Time
Board games	$\frac{1}{10}$
Park	$\frac{2}{5}$
Piano	$\frac{3}{7}$
Reading	$\frac{1}{12}$

19. Ricardo needs to pave the two rectangular sections shown. Determine the total area that Ricardo needs to pave. **N P MP FL**

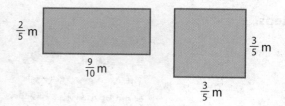

$\frac{2}{5}$ m

$\frac{9}{10}$ m

$\frac{3}{5}$ m

$\frac{3}{5}$ m

20. Without multiplying, determine where the product of $2 \times \frac{12}{7} \times \frac{1}{7}$ is located on the number line. Choose A, B, or C. Justify your reasoning. **N P MP**

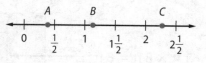

Dance Contest

On the first day of a dance contest registration, six people called the radio station to register. The next day, twice as many people called to register. Each day, the radio station received twice as many registrations as the day before.

If registration was limited to the first 300 participants, on what day did the radio station stop taking registrations?

Mathematical Process
6.1(B) Use a problem-solving model that incorporates analyzing given information, formulating a plan or strategy, determining a solution, justifying the solution, and evaluating the problem-solving process and the reasonableness of the solution.
Targeted TEKS 6.3(E)

 Analyze *What are the facts?*

- On the first day, 6 people registered.
- Each day, twice as many people registered.
- Registration was limited to 300 people.

 Plan *Choose a problem-solving strategy.*

I will use the _____ strategy.

 Solve *How can you apply the strategy?*

Create a table that shows the day, the number of registrations that day, and the running total of registrations.

Day	1	2	3	4	5	6
Number of Registrations	6	12	24			
Total Registrations	6	18	42			

Day 5 ended with _____ registrations, but during

Day _____, the 300th registration was received. So, the

radio station stopped taking registrations on Day _____.

 Justify and Evaluate

How do you know if your solution is reasonable?

The total for just Days 5 and 6 alone would be almost 300. It's reasonable that the radio station stopped taking registrations by Day 6.

Virtual DJ

Andrew is hiring a DJ for a community festival. They expect the festival to last for 5 hours. The cost to hire DJ Trax is shown in the table.

How much will it cost to hire DJ Trax for the festival?

 Analyze

Read the problem. Circle the information you know. Underline what the problem is asking you to find.

Cost to Hire DJ Trax	
Number of Hours	Total Cost ($)
2	251.00
4	502.00
6	753.00

 Plan

Choose a problem-solving strategy.

I will use the _____ strategy.

 Solve

How can you apply the strategy?

So, it will cost $ _____ to hire DJ Trax for 5 hours.

Justify and Evaluate

How do you know your solution is accurate?

_____

_____

Work with a small group to solve the following problems. Show your work on a separate piece of paper.

1. Gaming

The table at the right shows the cost of a subscription to the Action Gamers Channel.

Action Gamers Channel Prices	
Number of Months	Total Cost ($)
2	15.90
3	23.85
4	31.80

What is the cost of a 1-year subscription?

2. Number Theory

The diagram to the right is known as Pascal's Triangle.

If the pattern continues, what will the numbers in the next row be from left to right?

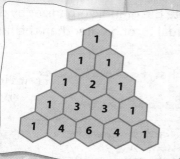

3. Number Sense

Describe the pattern below. Then find the next three numbers.

3.5, 13, 41.5, 127, ☐ , ☐ , ☐

4. Games

Claudio is purchasing a new gaming system. One Web site sells the system for $235.99 and the games for $45.99 each. He bought one system and 3 games.

If Claudio used a $400 gift card, how much will be left on the card?

Use any strategy!

Vocabulary Check

1. Define *Commutative Property*. Provide an example of an operation that is commutative. Provide an example of an operation which is not commutative. **TEKS** 6.7(D), 6.1(G)

_____

_____

_____

Key Concept Check

2. Complete the graphic organizer by determining if the product will be less than, equal to, or greater than the first factor. **TEKS** 6.3(E), 6.1(E)

First factor → Second factor ↓	Fraction Greater than One	Fraction Less than One
Fraction Greater than One		
Fraction Less than One		

3. The length of a pool table is 7.1 feet and the width is 3.6 feet. Determine the area of the surface of the pool table by multiplying the length by the width.

TEKS 6.3(E), 6.1(B) _____

Multi-Step Problem Solving

4. On a weekend trip, Ashton purchased gas twice. He bought 6 gallons of gasoline for $3.48 a gallon and later bought 6.6 gallons for $3.85 a gallon. He can drive, on average, 21.5 miles per gallon. How much did it cost, on average, to drive one mile? Round to the nearest cent.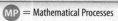

Ⓐ $0.17   Ⓒ $4.30

Ⓑ $0.51   Ⓓ $7.33

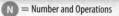 = Number and Operations   **MP** = Mathematical Processes

Use Models to Divide Whole Numbers by Fractions

INQUIRY HOW can I select tools and techniques to help me understand what it means to divide fractions?

Texas Essential Knowledge and Skills

Targeted TEKS
6.3(E) Multiply and divide positive rational numbers fluently.

Mathematical Processes
6.1(C), 6.1(D), 6.1(E), 6.1(F), 6.1(G)

Juan is building a set for the school musical. He has a 3-foot board that he needs to equally divide into $\frac{1}{2}$-foot pieces. How many pieces will he have after he cuts the board?

What do you know? _____

_____

What do you need to find? _____

_____

Hands-On Activity 1

Tools

Step 1 Draw a model that represents the length of the board. Draw lines to separate the board into thirds. Each third represents one foot.

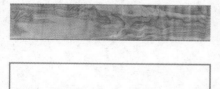

Step 2 Divide each third into halves.

Step 3 Determine how many sections of $\frac{1}{2}$ are in 3. Circle the groups that are the size of the divisor $\frac{1}{2}$.

There are ☐ groups of $\dfrac{☐}{☐}$. So, $3 \div \frac{1}{2} = $ ☐.

Check by multiplying: ☐ $\times \dfrac{☐}{☐} = $ ☐ ✔

Hands-On Activity 2

Determine $4 \div \frac{2}{3}$.

Step 1   The model represents 4.

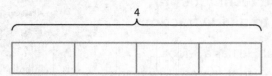

Step 2   Divide each whole into thirds.

Step 3   Circle groups of $\frac{2}{3}$ on the model.   Think: How many groups of $\frac{2}{3}$ are in 4?

There are $\boxed{}$ groups of $\frac{2}{3}$. So, $4 \div \frac{2}{3} = \boxed{}$.

Check by multiplying: $\boxed{} \times \dfrac{\boxed{}}{\boxed{}} = \boxed{}$ ✔

Hands-On Activity 3

Determine $2 \div \frac{3}{4}$.

Step 1   The model represents 2.

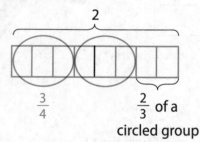

$\frac{3}{4}$ $\frac{2}{3}$ of a circled group

Step 2   Divide each whole into _____.

Step 3   Determine how many groups of $\dfrac{\boxed{}}{\boxed{}}$ are in $\boxed{}$.

Circle groups of $\dfrac{\boxed{}}{\boxed{}}$ on the model.

There are $\boxed{}$ groups of $\frac{3}{4}$ and $\frac{2}{3}$ of a group left over. So, $2 \div \frac{3}{4} = \boxed{} \dfrac{\boxed{}}{\boxed{}}$.

Check by multiplying: $\boxed{} \dfrac{\boxed{}}{\boxed{}} \times \dfrac{\boxed{}}{\boxed{}} = \boxed{}$ ✔

 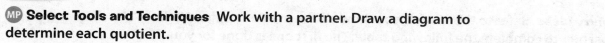 **Investigate**

MP Select Tools and Techniques Work with a partner. Draw a diagram to determine each quotient.

1. $3 \div \frac{1}{3} =$ _____

2. $2 \div \frac{1}{4} =$ _____

 Show your work.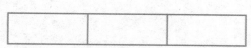

3. $6 \div \frac{2}{3} =$ _____

4. $4 \div \frac{1}{2} =$ _____

5. $3 \div \frac{3}{4} =$ _____

6. $4 \div \frac{3}{4} =$ _____

7. $5 \div \frac{2}{3} =$ _____

8. $2 \div \frac{4}{5} =$ _____

Analyze and Reflect

MP Organize Ideas Refer to the models you drew on the previous page. Work with a partner to complete the following table. The first one is done for you.

Division Problem	Quotient	Is the Quotient Less Than or Greater Than the Dividend?
$3 \div \frac{1}{3}$	9	greater
9. $2 \div \frac{1}{4}$		
10. $6 \div \frac{2}{3}$		
11. $4 \div \frac{1}{2}$		
12. $3 \div \frac{3}{4}$		
13. $4 \div \frac{3}{4}$		

14. **Connect Models to Rules** When a whole number is divided by a fraction that is less than one, will the quotient be less than or greater than the whole number? Explain.

_____

_____

_____

Create

15. **MP Apply Math to the Real World** Write a real-world problem that involves $4 \div \frac{4}{5}$. Solve the problem and multiply to check your answer.

_____

_____

16. **INQUIRY** HOW can I select tools and techniques to help me understand

what it means to divide fractions? _____

_____

_____

Divide Whole Numbers by Fractions

Launch the Lesson: Vocabulary

Texas Essential Knowledge and Skills

Targeted TEKS
6.3(E) Multiply and divide positive rational numbers fluently. *Also addresses 6.3(A).*

Mathematical Processes
6.1(A), 6.1(B), 6.1(D), 6.1(G)

Any two numbers with a product of 1 are called **reciprocals**.

Complete the table below by finding the reciprocal of $\frac{2}{3}$. Use the *guess, check,* and *revise* strategy. The first one is done for you.

Number	Product	Reciprocal
$\frac{1}{2}$	$\frac{1}{2} \times 2 = 1$	2
$\frac{2}{3}$	$\frac{2}{3} \times \dfrac{\square}{\square} = 1$	$\dfrac{\square}{\square}$

Vocab

Vocabulary
reciprocals

Essential Question
WHAT does it mean to multiply and divide fractions and decimals?

Describe the relationship between the numerator and the

denominator of a number and its reciprocal. _____

_____

 ## Real-World Investigation

Another name for reciprocal is *multiplicative inverse*. What are some words in everyday language that are similar to reciprocal or inverse?

_____

Pilots can fly in an *inverted* position, or upside down. How can you use the everyday meaning of *invert* to help you remember the mathematical

meaning of multiplicative inverse, or reciprocal? _____

_____

Which MP Mathematical Processes did you use?
Shade the circle(s) that applies.

Ⓐ Apply Math to the Real World.
Ⓑ Use a Problem-Solving Model.
Ⓒ Select Tools and Techniques.
Ⓓ Use Multiple Representations.
Ⓔ Organize Ideas.
Ⓕ Analyze Relationships.
Ⓖ Justify Arguments.

Find Reciprocals

Dividing 3 by $\frac{1}{2}$ gives the same result as multiplying 3 by 2, which is the reciprocal of $\frac{1}{2}$. Any two numbers with a product of 1 are called reciprocals.

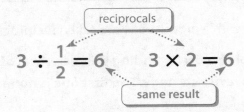

$$3 \div \frac{1}{2} = 6 \qquad 3 \times 2 = 6$$

reciprocals

same result

Tutor

Examples

1. **Determine the reciprocal of $\frac{2}{3}$.**

Since $\frac{2}{3} \times \frac{3}{2} = 1$, the reciprocal of $\frac{2}{3}$ is $\frac{3}{2}$.

2. **Determine the reciprocal of $\frac{1}{8}$.**

Since $\frac{1}{8} \times \frac{8}{1} = 1$, the reciprocal of $\frac{1}{8}$ is $\frac{8}{1}$ or 8.

3. **Determine the reciprocal of 5.**

Write the whole number as a fraction.

$$5 = \frac{\boxed{}}{1}$$

Determine the missing factor.

$$\frac{\boxed{}}{\boxed{}} \times \frac{\boxed{}}{\boxed{}} = 1$$

The reciprocal of 5 is $\frac{\boxed{}}{\boxed{}}$.

Got It? Do these problems to find out.

Determine the reciprocal of each number.

a. $\frac{3}{5}$ b. $\frac{1}{3}$ c. 11

Reciprocals

The examples suggest that you "invert" the fraction to find the reciprocal. That is, switch the numerator and denominator. You can use reciprocals to divide fractions.

 Show your work.

a. _____

b. _____

c. _____

Divide by a Fraction

Words   Dividing by a rational number and multiplying by its reciprocal result in equivalent values.

To divide a whole number by a fraction, multiply by its reciprocal.

Example $5 \div \frac{2}{3} = \frac{5}{1} \times \frac{3}{2}$

The division expression $5 \div \frac{2}{3}$ is read as 5 *divided by two thirds*. You need to find how many two-thirds are in 5.

Examples

Tutor

4. Determine $2 \div \frac{1}{3}$. **Write in simplest form.**

Method 1   **Use a model.**

Model the dividend, 2.

Divide each whole into thirds.

Think: How many thirds are in 2?

There are 6 total sections.

2

| $\frac{1}{3}$ | $\frac{1}{3}$ | $\frac{1}{3}$ | $\frac{1}{3}$ | $\frac{1}{3}$ | $\frac{1}{3}$ |

Method 2   **Multiply by the reciprocal.**

$2 \div \frac{1}{3} = \frac{2}{1} \times \frac{3}{1}$ Multiply by the reciprocal of $\frac{1}{3}$.

$= \frac{6}{1}$ or 6   Multiply the numerators.
Multiply the denominators.

- -

5. Determine $7 \div \frac{2}{3}$. **Write in simplest form.**

$7 \div \frac{2}{3} = \dfrac{\square}{\square} \times \dfrac{\square}{\square}$ Write the whole number as a fraction.
Multiply by the reciprocal of $\frac{2}{3}$.

$\dfrac{\square}{\square} \times \dfrac{\square}{\square} = \dfrac{\square}{\square}$ Multiply the numerators.
Multiply the denominators.

$\dfrac{\square}{\square} = \square \dfrac{\square}{\square}$ Simplify.

Show your work.

d. _____

e. _____

Got It? **Do these problems to find out.**

    d. $6 \div \frac{1}{3}$ **e.** $5 \div \frac{2}{3}$ **f.** $4 \div \frac{3}{4}$

f. _____

Example

6. At summer camp, the duration of a field hockey game is $\frac{3}{4}$ hour. The camp counselors have set aside 6 hours for field hockey games. How many games can be played?

Divide 6 by three-fourths.

$6 \div \frac{3}{4} = \frac{6}{1} \times \frac{4}{3}$ Multiply by the reciprocal.

$= \frac{\overset{2}{\cancel{6}}}{1} \times \frac{4}{\underset{1}{\cancel{3}}}$ Divide 3 and 6 by the GCF, 3.

$= \frac{8}{1}$ or 8   Simplify.

So, 8 games can be played.

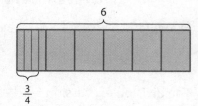

Guided Practice

Determine the reciprocal of each number. (Examples 1–3)

1. $\frac{2}{3}$ _____

2. $\frac{1}{7}$ _____

3. 4 _____

Show your work.

Write an equivalent multiplication expression. Then divide. Write in simplest form. (Examples 4 and 5)

4. $2 \div \frac{1}{3} =$ _____

5. $2 \div \frac{4}{5} =$ _____

6. $5 \div \frac{2}{7} =$ _____

7. A neighborhood development that is 4 acres is to be divided into $\frac{2}{3}$-acre lots. How many lots can be created?

(Example 6) _____

8. **Building on the Essential Question** Why does a whole number divided by a fraction less than one have a quotient greater than the whole number dividend?

_____
_____
_____
_____

Rate Yourself!

How well do you understand dividing whole numbers by fractions? Circle the image that applies.

Clear   Somewhat Clear   Not So Clear

Find out online. Use the Self-Check Quiz.

Check ✓

FOLDABLES Time to update your Foldable!

Independent Practice

Determine the reciprocal of each number. (Examples 1–3)

Show your work.

1. $\frac{3}{5}$ _____

2. $\frac{1}{4}$ _____

3. 1 _____

**Write an equivalent multiplication expression. Then divide.
Write in simplest form.** (Examples 4 and 5)

4. $3 \div \frac{3}{4} =$ _____

5. $5 \div \frac{3}{4} =$ _____

6. $8 \div \frac{4}{7} =$ _____

7. $6 \div \frac{3}{5} =$ _____

8. $2 \div \frac{5}{8} =$ _____

9. $4 \div \frac{8}{9} =$ _____

10. Jamar has an 8-foot-long piece of wood that he wants to cut to build a step stool for his tree house. If each piece is going to be $\frac{5}{6}$ foot long, what is the greatest number of pieces he will be able to use? (Example 6)

_____

11. The average adult horse needs $\frac{2}{5}$ bale of hay each day to meet dietary requirements. A horse farm has 44 bales of hay. How many horses can be fed in one day with 44 bales of hay? (Example 6)

_____

12. **MP** **Justify Arguments** Ethan ordered 4 sub sandwiches for a party. Each $\frac{1}{2}$ sandwich is one serving. Does he have enough to serve 7 friends? How much is leftover or how much more is needed? Explain. _____

_____

_____

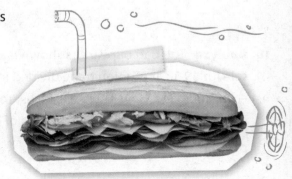

13. Chelsea has four hours of free time on Saturday. She would like to spend no more than $\frac{2}{3}$ of an hour on an activity. How many activities can she do during that time? Justify your procedure.

_____

14. (MP) **Apply Math to the Real World** Find an example of dividing a whole number by a fraction in a newspaper or on the Internet. Write a real-world problem in which you would divide a whole number by a fraction.

_____

15. (MP) **Analyze Relationships** Circle the expression that does not belong with the other three. Explain your reasoning.

$$\frac{7}{1} \times \frac{3}{2} \qquad 7 \div \frac{2}{3} \qquad 7 \times \frac{2}{3} \qquad 7 \times \frac{3}{2}$$

_____

16. Find the Error Daniella is solving $\frac{8}{9} \div 4$. Find her mistake and correct it.

_____

_____

_____

$$\frac{8}{9} \div 4 = \frac{8}{9} \times \frac{4}{1}$$
$$= \frac{32}{9} \text{ or } 3\frac{5}{9}$$

🔥 H.O.T. Problems Higher-Order Thinking

17. Analyze The Snack Shack is making a batch of trail mix. They use $9\frac{1}{3}$ pounds of granola, $9\frac{1}{3}$ pounds of mixed nuts, and $9\frac{1}{3}$ pounds of yogurt raisins to make the trail mix. They divide the mixture into 14 packages. How much is in each package? Explain.

_____

_____

_____

18. Analyze The bag of peanuts shown is on sale for $9.30. It is going to be divided into $\frac{3}{4}$-pound bags. How much will it cost to fill one smaller bag? How many pounds of peanuts will be remaining? _____

5 pounds

Name _____

Multi-Step Problem Solving

19. The table shows the ingredients needed to make one batch of salad dressing. A chef has 3 tablespoons of minced garlic. She made the greatest number of batches possible. How many tablespoons of garlic were left?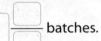

Ingredient	Amount
Oil	1 cup
Vinegar	$\frac{3}{4}$ cup
Minced garlic	$\frac{2}{3}$ tbsp

Ⓐ $\frac{1}{2}$ tablespoon   Ⓒ $\frac{2}{3}$ tablespoon

Ⓑ $\frac{1}{3}$ tablespoon   Ⓓ $\frac{5}{6}$ tablespoon

Use a problem-solving model to solve this problem.

1 Analyze

Read the problem. Circle the information you know.
Underline what the problem is asking you to find.

2 Plan

What will you need to do to solve the problem? Write your plan in steps.

Step 1   Divide to determine the number of batches made.

Step 2   Subtract to determine the amount remaining.

Read to Succeed! When dividing by fractions, multiply by the reciprocal.

3 Solve

Use your plan to solve the problem. Show your steps.

The chef could make $3 \div \frac{2}{3}$ or ⬚ $\frac{⬚}{⬚}$ batches.

Since she made ⬚ full batches, there is $\frac{⬚}{⬚}$ batch left.

One-half of a batch uses $\frac{1}{2} \times \frac{2}{3}$ or _____ tablespoon. The correct choice is _____. Fill in that answer choice.

4 Justify and Evaluate

How do you know your solution is accurate?

_____

_____

_____

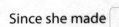

More Multi-Step Problem Solving

Use a problem-solving model to solve each problem.

20. The table shows the time it takes each person to build a house of cards. If there are 2 hours available to make houses of cards, how many more houses can Fina make than Logan?
N P MP

Person	Time (hours)
Jenna	$\frac{1}{4}$
Logan	$\frac{1}{3}$
Fina	$\frac{1}{5}$

Ⓐ 3

Ⓑ 4

Ⓒ 5

Ⓓ 6

21. Aria made 9 pounds of fudge. She separates the fudge into $\frac{3}{4}$-pound portions. She sells each portion for $6.50. If she sells all the fudge, how much money will she make?
N P MP

22. Robert and Judi are ordering lasagnas for a party. Robert ordered 10 large lasagnas. Each lasagna is cut into tenths. Judi ordered 6 smaller lasagnas. Each lasagna was cut into eighths. How many pieces did they order in all? N P MP

23. Cadence is making gift bags filled with different colored beads for her jewelry party. She fills the bags using a mixture of $1\frac{1}{2}$ pounds pink beads, $\frac{3}{4}$ pound purple beads, and $1\frac{1}{4}$ pounds green beads. She divides the mixture into 8 packages. How much is in each package? N P MP

N = Number and Operations   P = Proportionality   MP = Mathematical Processes

INQUIRY HOW can I select tools and techniques to help me divide one fraction by another fraction?

Toby bought $\frac{8}{9}$ pound of mixed candy from the grocery store. He wants to divide the candy into $\frac{2}{9}$-pound bags. How many bags can Toby make?

What do you know? _____

_____

What do you need to find? _____

_____

Texas Essential Knowledge and Skills TEKS

Targeted TEKS
6.3(E) Multiply and divide positive rational numbers fluently. *Also addresses 6.3(A).*

Mathematical Processes
6.1(C), 6.1(D), 6.1(E), 6.1(F)

Hands-On Activity 1

To solve the problem, use the division sentence $\frac{8}{9} \div \frac{2}{9}$. This shows how many groups of $\dfrac{\boxed{}}{\boxed{}}$ are in $\frac{8}{9}$.

Step 1 To make a bar diagram that represents the amount of Toby's candy, divide the bar into $\boxed{}$ sections.

$\boxed{}$

Step 2 Shade $\boxed{}$ of the sections to represent $\frac{8}{9}$ pound.

Step 3 Circle each group of $\frac{2}{9}$ in the shaded section. Determine the number of equal groups of $\frac{2}{9}$.

There are _____ groups of $\frac{2}{9}$ in $\frac{8}{9}$. So, $\frac{8}{9} \div \frac{2}{9} = \boxed{}$.

Toby can make _____ bags of candy that each have $\dfrac{\boxed{}}{\boxed{}}$ pound.

Hands-On Activity 2

Draw a diagram to determine $\frac{3}{4} \div \frac{3}{8}$.

Step 1   Rename so the fractions have common denominators. Since 8 is

a multiple of 4, rename the fraction $\frac{3}{4}$ as $\dfrac{\boxed{}}{\boxed{}}$.

Step 2   Draw a diagram with $\boxed{}$ sections and shade $\boxed{}$ of the sections
to represent $\frac{6}{8}$ pound.

Step 3   Circle each group of $\frac{3}{8}$ in the shaded section. Determine the number
of equal groups of $\frac{3}{8}$.

There are _____ groups of $\frac{3}{8}$ in $\frac{6}{8}$.

So, $\frac{3}{4} \div \frac{3}{8} = \boxed{}$.

Hands-On Activity 3

Draw a diagram to determine $\frac{2}{3} \div 2$.

Step 1   Draw a diagram and shade the sections to represent $\dfrac{\boxed{}}{\boxed{}}$.

Step 2   Divide the shaded sections into _____ equal groups.

Step 3   Write the fraction that names each group. $\dfrac{\boxed{}}{\boxed{}}$

So, $\frac{2}{3} \div 2 = \dfrac{\boxed{}}{\boxed{}}$.

Investigate

Select Tools and Techniques Work with a partner. Draw a diagram to determine each quotient.

1. $\frac{6}{7} \div \frac{2}{7} =$ _____

2. $\frac{4}{5} \div \frac{2}{5} =$ _____

3. $\frac{6}{7} \div \frac{3}{7} =$ _____

4. $\frac{8}{10} \div \frac{2}{5} =$ _____

5. $\frac{3}{4} \div \frac{1}{2} =$ _____

6. $\frac{5}{6} \div \frac{2}{3} =$ _____

7. $\frac{4}{7} \div 2 =$ _____

8. $\frac{12}{13} \div 3 =$ _____

MP Organize Ideas Work with a partner to complete the table. The first one is done for you.

	Division Expression	Quotient	Multiplication Sentence
	$\frac{4}{5} \div \frac{1}{5}$	4	$\frac{1}{5} \times 4 = \frac{4}{5}$
9.	$\frac{8}{9} \div 8$		
10.			$\frac{3}{4} \times \frac{1}{2} = \frac{3}{8}$
11.	$\frac{6}{8} \div \frac{2}{8}$		
12.			$\frac{3}{7} \times 1 = \frac{3}{7}$
13.	$\frac{10}{11} \div 5$		
14.			$\frac{5}{9} \times 1 = \frac{5}{9}$

15. **MP Analyze Relationships** Use the table to compare the divisor and dividend to the quotient. When is the quotient greater than 1?

_____

_____

Create
On Your Own

16. **Connect Models to Rules** Some quotients in the table are less than 1. Write a rule about when the quotient of two fractions will be less than 1.

_____

17. **MP Apply Math to the Real World** Write a real-world problem that involves $\frac{6}{8} \div \frac{2}{8}$. Solve the problem and multiply to check your answer.

_____

_____

18. **INQUIRY** HOW can I select tools and techniques to help me divide one fraction by another fraction?

_____

_____

Divide Fractions

Launch the Lesson: Real World

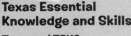 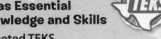

Texas Essential Knowledge and Skills

Targeted TEKS
6.3(E) Multiply and divide positive rational numbers fluently. *Also addresses 6.3(A).*

Mathematical Processes
6.1(A), 6.1(B), 6.1(C), 6.1(D), 6.1(E)

Three students are painting an equal part of an art mural. The art mural is half painted. What part of the whole mural has each student painted?

Essential Question

WHAT does it mean to multiply and divide fractions and decimals?

1. Divide the painted area into 3 equal parts.

2. Place an X over each part of the painted area. This represents the part each student has painted. Then divide the unpainted area into the same number of parts.

3. What fraction of the whole mural has each student painted? $\dfrac{\square}{\square}$

4. **Analyze** So, $\dfrac{1}{2} \div 3 = \dfrac{\square}{\square}$. It is also true that $\dfrac{1}{2} \times \dfrac{\square}{\square} = \dfrac{\square}{\square}$.

Compare and contrast the division problem and the multiplication problem.

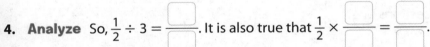

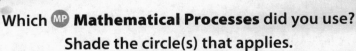

Which MP **Mathematical Processes** did you use?
Shade the circle(s) that applies.

(A) Apply Math to the Real World.

(B) Use a Problem-Solving Model.

(C) Select Tools and Techniques.

(D) Use Multiple Representations.

(E) Organize Ideas.

(F) Analyze Relationships.

(G) Justify Arguments.

Divide by a Fraction

Words	Dividing by a fraction and multiplying by its reciprocal result in equivalent values.
	To divide by a fraction, multiply by its reciprocal.

Example

Numbers

$$\frac{5}{6} \div \frac{2}{3} = \frac{5}{6} \times \frac{3}{2}$$

Algebra

$$\frac{a}{b} \div \frac{c}{d} = \frac{a}{b} \times \frac{d}{c}, \text{ where } b, c, \text{ and } d \neq 0$$

Work Zone

Tutor

Example

1. Find $\frac{1}{2} \div \frac{1}{3}$. **Write in simplest form.**

Method 1 **Use a model.**

Model the dividend, $\frac{1}{2}$.

Divide the whole into thirds.

$\frac{1}{2} \div \frac{1}{3}$ means how many

thirds are in $\frac{1}{2}$.

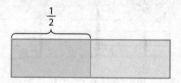

There are $1\frac{1}{2}$ one-third

sections in $\frac{1}{2}$.

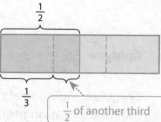

$\frac{1}{2}$ of another third

Method 2 **Multiply by the reciprocal.**

$$\frac{1}{2} \div \frac{1}{3} = \blacksquare$$

$$\frac{1}{2} \div \frac{1}{3} = \frac{1}{2} \times \frac{3}{1} \qquad \text{Multiply by the reciprocal, } \frac{3}{1}.$$

$$= \frac{3}{2} \text{ or } 1\frac{1}{2} \qquad \text{Multiply the numerators.}$$
$$\text{Multiply the denominators.}$$

Show your work.

So, $\frac{1}{2} \div \frac{1}{3} = 1\frac{1}{2}$.

Check by multiplying: $\frac{3}{2} \times \frac{1}{3} = \frac{1}{2}$ ✔

Got It? **Do these problems to find out.**

a. _____

b. _____

c. _____

a. $\frac{1}{4} \div \frac{3}{8}$ 　　　　 b. $\frac{2}{3} \div \frac{3}{8}$ 　　　　 c. $\frac{5}{6} \div \frac{1}{3}$

Example Tutor

2. **Write a real-world problem for $\frac{2}{3} \div \frac{1}{6}$. Use a model to solve.**

Mariska has $\frac{2}{3}$-pound of sunflower seeds. Each day, she feeds the cardinals in her yard $\frac{1}{6}$ pound of seeds. For how many days will she be able to feed the cardinals?

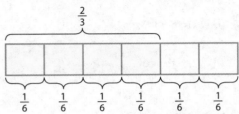

Model $\frac{2}{3}$. The whole is divided into six sections. Count the number of $\frac{1}{6}$ sections.

So, Mariska can feed the cardinals for 4 days.

Got It? Do this problem to find out.

d. Write a real-world problem for $\frac{3}{4} \div \frac{1}{8}$. Use a model to solve.

d. _____

Divide a Fraction by a Whole Number

When you divide a fraction by a whole number, express the whole number as a fraction. Then divide as with fractions.

Example Tutor

3. **Determine $\frac{5}{7} \div 10$. Write in simplest form.**

$\frac{5}{7} \div 10 = \frac{5}{7} \div \frac{10}{1}$ Express the whole number as a fraction with a denominator of 1.

$= \frac{5}{7} \times \frac{1}{10}$ Multiply by the reciprocal.

$= \frac{\overset{1}{\cancel{5}} \times 1}{7 \times \underset{2}{\cancel{10}}}$ Divide 5 and 10 by their GCF, 5.

$= \frac{1}{14}$ Multiply the numerators.
Multiply the denominators.

e. _____

f. _____

Got It? Do these problems to find out.

g. _____

e. $\frac{8}{9} \div 4$ **f.** $\frac{4}{5} \div 8$ **g.** $\frac{12}{13} \div 4$

Tutor

Example

4. Ramón is making party favors. He is dividing $\frac{3}{4}$ pound of almonds into 12 packages. Write and solve an equation to find how many pounds of almonds are in each package.

To find the number of pounds in each package, solve the equation $\frac{3}{4} \div 12 = \blacksquare$.

$$\frac{3}{4} \div 12 = \frac{3}{4} \times \frac{1}{12}$$ Multiply by the reciprocal, $\frac{1}{12}$.

$$= \frac{\overset{1}{\cancel{3}} \times 1}{4 \times \underset{4}{\cancel{12}}}$$ Divide 3 and 12 by their GCF, 3.

$$= \frac{1}{16}$$ Multiply the numerators.
Multiply the denominators.

There will be $\frac{1}{16}$ pound of almonds in each package.

Guided Practice

Write an equivalent multiplication expression. Then divide. Write in simplest form. Check by multiplying. (Examples 1 and 3)

1. $\frac{1}{4} \div \frac{1}{2} =$ _____

Show your work.

2. $\frac{5}{6} \div \frac{2}{3} =$ _____

3. $\frac{1}{8} \div 3 =$ _____

4. Write a real-world problem for $\frac{2}{3} \div \frac{5}{6}$. Use a model to solve. (Example 2)

_____

_____

5. A neighborhood garden that is $\frac{2}{3}$ of an acre is to be divided into 4 equal-size sections. Write and solve an equation to find the size of each section. (Example 4)

_____

6. **?** **Building on the Essential Question** How is the process used to divide fractions similar to the process used to multiply fractions?

_____

_____

Rate Yourself!

How confident are you about dividing fractions? Shade the ring on the target.

☹   ☹   ☺
☐ ☐ ☐ ☐ ☐

Find out online. Use the Self-Check Quiz.

Check

FOLDABLES Time to update your Foldable!

Independent Practice

6.3(A), 6.3(E), 6.1(C), 6.1(D), 6.1(E) TEKS

Write an equivalent multiplication expression. Then divide. Write in simplest form. Check by multiplying. (Examples 1 and 3)

1. $\frac{1}{8} \div \frac{1}{2} =$ _____

Show your work.

2. $\frac{3}{4} \div \frac{2}{3} =$ _____

3. $\frac{3}{4} \div 9 =$ _____

4. $\frac{1}{6} \div \frac{4}{7} =$ _____

5. $\frac{1}{3} \div 8 =$ _____

6. $\frac{1}{3} \div \frac{5}{6} =$ _____

7. Write a real-world problem for $\frac{5}{6} \div \frac{1}{12}$. Use a model to solve. (Example 2)

_____

_____

_____

Write and solve an equation. (Example 4)

8. A piece of licorice is to be cut into 10 equal-size pieces. If the length of the piece of licorice is $\frac{2}{3}$ yard, how long will each piece of licorice be?

_____

_____

9. **MP Select Tools and Techniques** To tie-dye one T-shirt, $\frac{3}{8}$ cup of dye is needed. The table shows the number of cups of each color of dye in Mr. Galvez's art class. How many T-shirts can be made using only orange dye?

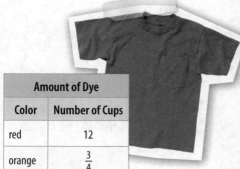

Amount of Dye	
Color	Number of Cups
red	12
orange	$\frac{3}{4}$

_____

10. Carlota has $\frac{3}{4}$ ton of mulch she is going to divide evenly among 5 flower beds. How much mulch will each flower bed contain?

_____

11. **MP** **Organize Ideas** Complete the Venn diagram to compare and contrast the division and multiplication problems.

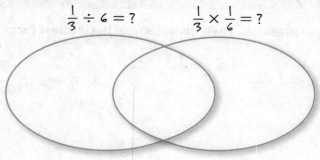

$$\frac{1}{3} \div 6 = ? \qquad \frac{1}{3} \times \frac{1}{6} = ?$$

 H.O.T. Problems Higher-Order Thinking

12. **Create** Find two positive fractions with a quotient of $\frac{5}{6}$. Give the equivalent multiplication sentence.

_____

13. **Analyze** Is the quotient $\frac{2}{3} \div \frac{1}{2}$ greater than or less than 1? Is the quotient of $\frac{1}{2} \div \frac{2}{3}$ greater than or less than 1? Explain your reasoning.

_____

_____

14. **Analyze** Complete the steps to demonstrate why you multiply by the reciprocal when dividing fractions. Determine $\frac{1}{4} \div \frac{3}{8}$.

Step 1 Rewrite it as $\dfrac{\frac{1}{4}}{\frac{3}{8}}$.

Step 2 Multiply the numerator and the denominator by the reciprocal of $\frac{3}{8}$. $\dfrac{\frac{1}{4}}{\frac{3}{8}} = \dfrac{\frac{1}{4} \times \boxed{}/\boxed{}}{\frac{3}{8} \times \boxed{}/\boxed{}}$

Step 3 Simplify the denominator. $\dfrac{\frac{1}{4} \times \frac{8}{3}}{\boxed{}}$

Step 4 Simplify the fraction. $\dfrac{\boxed{}}{\boxed{}} \times \dfrac{\boxed{}}{\boxed{}}$

15. **Analyze** In cooking, 1 drop is equal to $\frac{1}{6}$ of a dash. If a recipe calls for $\frac{2}{3}$ of a dash, write an expression that would give the number of drops that are needed.

_____

Multi-Step Problem Solving

16. Alfonso is making snack bags with different types of nuts as shown in the table. Each snack bag contains $\frac{1}{8}$ pound of one type of nut. How many more whole servings of walnuts can he make than peanuts?

Type of Nut	Weight (lb)
Almonds	$\frac{1}{2}$
Cashews	$\frac{1}{4}$
Peanuts	$\frac{2}{5}$
Walnuts	$\frac{3}{4}$

(A) 1   (C) 3

(B) 2   (D) 6

Use a problem-solving model to solve this problem.

1 Analyze

Read the problem. Circle the information you know.
Underline what the problem is asking you to find.

2 Plan

What will you need to do to solve the problem? Write your plan in steps.

Step 1   Divide to determine the number of servings of walnuts and peanuts.

Step 2   Subtract to determine how many more servings of walnuts than peanuts.

3 Solve

Use your plan to solve the problem. Show your steps.

Walnuts: $\frac{3}{4} \div \frac{1}{8} = \frac{3}{4} \cdot \frac{8}{1}$ or ☐ servings

Peanuts: $\frac{2}{5} \div \frac{1}{8} = \frac{2}{5} \cdot \frac{8}{1}$ or ☐$\frac{☐}{☐}$ servings

So, Alfonso made 6 − 3 or ____ more whole servings of walnuts

than peanuts. The correct choice is ____.

Read to Succeed!

The number of whole servings of peanuts is 3 because $\frac{1}{5}$ is not a whole serving.

4 Justify and Evaluate

How do you know your solution is accurate?

_____

_____

N = Number and Operations   **MP** = Mathematical Processes

Use a problem-solving model to solve each problem.

17. Anabella is using ribbon to decorate the edge of a picture frame with a length of $\frac{1}{4}$ yard and a width of $\frac{1}{6}$ yard. She will only use one color to decorate the frame. Each color of ribbon is available in lengths as shown in the table. How many more strips of green ribbon than blue ribbon would she need for the frame? Ⓝ Ⓜ🅟

Color	Strip Length (yd)
Black	$\frac{1}{2}$
Blue	$\frac{2}{3}$
Green	$\frac{1}{6}$

Ⓐ 5

Ⓑ 3

Ⓒ 2

Ⓓ 1

18. Camillo is decorating birthday cards with glitter to send to his friends. The table shows the different colors of glitter that he has. He will mix all these colors together, and then use $\frac{1}{4}$ tube of glitter on each card. How many birthday cards can he decorate? Ⓝ Ⓜ🅟

Color	Tubes
Red	2
Yellow	$\frac{3}{5}$
Purple	$\frac{3}{8}$
Pink	$\frac{1}{2}$

19. Stephanie usually jogs $\frac{3}{4}$ mile every day. She decides that she wants to sprint for a part of this distance. She will jog for $\frac{1}{2}$ of $\frac{3}{4}$ mile and will sprint the rest, but she only sprints $\frac{1}{8}$ mile at a time before resting. How many sprints will Stephanie do each day? Ⓝ Ⓜ🅟

20. Without doing any calculations, which expression does not have the same value as $\frac{1}{2} \div \frac{2}{3}$? Explain. Ⓝ 🅟 Ⓜ🅟

A	$\frac{1}{2} \div \frac{4}{6}$
B	$\frac{1}{2} \times \frac{3}{2}$
C	$\frac{3}{6} \times \frac{3}{2}$
D	$\frac{3}{6} \div \frac{6}{4}$

Ⓝ = Number and Operations 🅟 = Proportionality Ⓜ🅟 = Mathematical Processes

Multiply and Divide Mixed Numbers

The eyeball of an Atlantic Giant Squid is about 12 times as large as the average human eyeball. The average human eyeball is $1\frac{1}{4}$ inches across. Draw a bar diagram to compare the average size of a human eyeball to the average size of an Atlantic Giant Squid's eyeball.

Texas Essential Knowledge and Skills

Targeted TEKS
6.3(E) Multiply and divide positive rational numbers fluently. *Also addresses 6.3(A).*

Mathematical Processes
6.1(A), 6.1(B), 6.1(D), 6.1(G)

Essential Question
WHAT does it mean to multiply and divide fractions and decimals?

1. Use your diagram to write a multiplication expression that shows the size of the Atlantic Giant Squid's eyeball. _____

2. Write your multiplication expression from Exercise 1 using improper fractions. Multiply to find the size of the squid's eyeball. _____

3. Write a related division expression for your multiplication expression. What is the quotient? _____

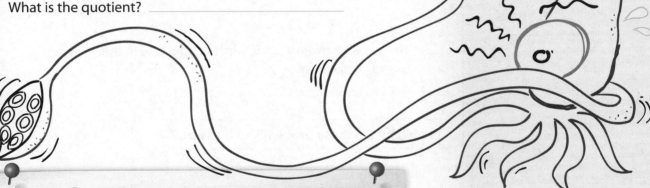

Which MP Mathematical Processes did you use?
Shade the circle(s) that applies.

Ⓐ Apply Math to the Real World.　　Ⓔ Organize Ideas.

Ⓑ Use a Problem-Solving Model.　　Ⓕ Analyze Relationships.

Ⓒ Select Tools and Techniques.　　Ⓖ Justify Arguments.

Ⓓ Use Multiple Representations.

Multiply Mixed Numbers

To multiply with mixed numbers, write each mixed number as an improper fraction. Use the greatest common factor, or GCF, to simplify.

Examples

1. Determine $\frac{1}{3} \times 1\frac{3}{4}$. Write in simplest form.

Estimate   Use compatible numbers. $\frac{1}{2} \times 2 = 1$

$$\frac{1}{3} \times 1\frac{3}{4} = \frac{1}{3} \times \frac{7}{4} \qquad \text{Write } 1\frac{3}{4} \text{ as } \frac{7}{4}.$$

$$= \frac{1 \times 7}{3 \times 4} \qquad \text{Multiply.}$$

$$= \frac{7}{12} \qquad \text{Simplify. Compare to the estimate.}$$

2. The Hoover Dam contains $4\frac{1}{2}$ million cubic yards of concrete. The Grand Coulee Dam, in Washington state, contains $2\frac{2}{3}$ times as much concrete. How much concrete does it contain?

Estimate $4 \times 3 = 12$

$$4\frac{1}{2} \times 2\frac{2}{3} = \frac{9}{2} \times \frac{8}{3} \qquad \text{Write the mixed numbers as improper fractions.}$$

$$= \frac{\overset{3}{\cancel{9}}}{2} \times \frac{\overset{4}{\cancel{8}}}{\cancel{3}} \qquad \begin{array}{l}\text{Divide 9 and 3 by their GCF, 3.}\\ \text{Then divide 8 and 2 by their GCF, 2.}\end{array}$$

$$= \frac{3}{1} \times \frac{4}{1} \qquad \text{Multiply the numerators and multiply the denominators.}$$

$$= \frac{12}{1} \text{ or } 12 \qquad \text{Simplify.}$$

There are 12 million cubic yards of concrete in the Grand Coulee Dam.

Check for Reasonableness $12 = 12$ ✔

STOP and Reflect

Is the product of two mixed numbers greater than or less than both the factors? Explain below.

Got It? Do these problems to find out.

a. $\frac{3}{8} \times 3\frac{1}{3}$

b. Mr. Wilkins is laying bricks to make a rectangular patio. The area he is covering with bricks is $15\frac{1}{2}$ feet by $9\frac{3}{4}$ feet. What is the area of the patio?

Show your work.

a. _____

b. _____

Divide by a Mixed Number

To divide with mixed numbers, express any mixed numbers as improper fractions. Remember to simplify before you multiply.

Examples

Tutor

3. Determine $1\frac{3}{4} \div \frac{2}{5}$.

Estimate $2 \div \frac{1}{2} = 4$

$1\frac{3}{4} \div \frac{2}{5} = \frac{7}{4} \div \frac{2}{5}$ Write the mixed number as an improper fraction.

$= \frac{7}{4} \times \frac{5}{2}$ Multiply by the reciprocal.

$= \frac{35}{8}$ or $4\frac{3}{8}$ Simplify.

Check for Reasonableness $4\frac{3}{8} \approx 4$ ✓

4. Determine $4\frac{2}{3} \div 1\frac{3}{4}$.

Estimate $\boxed{} \div \boxed{} = \boxed{}\dfrac{\boxed{}}{\boxed{}}$

$4\frac{2}{3} \div 1\frac{3}{4} = \dfrac{\boxed{}}{\boxed{}} \div \dfrac{\boxed{}}{\boxed{}}$ Write the mixed numbers as improper fractions.

$= \dfrac{\overset{2}{\boxed{}}}{\boxed{}} \times \dfrac{\boxed{}}{\underset{1}{\boxed{}}}$ Multiply by the reciprocal. Divide by the GCF.

$= \dfrac{\boxed{}}{\boxed{}}$ or $\boxed{}\dfrac{\boxed{}}{\boxed{}}$ Simplify.

Check for Reasonableness $\boxed{}\dfrac{\boxed{}}{\boxed{}} \approx \boxed{}\dfrac{\boxed{}}{\boxed{}}$ ✓

Got It? Do these problems to find out.

c. $4\frac{1}{5} \div \frac{1}{3}$ **d.** $8 \div 2\frac{1}{2}$ **e.** $1\frac{5}{9} \div 2\frac{1}{3}$

STOP and Reflect

How is dividing two mixed numbers similar to dividing two fractions?

Show your work.

c. _____

d. _____

e. _____

Example

5. Mr. Conrad's pecan pie recipe calls for $1\frac{3}{4}$ cups of pecans. He plans to make 8 pies for his family reunion. How many cups of pecans will Mr. Conrad need?

Estimate $2 \times 8 = 16$

$$1\frac{3}{4} \times 8 = \frac{7}{4} \times \frac{8}{1}$$ Write the mixed number as an improper fraction. Write the whole number as a fraction with a denominator of 1.

$$= \frac{7}{\overset{1}{\cancel{4}}} \times \frac{\overset{2}{\cancel{8}}}{1}$$ Divide 8 and 4 by their GCF, 4.

$$= \frac{7}{1} \times \frac{2}{1}$$ Multiply the numerators and multiply the denominators.

$$= \frac{14}{1} \text{ or } 14$$ Simplify.

Check for Reasonableness $14 \approx 16$ ✔

Mr. Conrad will need 14 cups of pecans.

Guided Practice

Multiply or divide. Write in simplest form. (Examples 1–4)

1. $\frac{1}{2} \times 2\frac{3}{8} = $ _____

2. $1\frac{3}{4} \times 2\frac{4}{5} = $ _____

3. $2\frac{2}{3} \div 1\frac{1}{6} = $ _____

4. A box of snack-size cracker packs weighs $28\frac{1}{2}$ ounces. Each snack pack weighs $4\frac{3}{4}$ ounces. How many snack packs are in the box? (Example 5)

_____

5.  **Building on the Essential Question** How can estimation be used when multiplying and dividing mixed numbers?

_____

_____

_____

_____

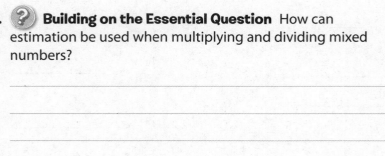

Rate Yourself!

☐ I understand how to multiply and divide mixed numbers.

▶▶ Great! You're ready to move on!

☐ I still have some questions about multiplying and dividing mixed numbers.

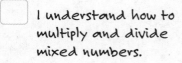

📖 Find out online. Use the Self-Check Quiz.

Check ✔

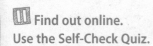
FOLDABLES Time to update your Foldable!

Independent Practice

6.3(E), 6.1(A), 6.1(F) TEKS

Multiply. Write in simplest form. (Examples 1, 2)

1. $\frac{1}{2} \times 2\frac{1}{3} =$ _____

2. $1\frac{7}{8} \times \frac{4}{5} =$ _____

3. $6\frac{2}{3} \times 3\frac{3}{10} =$ _____

Show your work.

Divide. Write in simplest form. Check by multiplying. (Examples 3, 4)

4. $4\frac{1}{6} \div 10 =$ _____

5. $6\frac{1}{2} \div \frac{3}{4} =$ _____

6. $3\frac{3}{4} \div 5\frac{5}{8} =$ _____

7. A carp can travel at a speed of $3\frac{7}{10}$ miles per hour. At this rate, how far can a carp travel in $2\frac{1}{2}$ hours? (Example 5)

_____

_____

8. Juliette is making fruit salad. She purchased $9\frac{2}{3}$ ounces each of 6 different fruits. How many ounces of fruit did she purchase? (Example 5)

_____

_____

9. The length of a kitchen wall is $24\frac{2}{3}$ feet long. A border will be placed along the wall of the kitchen. If the border comes in strips that are each $1\frac{3}{4}$ feet long, how many strips of border are needed? (Example 5)

_____

_____

10. Jay is cutting a roll of biscuit dough into slices that are $\frac{3}{8}$ inch thick. If the roll is $10\frac{1}{2}$ inches long, how many slices can he cut? (Example 5)

_____

_____

11. **STEM** Earth is about $92\frac{9}{10}$ million miles from the Sun. Use the table shown.

   a. How far is Venus from the Sun? _____

   b. How far is Mars from the Sun? _____

   c. How far is Jupiter from the Sun? _____

   d. How far is Saturn from the Sun? _____

Planet	Approximate Number of Times as Far from the Sun as Earth
Venus	$\frac{3}{4}$
Mars	$1\frac{1}{2}$
Jupiter	$5\frac{1}{4}$
Saturn	$9\frac{1}{2}$

12. **MP Analyze Relationships** Refer to the graphic novel frame below for Exercises a–c.

a. What is the total weight of the birdseed they bought? _____

b. If each bag contains $1\frac{1}{2}$ pounds, how many bags can they make? _____

c. Will there be any birdseed left over? Explain. _____
_____

 H.O.T. Problems Higher-Order Thinking

13. **Analyze** Analyze each product in the table.

a. Why is the first product less than $\frac{3}{4}$?
_____
_____
_____

First Factor		Second Factor		Product
$\frac{1}{2}$	$\times$	$\frac{3}{4}$	$=$	$\frac{3}{8}$
1	$\times$	$\frac{3}{4}$	$=$	$\frac{3}{4}$
$\frac{3}{2}$	$\times$	$\frac{3}{4}$	$=$	$\frac{9}{8}$

b. Why is the second product equal to $\frac{3}{4}$?
_____
_____
_____

c. Why is the third product greater than $\frac{3}{4}$?
_____
_____
_____

14. **Analyze** Without multiplying, determine whether the product of $2\frac{1}{2} \times \frac{2}{3}$ is located on the number line at point A, B, or C. Explain your reasoning. _____

A   B   C

0   1   2   3

Multi-Step Problem Solving

15. The table shows the side lengths of four square mirrors. How many times greater is the area of mirror B than the area of mirror C?

(A) $2\frac{2}{49}$ (C) $3\frac{3}{16}$

(B) $3\frac{1}{16}$ (D) $6\frac{1}{4}$

Mirror	Side Length (ft)
A	$1\frac{1}{4}$
B	$2\frac{1}{2}$
C	$1\frac{3}{4}$
D	$3\frac{1}{6}$

Use a problem-solving model to solve this problem.

1 Analyze

Read the problem. Circle the information you know.
Underline what the problem is asking you to find.

2 Plan

What will you need to do to solve the problem? Write your plan in steps.

Step 1   Use the formula $A = \ell \cdot w$ to determine the area of each mirror.

Step 2   Divide to determine how many times greater mirror B is than mirror C.

3 Solve

Use your plan to solve the problem. Show your steps.

Mirror B: $2\frac{1}{2} \cdot 2\frac{1}{2} = \frac{5}{2} \cdot \frac{5}{2} = \frac{25}{4}$ or ⬚⬚/⬚ square feet

Mirror C: $1\frac{3}{4} \cdot 1\frac{3}{4} = \frac{7}{4} \cdot \frac{7}{4} = \frac{49}{16}$ or ⬚⬚/⬚ square feet

So, Mirror B is $6\frac{1}{4} \div 3\frac{1}{16}$ or _____ times larger than Mirror C.

Choice _____ is correct. Fill in that answer choice.

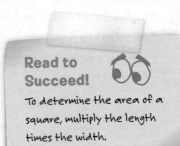

Read to Succeed!

To determine the area of a square, multiply the length times the width.

4 Justify and Evaluate

How do you know your solution is accurate?

_____

N = Number and Operations   **MP** = Mathematical Processes

More **Multi-Step** Problem Solving

Use a problem-solving model to solve each problem.

16. The table shows the dimensions of two fenced-in areas at a dog park. How many times greater is the area enclosed by the wood fence than the area enclosed by the metal fence?

Fence	Length (yd)	Width (yd)
Wood	$6\frac{1}{2}$	$2\frac{1}{4}$
Metal	$2\frac{3}{4}$	$2\frac{1}{2}$

Ⓐ $1\frac{1}{9}$

Ⓑ $2\frac{7}{55}$

Ⓒ $2\frac{4}{11}$

Ⓓ $7\frac{3}{4}$

17. Horacio's garden is shown below. He needs $1\frac{1}{3}$ scoops of fertilizer for each square foot of the garden. How many scoops of fertilizer does Horacio need for the entire garden?

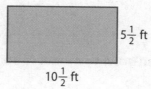

$5\frac{1}{2}$ ft

$10\frac{1}{2}$ ft

18. On Saturday, Justine studied $1\frac{1}{4}$ times as long as Shantel and $1\frac{3}{4}$ times as long as Nicole. If Justine studied $3\frac{1}{2}$ hours on Saturday, how much longer did Shantel study than Nicole on Saturday? Express your answer as a number of hours in decimal notation. N EE MP

19. Without dividing, explain whether $1\frac{1}{2} \div 3\frac{1}{4} \div 2\frac{5}{6}$ is greater or less than $2\frac{5}{6} \div 3\frac{1}{4} \div 1\frac{1}{2}$. N MP

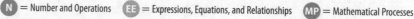
N = Number and Operations   EE = Expressions, Equations, and Relationships   MP = Mathematical Processes

Mixed Problem Solving with Rational Numbers

 Launch the Lesson: Real World

Financial Literacy Elyse bought a gallon of lemonade for $3.59. She plans to sell cups of lemonade for $0.50 each. Follow the steps below to find how much profit she will make if she sells all of the lemonade. Write and find the value of a numerical expression for each step. (*Hint: One gallon has 128 ounces. One cup has 8 ounces. Profit equals revenue minus expenses.*)

Step 1 How many cups are in one gallon?

_____

Step 2 How much revenue will she bring in for selling the whole gallon of lemonade?

_____

Step 3 How much profit will she make if she sells all of the lemonade?

_____

1. What if Elyse found another store that sells a gallon of lemonade for $3.15. How much profit would she make?

_____

2. If Elyse bought a gallon of lemonade for $3.15 and sold cups of lemonade for $0.75 each, how much more profit would she make than her original profit?

_____

Which **MP** **Mathematical Processes** did you use?
Shade the circle(s) that applies.

Ⓐ Apply Math to the Real World.
Ⓑ Use a Problem-Solving Model.
Ⓒ Select Tools and Techniques.
Ⓓ Use Multiple Representations.
Ⓔ Organize Ideas.
Ⓕ Analyze Relationships.
Ⓖ Justify Arguments.

Texas Essential Knowledge and Skills TEKS

Targeted TEKS
6.3(E) Multiply and divide positive rational numbers fluently.
Mathematical Processes
6.1(A), 6.1(B)

Essential Question ?
WHAT does it mean to multiply and divide fractions and decimals?

Expressions with Rational Numbers

You can determine the value of numerical expressions that include rational numbers.

Tutor

Examples

Determine the value of each expression.

1. $6\left(\dfrac{1}{3}\right) + 7$

$$6\left(\dfrac{1}{3}\right) + 7 = \dfrac{6}{1} \cdot \left(\dfrac{1}{3}\right) + 7 \qquad \text{Write 6 as } \dfrac{6}{1}.$$

$$= 2 + 7 \qquad \text{Multiply. } \dfrac{6 \times 1}{1 \times 3} = \dfrac{6}{3} \text{ or } 2$$

$$= 9 \qquad \text{Add.}$$

2. $\dfrac{5}{6}\left(\dfrac{4}{5}\right) - \dfrac{1}{6}$

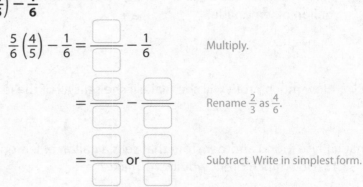

$$\dfrac{5}{6}\left(\dfrac{4}{5}\right) - \dfrac{1}{6} = \dfrac{\square}{\square} - \dfrac{1}{6} \qquad \text{Multiply.}$$

$$= \dfrac{\square}{\square} - \dfrac{\square}{\square} \qquad \text{Rename } \dfrac{2}{3} \text{ as } \dfrac{4}{6}.$$

$$= \dfrac{\square}{\square} \text{ or } \dfrac{\square}{\square} \qquad \text{Subtract. Write in simplest form.}$$

3. $5.4(3) - 1.28$

$$5.4(3) - 1.28 = \boxed{} - 1.28 \qquad \text{Multiply.}$$

$$= \boxed{} \qquad \text{Subtract.}$$

a. _____

b. _____

Got It? Do these problems to find out.

a. $3\left(\dfrac{5}{9}\right) + \dfrac{1}{3}$

b. $7.5(0.5) - 2.35$

Solve Multi-Step Problems with Rational Numbers

You can solve multi-step problems involving rational numbers by using the four-step plan. First, analyze the information given. Then formulate a plan and determine the solution using your plan. Finally, justify your solution by evaluating the problem-solving process and the reasonableness of the solution.

Multi-Step Example

Tutor

4. **Craig has 42 books he wants to store on shelves. Each book is $1\frac{3}{4}$ inches thick. He can buy 3-foot-long shelves for $27.99 each. How much will it cost to shelve the books?**

Step 1 Determine how much space he will need by multiplying the number of books by the thickness of each book.

$$42 \times 1\frac{3}{4} = \frac{42}{1} \times \frac{7}{4}$$

Write 42 as $\frac{42}{1}$. Rename $1\frac{3}{4}$ as $\frac{7}{4}$.

$$= \frac{147}{2} \text{ or } 73\frac{1}{2}$$

Multiply. Then simplify.

Craig needs $73\frac{1}{2}$ inches of shelving.

Step 2 Determine the number of shelves he needs by dividing the shelving needed by the length of one shelf.

$$73\frac{1}{2} \div 36 = \frac{147}{2} \times \frac{1}{36}$$

One shelf is 3 feet or 36 inches.

$$= \frac{147}{72} \text{ or } 2\frac{1}{24}$$

Multiply. Then simplify.

He will need a little over two shelves, so he will have to buy three shelves.

Step 3 Determine the total cost of the shelves by multiplying the number of shelves by the cost of one shelf.

$$3 \times \$27.99 = \$83.97$$

It will cost Craig $83.97 for the three shelves.

Got It? Do this problem to find out.

c. A peach contains 11.6 milligrams of Vitamin C. An orange contains 95.8 milligrams of Vitamin C. Simone would like to get at least 315 milligrams of Vitamin C each week. She has already eaten 3 oranges this week. How many peaches should she have to reach her goal?

c. _____

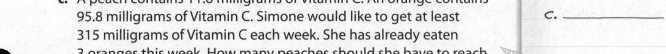

 **Multi-Step Example**

5. A United States quarter is 1.75 millimeters thick. How many centimeters thick is $10 in quarters?

To find the thickness, first determine how many quarters are in $10. Then multiply by the thickness of one quarter. Finally, convert the total thickness to centimeters

Step 1 $10.00 ÷ $0.25 = 40   There are 40 quarters in $10.

Step 2 40 × 1.75 mm = 70 mm   40 quarters are 70 mm thick.

Step 3 70 mm ÷ 10 = 7 cm   10 mm = 1 cm

So, $10 in quarters is 7 centimeters thick.

Guided Practice

Determine the value of each expression. (Examples 1–3)

1. $8\left(\dfrac{3}{4}\right) - 3 =$ _____

2. $\dfrac{3}{5}\left(\dfrac{20}{21}\right) + \dfrac{3}{7} =$ _____

3. Patrick made $\dfrac{13}{15}$ of his free throw shots. Isaiah missed 0.24 of his free throw shots. What fraction more did Isaiah make than Patrick? (Example 4) _____

4. Morgan is deciding between incandescent light bulbs and halogen light bulbs. The incandescent bulbs last for 1,000 hours each, come in a pack of 4, and cost $1.49. The halogen light bulbs last for 2,000 hours each and cost $5.49 for one bulb. What is the cost for 100 hours for each type of bulb? Round to the nearest cent.

(Example 5) _____

5. ❓ **Building on the Essential Question** How can you begin solving a multi-step problem? _____

_____

Rate Yourself!

How confident are you about solving multi-step problems with rational numbers? Shade the ring on the target.

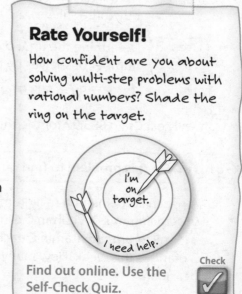

I'm on target.

I need help.

Find out online. Use the Self-Check Quiz.

Check ✓

Independent Practice

Determine the value of each expression. (Examples 1–3)

1. $3\left(\dfrac{4}{15}\right) + \dfrac{7}{10} =$ _____

2. $\dfrac{6}{7}\left(\dfrac{7}{9}\right) - \dfrac{1}{4} =$ _____

3. $\dfrac{3}{7}\left(\dfrac{5}{6}\right) + \dfrac{1}{2} =$ _____

4. $5.39(1.2) - 1.308 =$ _____

5. Kelli wants to sew trim around the sleeves and hem of a dance costume. She needs a piece of trim that is $8\dfrac{1}{8}$ inches long for the sleeves and a piece that is $40\dfrac{5}{8}$ inches long for the hem. If the package contains 5 feet of trim, how much trim will she have left after making the costume? (Example 4)

_____

6. Andrew is making cranberry-apple crisp for a family reunion. He needs to make enough for 20 people. He has 1 cup of brown sugar. How much more brown sugar does he need? (Example 5)

_____

Cranberry Apple Crisp (serves 8)
5 cups cored, sliced apples
1 cup cranberries
$\frac{1}{3}$ cup sugar
$\frac{1}{2}$ cup flour
$\frac{1}{2}$ cup brown sugar
1 teaspoon cinnamon
$\frac{1}{4}$ cup butter

7. **STEM** An average adult male's heart will pump about $\dfrac{1}{15}$ pint of blood with every heartbeat. If the heart beats 60 times per minute, how many gallons of blood are pumped every hour?

_____

8. Adel City is enclosing a skate park with fencing. The skate park is $17\dfrac{1}{3}$ yards wide and $24\dfrac{2}{3}$ yards long. Fencing is sold in 8-foot sections and costs $67.99 per section. How much will it cost to fence in the entire skate park?

_____

9. Justin is making homemade bouncy balls using the recipe at the right. He wants to make 75 of them to sell at a craft fair. If three teaspoons equal one tablespoon, how many tablespoons of sodium borate will he need? _____

Bouncy Balls
- 2 tablespoons warm water
- $\frac{1}{2}$ teaspoon sodium borate
- 1 tablespoon glue
- 1 tablespoon corn starch

10. Members of the Drama Club are building a set for a play. They need 6 pieces of wood. Each piece of wood needs to be $3\frac{3}{4}$ feet long. The wood comes in 12-foot lengths. After the pieces are cut off, how much wood will be left over? _____

11. **Find the Error** Mark earns $12 an hour mowing lawns. He mowed a rectangular lawn that measured $33\frac{1}{3}$ yards by $26\frac{2}{3}$ yards in $\frac{3}{4}$ hour. By rounding to the nearest hundredth, Mark determined that he earned $98.77 per square yard mowing that particular lawn. Explain and correct Mark's error. _____

_____

_____

H.O.T. Problems Higher-Order Thinking

12. **Analyze** Shayla filled 5 baskets of raspberries while hiking. Each basket contained $1\frac{2}{5}$ pounds of raspberries. She used $2\frac{1}{4}$ pounds to make raspberry jam. Shayla estimated that she has about 5 pounds of raspberries left. Explain how you know whether her estimate is reasonable. _____

_____

_____

13. **Create** Write a real-world multi-step problem in which you would multiply and then subtract decimals. _____

_____

_____

14. **Evaluate** A bead store has 1,230 beads for sale. One-third of the beads are priced at $0.25 each. One-half of the beads are priced at $1.80 each. The remaining beads are priced at $3.00 each. What is the total dollar value of the beads in the store? Write a single numerical expression that can be used to solve the problem. Then solve the problem.

_____

_____

Multi-Step Problem Solving

15. The table shows the cost per yard for different types of ribbon. Chase bought $3\frac{1}{4}$ yards of knitted ribbon and $1\frac{3}{4}$ yards of crocheted ribbon to use for his art project. How much money did he spend, in dollars? Round to the nearest cent. (N) (MP)

Ribbon	Cost per Yard ($)
Woven	1.75
Knitted	2.00
Crocheted	2.10
With pearls	2.45

Use a problem-solving model to solve this problem.

1 Analyze

Read the problem. Circle the information you know.
Underline what the problem is asking you to find.

2 Plan

What will you need to do to solve the problem? Write your plan in steps.

Step 1 Multiply to determine the amount spent on knitted ribbon and crocheted ribbon.

Step 2 Add to determine the total spent.

Read to Succeed!
When rounding, wait to round until the end of the problem.

3 Solve

Use your plan to solve the problem. Show your steps.

Knitted ribbon: $3\frac{1}{4} \times \$2.00$ or $ _____

Crocheted ribbon: $1\frac{3}{4} \times \$2.10$ or $ _____

So, Chase spent $ _____ + $ _____ or $ _____.
Complete the grid.

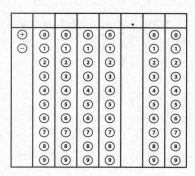

4 Justify and Evaluate

How do you know your solution is accurate?

_____

_____

_____

(N) = Number and Operations (MP) = Mathematical Processes

Use a problem-solving model to solve each problem.

16. The table shows the amount of time Domingo spent practicing the violin last week. How many hours longer did he practice on Thursday and Friday combined than on Monday and Tuesday combined? Write your answer as a decimal.

Day	Time (hr)
Monday	$\frac{1}{2}$
Tuesday	$1\frac{1}{5}$
Wednesday	1
Thursday	$\frac{4}{5}$
Friday	$1\frac{1}{2}$

17. Briana is making a necklace using rectangular beads. Two of the beads are shown below. How many times larger is the area of the blue bead than the area of the yellow bead?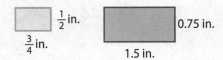

$\frac{1}{2}$ in.

$\frac{3}{4}$ in.

0.75 in.

1.5 in.

18. Gavin bicycles 3.5 miles on Saturday. He walks $1\frac{1}{3}$ miles on Sunday, and runs $\frac{1}{2}$ mile on Monday. How many times farther did he ride his bicycle than walk and run combined? Round your answer to the nearest hundredth.

19. Janice wants to use tiny boxes to store buttons in her craft room. One of the boxes is shown below. The space available on her shelf for these boxes is 9 in³. How many tiny boxes will fit in this space?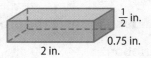

$\frac{1}{2}$ in.

0.75 in.

2 in.

N = Number and Operations   **P** = Proportionality   **EE** = Expressions, Equations, and Relationships   **MP** = Mathematical Processes

186   **Chapter 2** Multiply and Divide Rational Numbers

21ST CENTURY CAREER

Mathematical Process
6.1(A) Apply mathematics to problems arising in everyday life, society, and the workplace.
Targeted TEKS 6.3(E)

TEKS

Sports Equipment Designer

Do you have a passion for sports and a strong interest in science? Are you a creative thinker who always has new ideas or better ways of doing things? If so, then you should consider a career designing sports equipment. Sports equipment designers combine creativity and engineering principles to create equipment that is cutting edge and helps improve athletic performance. They design everything from baseball bats and footballs to lacrosse protective gear and racing wheelchairs.

Is This the Career for You?

Are you interested in a career as a sports equipment designer? Take some of the following courses in high school.

◆ Algebra
◆ Biology
◆ Calculus
◆ Computer Science
◆ Physics

College & Career
READINESS

Explore college and careers at ccr.mcgraw-hill.com

Gaining a Competitive Edge

When a punter kicks a football, the ball has both horizontal motion and vertical motion. The table shows these values when a football is kicked at 25 meters per second.

Use the information in the table to solve each problem. Assume that each football is kicked at 25 meters per second. Round to the nearest tenth if necessary.

1. The *hang time*, or time that a football is in the air, of a football that is kicked at a 27° angle is given by 0.204 × 11.3. What is the

   approximate hang time? _____

2. How much greater is the hang time of a football that is kicked at a 62° angle than one that is kicked at a 45° angle? Use the expressions

   0.204 × 22.1 and 0.204 × 17.7. _____

3. The final distance from the punter to a football kicked at a 27° angle is approximately 22.3 × 11.3 × 0.2. What is the distance from

   the punter to the football? _____

4. Find the distance of a football that is kicked at an angle of 62° if the distance is found by using the expression 11.7 × 22.1 × 0.2.

   _____

5. The hang time of a football is about 3 seconds. Find 3 ÷ 0.204 to determine the vertical

   motion of the football. _____

6. A football reaches its maximum height in y ÷ 9.8 seconds. A football is kicked at a 62° angle. At the same time, another football is kicked at a 27° angle. Which reaches its maximum height first? Explain.

   _____

   _____

Punting A Football		
Angle of Kick	Horizontal Motion (m/s)	Vertical Motion (m/s)
	x	y
27°	22.3	11.3
45°	17.7	17.7
62°	11.7	22.1

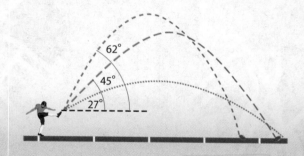

 Career Project

It's time to update your career portfolio! Choose a piece of sports equipment and describe how it has changed over the past 20 years. List the reasons for the changes. Prepare a brief oral presentation and present it to your classmates. as others are presenting, listen carefully to their presentations. At the end, ask any clarifying questions.

Suppose you are an employer hiring a sports equipment designer. What questions would you ask a potential employee?

_____

_____

_____

Chapter Review

Vocabulary Check

Work with a partner to complete each sentence using the vocabulary list at the beginning of the chapter. Take turns saying each sentence aloud while the other student listens carefully. Then circle the word that completes the sentence in the word search.

1. A number that has a whole number part and a fraction part is a _____.

2. The _____ is the greatest of the common factors of two or more numbers.

3. The product of a number and its _____ is one.

4. The number above the fraction bar is the _____.

5. The number below the fraction bar is the _____.

6. A _____ is a number that represents part of a whole or part of a set.

7. A fraction with a numerator that is greater than or equal to the denominator is an _____.

8. _____ are numbers that are easy to divide mentally.

9. A fraction in which the GCF of the numerator and the denominator is 1 is written in _____.

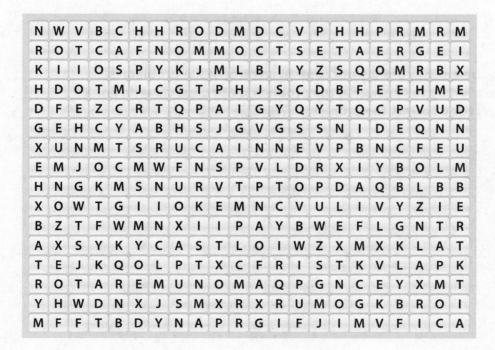

```
N W V B C H H R O D M D C V P H H P R M R M
R O T C A F N O M M O C T S E T A E R G E I
K I I O S P Y K J M L B I Y Z S Q O M R B X
H D O T M J C G T P H J S C D B F E E H M E
D F E Z C R T Q P A I G Y Q Y T Q C P V U D
G E H C Y A B H S J G V G S S N I D E Q N N
X U N M T S R U C A I N N E V P B N C F E U
E M J O C M W F N S P V L D R X I Y B O L M
H N G K M S N U R V T P T O P D A Q B L B B
X O W T G I I O K E M N C V U L I V Y Z I E
B Z T F W M N X I I P A Y B W E F L G N T R
A X S Y K Y C A S T L O I W Z X M X K L A T
T E J K Q O L P T X C F R I S T K V L A P K
R O T A R E M U N O M A Q P G N C E Y X M T
Y H W D N X J S M X R X R U M O G K B R O I
M F F T B D Y N A P R G I F J I M V F I C A
```

Use Your FOLDABLES

Collaborate

Use your Foldable to help review the chapter. Share your Foldable with a partner and take turns summarizing what you learned in this chapter, while the other partner listens carefully. Seek clarification of any concepts, as needed. **TEKS** 6.1(E)

Tape here

Tab 3	Multiply and Divide Rational Numbers
Tab 2	
Tab 1	

Example	Example
fraction × mixed number	**mixed number ÷ fraction**

Got it?

The problems below may or may not contain an error. If the problem is correct, write a "✓" by the answer. If the problem is not correct, write an "X" over the answer and correct the problem. **TEKS** 6.3(E)

1. $13 \times \frac{1}{3} = 4\frac{2}{3}$

The first one is done for you. ➡ $13 \times \frac{1}{3} = \frac{13}{3}$ or $4\frac{1}{3}$

2. $16 \times \frac{5}{6} = 19\frac{1}{5}$

3. $18.5 \times 0.40 = 7.4$

4. $\frac{5}{8} \div \frac{3}{4} = \frac{15}{32}$

5. $3\frac{2}{3} \div \frac{5}{6} = 4\frac{2}{5}$

6. $569.6 \div 3.2 = 17.8$

Multi-Step Problem Solving

7. The table shows the amount of milk needed for different family recipes for one batch of pancakes. Suppose you have 6 cups of milk to make pancakes. If you use all 6 cups of milk, whose recipe will make more pancakes and how many more pancakes? Show the steps you used and justify your solution.

Pancake Recipes		
Recipe	Milk (Cup)	Number of Pancakes Made Per Batch
Mother's	$\frac{3}{4}$	9
Grandma's	$\frac{2}{3}$	7

1 Analyze

2 Plan

3 Solve

4 Justify and Evaluate

_____

_____

_____

Got it?

8. Tom has 48 coins in nickels, dimes, and quarters. Of the coins, $\frac{3}{8}$ are dimes and $\frac{1}{4}$ are nickels. How much money does he have in nickels, dimes, and quarters? Show the steps you used and justify your solution.

_____

_____

_____

_____

N = Number and Operations   **MP** = Mathematical Processes

Reflect

? Answering the Essential Question

Use what you learned about multiplying and dividing fractions and decimals to complete the graphic organizer. **TEKS** 6.1(D), 6.1(E), 6.1(G)

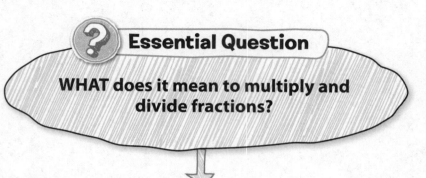

? Essential Question

WHAT does it mean to multiply and divide fractions?

Operation	Dividend and Divisor	Is the answer less than or greater than the dividend? Provide an example.
multiply	decimal by decimal	
divide	decimal by decimal	
multiply	whole number by whole number	
multiply	fraction by fraction	
divide	whole number by whole number	
divide	fraction by fraction	

 ? Answer the Essential Question. WHAT does it mean to multiply and divide fractions? Verbally share your response with a partner, seeking and providing clarification as needed.

Collaborate

Chapter 3

Operations with Integers

Texas Essential Knowledge and Skills

Targeted TEKS

6.3 The student applies mathematical process standards to represent addition, subtraction, multiplication, and division while solving problems and justifying solutions.

Mathematical Processes

6.1, 6.1(A), 6.1(B), 6.1(C), 6.1(D), 6.1(E), 6.1(F), 6.1(G)

Essential Question

WHAT happens when you add, subtract, multiply, and divide integers?

Math in the Real World

Natural Resources, such as crude oil, can be found in the Edwards Plateau region of Texas. To obtain the oil, a drilling rig will drill a depth around −2,000 feet. The number −2,000 is a negative integer.

On the graph below, graph a point at the depth crude oil can be found.

Vocabulary

additive inverse

opposites

zero pair

Writing Math

Compare and Contrast When you *compare*, you notice how things are alike. When you *contrast*, you notice how they are different. Here are two cell phone plans.

Plan B

$34.99

300 anytime minutes

100 text messages

Free weekend minutes

Plan A

$34.99

200 anytime minutes

200 text messages

Free weekend minutes

Compare and contrast the monthly plans. Make a list of how they are alike and how they are different.

Alike/Compare	Different/Contrast

Quick Review

Review 6.2(B), 6.2(C)

Example 1

Determine $|{-6}|$.

The absolute value of a number is the distance the number is from zero.

$|{-6}| = 6$ −6 is 6 units from 0.

Example 2

Locate the set $\{-3, -1, 0, 4\}$ on a number line.

Place a dot at each integer on the number line.

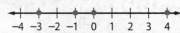

Quick Check

Check ✓

Absolute Value Determine the absolute value.

1. $|{-9}| = $ _____

2. $|17| = $ _____

3. $|{-100}| = $ _____

Show your work.

4. $|0| = $ _____

5. $|10 + 9| = $ _____

6. $|14 - 8| = $ _____

Integers Locate the set of numbers on a number line.

7. $\{-2, 1, 3\}$

8. $\{-1, 0, 4, -6\}$

9. $\{-8, -4, -1\}$

10. $\{-11, 13, -7, 9\}$

11. $\{8, -8, 0\}$

12. $\{17, -6, 13, 9\}$

How Did You Do?

Which problems did you answer correctly in the Quick Check?
Shade those exercise numbers below.

   4 5 6 8 10

FOLDABLES® Use the Foldable throughout this chapter to help you learn about operations with integers.

✂ cut on all dashed lines   📄 fold on all solid lines   tape to page 260

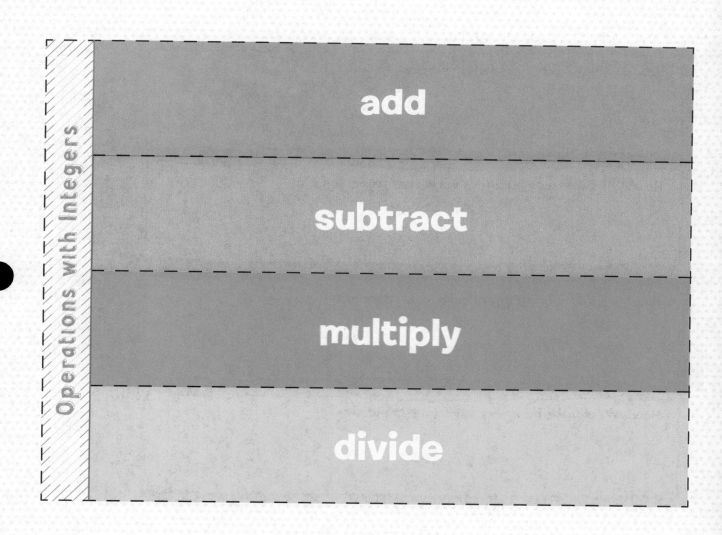

FOLDABLES® Use the Foldable throughout this chapter to help you learn about operations with integers.

✂ cut on all dashed lines ☐ fold on all solid lines ▨ tape to page 260

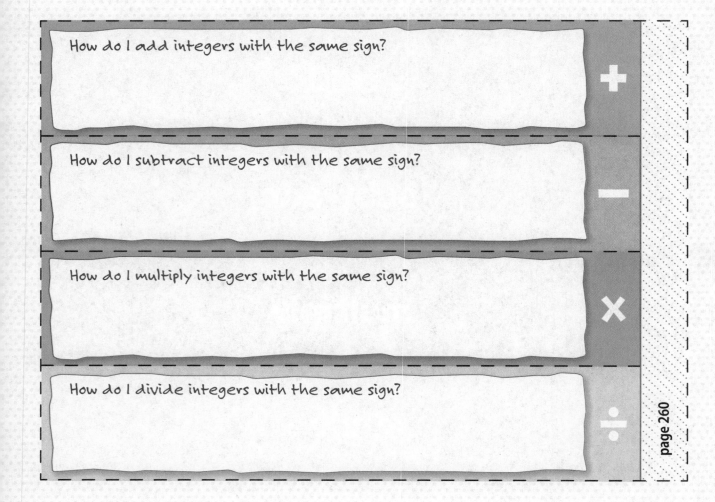

How do I add integers with the same sign?

+

How do I subtract integers with the same sign?

−

How do I multiply integers with the same sign?

×

How do I divide integers with the same sign?

÷

page 260

Use Models to Add Integers

INQUIRY HOW can I select tools and techniques to determine when the sum of two integers is a negative number?

In football, forward progress is represented by a positive integer. Losing yardage is represented by a negative integer. On the first play, a team lost 5 yards. On the second play, the team lost 2 yards. What was the team's total yardage on the two plays? Find out in Hands-On Activity 1.

Texas Essential Knowledge and Skills

Targeted TEKS
6.3(C) Represent integer operations with concrete models and connect the actions with the models to standardized algorithms.

Mathematical Processes
6.1(C), 6.1(D), 6.1(E)

Vocabulary
zero pair

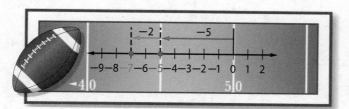

Hands-On Activity 1

Watch Tools

You can use concrete objects, such as counters, to find the total yardage.

Step 1 Use negative integers to represent the yards lost on each play.

☐ + ☐

a loss of 5 yards   a loss of 2 yards

Step 2 Combine a set of 5 negative counters and a set of 2 negative counters.

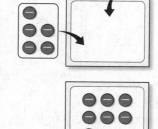

Step 3 There is a total of ☐ negative counters. The model shows that adding a negative number to another negative number results in a negative sum.

So, $-5 + (-2) =$ ☐ . The team lost a total of ☐ yards on the first two plays.

The following two properties are important when modeling operations with integers.

- When one positive counter is paired with one negative counter, the result is called a **zero pair**. The value of a zero pair is 0.

- You can add or remove zero pairs from a mat because adding or removing zero does not change the value of the counters on the mat.

Hands-On Activity 2

Use counters to determine −4 + 2.

Step 1 Combine [ ] negative counters with [ ] positive counters.

The addends have different signs.

Step 2 Remove all zero pairs.

There are more negative counters than positive counters.

4 > 2

Step 3 Find the number of counters remaining.

The model shows that the sum has the same sign as the greater number of counters.

There are [ ] negative counters remaining.

So, −4 + 2 = [ ].

1. **MP Analyze Relationships** How would the model and sum change if the addition expression was 4 + (−2)?

_____

_____

Investigate

Collaborate

MP **Use Multiple Representations** Work with a partner. Determine each sum. Show your work using drawings.

2. $5 + 6 =$ _____

Show your work.

3. $-3 + (-5) =$ _____

4. $-5 + (-4) =$ _____

5. $7 + 3 =$ _____

6. $-6 + 5 =$ _____

7. $-2 + 7 =$ _____

8. $8 + (-3) =$ _____

9. $3 + (-6) =$ _____

10. Connect Models to Rules Study the exercises in which both addends are negative. What do you notice about the sum?

_____

11. Connect Models to Rules Study the exercises in which one addend is negative and one is positive. What do you notice about the sum?

_____

MP Organize Ideas Work with a partner to complete the table. The first one is done for you.

	Addition Expression	Sum	Sign of Addend with Greater Absolute Value	Sign of Sum
	$5 + (-2)$	3	positive	positive
12.	$-6 + 2$			
13.	$7 + (-12)$			
14.	$-4 + 9$			
15.	$-12 + 20$			
16.	$15 + (-18)$			

Create

On Your Own

17. **Connect Models to Rules** Write a rule you can use to find the sum of two negative integers without using counters.

_____

_____

18. **Connect Models to Rules** Write a rule you can use to find the sum of a positive integer and a negative integer without using counters.

_____

_____

19. **MP Use Multiple Representations** Write two addition sentences where the sum is zero. Describe the numbers.

_____

_____

20. **INQUIRY** HOW can I select tools and techniques to determine when the sum of two integers is a negative number?

_____

_____

Add Integers

 Launch the Lesson: Vocabulary ▶ Watch

Texas Essential Knowledge and Skills

Targeted TEKS
6.3(D) Add, subtract, multiply, and divide integers fluently. *Also addresses 6.3(C).*

Mathematical Processes
6.1(A), 6.1(B), 6.1(D), 6.1(F)

Integers like 2 and −2 are called **opposites** because they are the same distance from 0, but on opposite sides. Complete the graphic organizer about opposites.

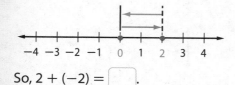

Model It

$$-3 \quad -2 \quad -1 \quad 0 \quad 1 \quad 2 \quad 3$$

Real-World Example | Math Example

Vocab

Vocabulary
opposites
additive inverse

Two integers that are opposites are also called **additive inverses**. The Additive Inverse Property states that the sum of any number and its additive inverse is zero. You can model $2 + (-2)$ on a number line.

 Essential Question
WHAT happens when you add, subtract, multiply, and divide integers?

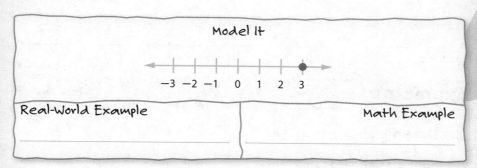

$$-4 \quad -3 \quad -2 \quad -1 \quad 0 \quad 1 \quad 2 \quad 3 \quad 4$$

Start at zero.
Move 2 units to the right to show 2.
Then move 2 units to the left to show −2.

So, $2 + (-2) =$ ☐.

 ## Real-World Link

The temperature outside is −5°. Name the temperature that would make the sum of the two temperatures 0°. ☐

Which **MP Mathematical Processes** did you use?
Shade the circle(s) that applies.

Ⓐ Apply Math to the Real World.
Ⓑ Use a Problem-Solving Model.
Ⓒ Select Tools and Techniques.
Ⓓ Use Multiple Representations.
Ⓔ Organize Ideas.
Ⓕ Analyze Relationships.
Ⓖ Justify Arguments.

Add Integers with the Same Sign

Words To add integers with the same sign, add their absolute values. The sum is:

- positive if both integers are positive.
- negative if both integers are negative.

Models

Examples $3 + 4 = 7$ $\qquad\qquad\qquad$ $-3 + (-4) = -7$

Work Zone

Examples

Tutor

1. **Determine** $-3 + (-2)$.

Start at 0. Move 3 units down to show -3.

From there, move 2 units down to show -2.

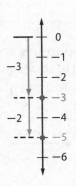

The model shows that the sum of 2 negative integers is negative.

So, $-3 + (-2) = -5$.

2. **Determine** $-26 + (-17)$.

$-26 + (-17) = -43$ $\qquad$ Both integers are negative, so the sum is negative.

3. **Determine** $-4 + (-3) + (-5)$.

> Show your work.

$$-4 + (-3) + (-5) = -7 + (-5) \qquad \text{Add } -4 \text{ and } (-3).$$
$$= -12 \qquad \text{Add.}$$

Got It? Do these problems to find out.

a. $-5 + (-7)$ $\qquad\qquad$ **b.** $-10 + (-4)$

c. $-14 + (-16)$ $\qquad\qquad$ **d.** $-8 + (-10) + (-7)$

a. _____

b. _____

c. _____

d. _____

Add Integers with Different Signs

Words To add integers with different signs, subtract their absolute values. The sum is:

- positive if the positive integer's absolute value is greater.
- negative if the negative integer's absolute value is greater.

Models

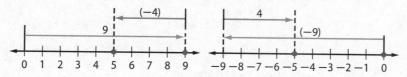

Examples $9 + (-4) = 5$ $-9 + 4 = -5$

Examples

Tutor

4. **Determine $5 + (-3)$.**

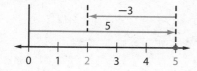

So, $5 + (-3) = 2$.

5. **Determine $-3 + 2$.**

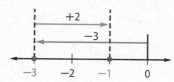

So, $-3 + 2 = -1$.

6. **Determine $2 + (-15) + (-2)$.**

$2 + (-15) + (-2) = 2 + (-2) + (-15)$ Commutative Property (+)

$= [2 + (-2)] + (-15)$ Associative Property (+)

$= 0 + (-15)$ Additive Inverse Property

$= -15$ Additive Identity Property

Got It? Do these problems to find out.

e. $6 + (-7)$ **f.** $-15 + 19$ **g.** $10 + (-12)$

h. $-13 + 18$ **i.** $(-14) + (-6) + 6$

Adding Integers

When you add integers with different signs, start at zero. Move right for positive integers. Move left for negative integers. So, the sum of $p + q$ is located a distance $|q|$ from p.

Show your work.

e. _____

f. _____

g. _____

h. _____

i. _____

Example

7. A roller coaster starts at point *A*. It goes up 20 feet, down 32 feet, and then up 16 feet to point *B*. Write an addition sentence to find the height at point *B* in relation to point *A*. Then find the sum and explain its meaning.

$$20 + (-32) + 16 = 20 + 16 + (-32) \qquad \text{Commutative Property } (+)$$
$$= 36 + (-32) \qquad 20 + 16 = 36$$
$$= 4 \qquad \text{Subtract absolute values.}$$

Point *B* is 4 feet higher than point *A*.

Guided Practice

Add. Use a number line. (Examples 1–6)

1. $-6 + (-8) =$ _____

Show your work.

2. $-3 + 10 =$ _____

3. $-8 + (-4) + 12 =$ _____

4. $-9 + (-5) + (-6) =$ _____

5. Sofia owes her brother $25. She gives her brother the $18 she earned dog-sitting. Write an addition expression to describe this situation. Then find the sum and explain its meaning. (Example 7) _____

_____

6. **?** **Building on the Essential Question** Explain how you know whether a sum is positive, negative, or zero without actually adding. _____

_____

_____

_____

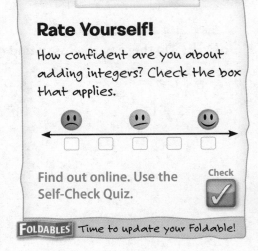

Rate Yourself!

How confident are you about adding integers? Check the box that applies.

Find out online. Use the Self-Check Quiz.

Check ✓

FOLDABLES Time to update your Foldable!

Independent Practice

6.3(D), 6.1(A), 6.1(F) TEKS

Add. (Examples 1–6)

1. $-22 + (-16) =$ _____

2. $-10 + (-15) =$ _____

3. $6 + 10 =$ _____

4. $21 + (-21) + (-4) =$ _____

5. $-17 + 20 + (-3) =$ _____

6. $-34 + 25 + (-25) =$ _____

7. $-4 + 5 =$ _____

8. $-15 + 8 =$ _____

9. $-7 + (-11) =$ _____

10. Financial Literacy Stephanie has $152 in the bank. She withdraws $20. Then she deposits $84. Write an addition expression to represent this situation. Then find the sum and explain its meaning. (Example 7)

_____

11. **MP Apply Math to the Real World** Find the total profit or loss for each color of T-shirt. _____

Green T-shirt:
  Short-sleeve shirt: $8.00
  Printing: $6.00
  Selling price: $15.00
White T-shirt:
  Long-sleeve shirt: $10.00
  Printing: $7.00
  Selling price: $20.00
Black T-shirt:
  Short-sleeve shirt: $8.00
  Printing on Front: $4.00
  Printing on Back: $3.00
  Selling price: $18.00

We are creating T-shirts to be sold for homecoming!

12. **Analyze Relationships** Lena deposits and withdraws money from a bank account. The table shows her transactions for March. Write an addition expression to describe her transactions. Then find the sum and explain its meaning.

March	
Week	Transaction
1	deposit $300
2	withdraw $50
3	withdraw $75
4	deposit $225

_____

_____

_____

H.O.T. Problems Higher-Order Thinking

13. Create Describe two situations in which opposite quantities combine to make zero.

_____

_____

_____

14. Analyze Explain why you add to find the sum of two negative integers, but subtract to find the sum of a positive and a negative integer. Use a number line or counters in your explanation.

_____

_____

_____

_____

_____

_____

Analyze Simplify.

15. $8 + (-8) + a$ _____

16. $x + (-5) + 1$ _____

17. $-9 + m + (-6)$ _____

18. Create Write an expression that can represented by the number

line below. _____

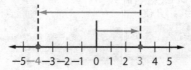

Multi-Step Problem Solving

19. Carlos is swimming at the beach. The number line shows his vertical movement in feet. Which expression is represented on the number line model? Describe his vertical movement in relation to the surface of the water. **N** **MP**

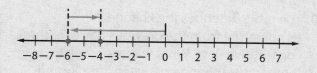

Ⓐ $(-6) + (-4)$; He swam 6 feet down and then 4 feet down. He is 10 feet below the surface.

Ⓑ $0 + (-6)$; He swam 6 feet down and is 6 feet below the surface of the water.

Ⓒ $(-4) + (-2)$; He swam 4 feet down and then 2 feet down. He is 6 feet below the surface.

Ⓓ $(-6) + 2$; He swam 6 feet down and then 2 feet up. He is 4 feet below the surface.

Use a problem-solving model to solve this problem.

1 Analyze

Read the problem. Circle the information you know. Underline what the problem is asking you to find.

2 Plan

What will you need to do to solve the problem? Write your plan in steps.

Step 1 Determine the direction and length of the red arrow.

Step 2 Determine the direction and length of the blue arrow.

3 Solve

Use your plan to solve the problem. Show your steps.

The red arrow starts at 0 and goes to the left to _____. Then,

the blue arrow goes to the right 2 units and ends at _____.

So, Carlos swims 6 feet down to −6, then 2 feet up to −4.

He is _____ feet _____ the surface. Choice _____ is correct.

Read to Succeed!

When an arrow goes to the right, it means adding or a positive number. When it goes to the left, then it means subtraction or a negative number.

4 Justify and Evaluate

How do you know your solution is accurate?

_____

N = Number and Operations   **MP** = Mathematical Processes

Use a problem-solving model to solve each problem.

20. The table describes the change in temperature from the previous day over three consecutive days. What was the overall temperature change between Sunday and Wednesday as an integer? **N** **MP**

Day	Change in Temperature (°F)
Monday	dropped 2°
Tuesday	dropped 5°
Wednesday	rose 3°

Ⓐ 3°F

Ⓑ 0°F

Ⓒ −4°F

Ⓓ −10°F

21. In golf, a score of 0 is called *par*. A score *over par* is represented with a positive integer, and a score *under par* is represented with a negative integer. The goal is to get the lowest score possible. Justin and André played three rounds of golf, with their scores for each round as shown in the table. What is the winning final score? **N** **MP**

	Round 1	Round 2	Round 3
Justin	−2	0	3
André	2	−3	1

22. The table shows the transactions of Sierra's checking account during one week. What is her account balance at the end of the week? **N** **FL** **MP**

Transaction	Amount
Beginning balance	$124
ATM withdrawal	$20
Deposit	$35
Bank card purchase	$12

23. In a convenience store, there is a tray by the register that contains leftover change. Customers can use this change for their purchases, or place their change in the tray for other customers to use. At the beginning of the day, there is 27¢ in the change tray. By the end of the day, there is only 15¢ left in the tray. Only two costumers used the change tray, and one of these costumers added 6¢. How did the other costumer use the tray? Justify your response. **N** **EE** **MP**

_____

_____

_____

_____

N = Number and Operations **EE** = Expressions, Equations, and Relationships **FL** = Personal Financial Literacy **MP** = Mathematical Processes

210 **Chapter 3** Operations with Integers

Use Models to Subtract Integers

INQUIRY HOW can I select tools to show how the subtraction of integers is related to the addition of integers?

A dolphin swims 6 meters below the surface of the ocean. Then it jumps to a height of 5 meters above the surface of the water. Determine the difference between the two distances.

Texas Essential Knowledge and Skills

Targeted TEKS
6.3(C) Represent integer operations with concrete models and connect the actions with the models to standardized algorithms.

Mathematical Processes
6.1(C), 6.1(D), 6.1(E)

Hands-On Activity 1

Watch   Tools

You can use concrete objects, such as counters, to find $5 - (-6)$, the difference between the distances.

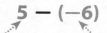

$$5 - (-6)$$

the number of positive counters placed on the mat

the number of negative counters that need removed from the mat

Step 1 Place 5 positive counters on the mat. Remove 6 negative counters. However, there are 0 negative counters.

Step 2 Add ☐ zero pairs to the mat.

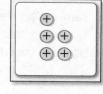

Step 3 Now you can remove ☐ negative counters. Count the remaining positive counters.

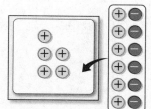

So, $5 - (-6) =$ ☐. The difference between the distances is ☐ meters.

The model shows that removing 6 negative counters yielded the same result as adding 6 positive counters.

Hands-On Activity 2

Use counters to determine $-6 - (-3)$.

$$-6 - (-3)$$

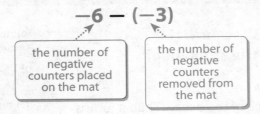

the number of negative counters placed on the mat

the number of negative counters removed from the mat

Step 1 Place 6 negative counters on the mat.

Step 2 Remove 3 negative counters.

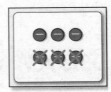

There are ☐ negative counters remaining. So, $-6 - (-3) = $ ☐.

Hands-On Activity 3

Use counters to determine $-5 - 1$.

Step 1 Place ☐ negative counters on the mat.
You need to remove 1 positive counter.
However, there are 0 positive counters.

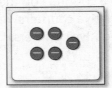

Step 2 Add 1 zero pair to the mat.

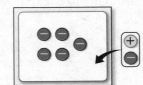

Step 3 Now you can remove 1 positive counter.
Find the remaining number of counters.

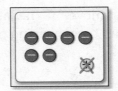

There are ☐ negative counters remaining.

So, $-5 - 1 = $ ☐.

The model shows that removing 1 positive counter yielded the same result as adding 1 negative counter.

Check Find $-5 + (-1)$. Is it the same as $-5 - 1$? $-5 + (-1) = -6$ ✓

Investigate

Work with a partner. Determine each difference. Show your work using drawings.

1. $7 - 6 =$ _____

Show your work.

2. $5 - (-3) =$ _____

3. $6 - (-2) =$ _____

4. $5 - 8 =$ _____

5. $-7 - (-2) =$ _____

6. $-7 - 3 =$ _____

7. Refer to Exercises 2 and 3. How can you remove negative counters from a set of positive counters? What is the net effect?

_____

_____

_____

_____

8. Refer to Exercise 4. How can you remove a greater number of positive counters from a smaller set of positive counters?

_____

_____

_____

_____

Analyze and Reflect

Collaborate

MP Organize Ideas Work with a partner. Circle an expression that is equivalent to the expression in the first column. The first one is done for you.

	$-3 - 1$	$-3 + 1$	$\boxed{-3 + (-1)}$	$-3 - (-1)$
9.	$-2 - 9$	$-2 - (-9)$	$-2 + 9$	$-2 + (-9)$
10.	$-8 - 4$	$-8 + 4$	$-8 + (-4)$	$-8 - (-4)$
11.	$6 - (-2)$	$6 + 2$	$6 - 2$	$6 + (-2)$
12.	$5 - (-7)$	$5 - 7$	$5 + (-7)$	$5 + 7$
13.	$-1 - (-3)$	$-1 - 3$	$-1 + 3$	$-1 + (-3)$
14.	$-3 - (-8)$	$-3 + 8$	$-3 - 8$	$-3 + (-8)$

15. **Connect Models to Rules** Study the pattern in the table. Write a rule you can use to find the difference of two integers without using counters. Test your rule by finding $3 - (-2)$ two different ways using counters.

_____

_____

Create

On Your Own

16. **MP Analyze Relationships** Write a subtraction sentence where the difference is positive. Use a positive and a negative integer.

_____

17. **MP Analyze Relationships** Write a subtraction sentence where the difference is negative. Use a positive and a negative integer.

_____

18. **INQUIRY** HOW can I select tools to show how the subtraction of integers is related to the addition of integers?

_____

_____

_____

Subtract Integers

 Launch the Lesson: Real World

The platform on a diving board is 3 meters high. The actions of a diver climbing up to the diving board platform and diving 1 meter below the water's surface are shown on the number line at the right.

The diver's actions can be represented by the subtraction equation $3 - 4 = -1$.

1. Use the model to explain how to subtract 4 from 3.

_____

_____

_____

_____

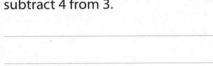

2. Evaluate Explain how a model could illustrate how to subtract 5 from 1.

_____

_____

3. Refer to the model above. How do the models also show addition? Write an addition sentence represented by each model.

_____

_____

Texas Essential Knowledge and Skills

 TEKS

Targeted TEKS
6.3(D) Add, subtract, multiply, and divide integers fluently. *Also addresses 6.3(C).*

Mathematical Processes
6.1(A), 6.1(B), 6.1(D), 6.1(F)

Essential Question
WHAT happens when you add, subtract, multiply, and divide integers?

Which MP Mathematical Processes did you use?
Shade the circle(s) that applies.

Ⓐ Apply Math to the Real World.

Ⓑ Use a Problem-Solving Model.

Ⓒ Select Tools and Techniques.

Ⓓ Use Multiple Representations.

Ⓔ Organize Ideas.

Ⓕ Analyze Relationships.

Ⓖ Justify Arguments.

Subtract Integers

Words To subtract an integer, add its additive inverse.

Symbols $p - q = p + (-q)$

Examples $4 - 9 = 4 + (-9) = -5$ $7 - (-10) = 7 + (10) = 17$

The model shows that when you subtract 7 the result is the same as adding its additive inverse, -7.

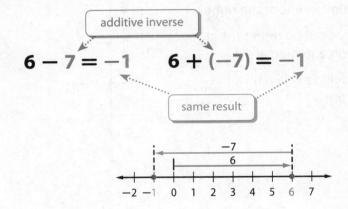

additive inverse

$$6 - 7 = -1 \qquad 6 + (-7) = -1$$

same result

Examples

Tutor

1. **Determine $8 - 13$.**

$8 - 13 = 8 + (-13)$ To subtract 13, add -13.

$\qquad = -5$ Simplify.

Check by adding $-5 + 13 \overset{?}{=} 8$

$\qquad\qquad\qquad 8 = 8$ ✓

2. **Determine $-10 - 7$.**

$-10 - 7 = -10 + (-7)$ To subtract 7, add -7.

$\qquad = -17$ Simplify.

Check by adding $-17 + 7 \overset{?}{=} -10$

$\qquad\qquad\qquad -10 = -10$ ✓

Show your work.

Got It? Do these problems to find out.

a. _____

b. _____

c. _____

a. $6 - 12$ **b.** $-20 - 15$ **c.** $-22 - 26$

Examples

Tutor

3. **Determine 1 − (−2).**

$1 - (-2) = 1 + 2$ To subtract −2, add 2.

$= 3$ Simplify.

4. **Determine −10 − (−7).**

$-10 - (-7) = -10 + 7$ To subtract −7, add 7.

$= -3$ Simplify.

5. **Determine $|6 - 10| - |-8|$.**

The absolute value bars act like grouping symbols.

$|6-10| - |-8| = |6 + (-10)| - |-8|$ To subtract 10, add −10.

$= |-4| - |-8|$ Add.

$= 4 - 8$ $|-4| = 4$ and $|-8| = 8$

$= 4 + (-8)$ To subtract 8, add −8.

$= -4$ Add.

6. **Determine $-|-4 - 1| - |-3|$.**

$-|-4 - 1| - |-3| = -\left|-4 \boxed{} \left(\boxed{}\right)\right| - |-3|$ To subtract 1, add −1.

$= -\left|\boxed{}\right| - |-3|$ Add.

$= -\boxed{} - \boxed{}$ $|-5| = 5$ and $|-3| = 3$

$= -5 \boxed{} \left(\boxed{}\right)$ To subtract 3, add −3.

$= \boxed{}$ Add.

Got It? Do these problems to find out.

d. $4 - (-12)$

e. $-15 - (-5)$

f. $18 - (-6)$

g. $|-4 - 9| - |7 - (-3)|$

h. $|-8 - (-1)| - |6|$

STOP and Reflect

Circle the integer below that will make this number sentence true.

$-5 - (?) = -3$

−8   −2   2

Show your work.

d. _____

e. _____

f. _____

g. _____

h. _____

Example

7. The temperatures on the Moon vary from −173°C to 127°C. Determine the difference between the maximum and minimum temperatures.

Subtract the lower temperature from the higher temperature.

Estimate $100 - (-200) = 300$

$127 - (-173) = 127 + 173$ To subtract −173, add 173.

$= 300$ Simplify.

So, the difference between the temperatures is 300°C.

Got It? Do this problem to find out.

i. Brenda had a balance of −$52 in her account. The bank charged her a fee of $10 for having a negative balance. What is her new balance?

i. _____

Guided Practice

Subtract. (Examples 1–4)

1. $14 - 17 =$ _____

2. $14 - (-10) =$ _____

3. $12 - 26 =$ _____

4. Determine $-|-3-4| - |-1|$. (Examples 5 and 6)

_____

5. **STEM** The sea surface temperatures range from −2°C to 31°C. Determine the difference between the maximum and minimum temperatures. (Example 7) _____

6. ? **Building on the Essential Question** If x and y are positive integers, is $x - y$ always positive? Explain.

_____

_____

Rate Yourself!

How well do you understand subtracting integers? Circle the image that applies.

Clear   Somewhat Clear   Not So Clear

Find out online. Use the Self-Check Quiz.

 Check

FOLDABLES Time to update your Foldable!

Independent Practice

6.3(D), 6.1(C)

Subtract. (Examples 1–4)

1. $0 - 10 =$ _____

Show your work.

2. $-9 - 5 =$ _____

3. $-4 - 8 =$ _____

4. $31 - 48 =$ _____

5. $-25 - 5 =$ _____

6. $-44 - 41 =$ _____

7. $4 - (-19) =$ _____

8. $-11 - (-42) =$ _____

9. $52 - (-52) =$ _____

Determine the value of each expression. (Examples 5 and 6)

10. $|-2 - 8| - |-5|$ _____

11. $-|-3 - (-9)| - |16|$ _____

12. **MP Select Tools and Techniques** Use the information below. (Example 7)

State	Alabama	California	Florida	Louisiana	New Mexico
Lowest Elevation (ft)	0	−282	0	−8	2,842
Highest Elevation (ft)	2,407	14,494	345	535	13,161

a. What is the difference between the highest elevation in Alabama and the

lowest elevation in Louisiana? _____

b. Determine the difference between the lowest elevation in New Mexico

and the lowest elevation in California. _____

c. Which state has the greatest difference in elevation? _____

d. Which state has the least difference in elevation? _____

13. Find the Error Hiroshi is finding $-15 - (-18)$. Determine his mistake and correct it.

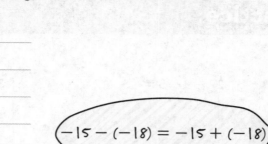

 H.O.T. Problems Higher-Order Thinking

14. Create Write a subtraction sentence using integers. Then, write the equivalent addition sentence and explain how to find the sum.

15. Analyze Use the properties of operations.

   a. The Commutative Property is true for addition. For example, $7 + 2 = 2 + 7$. Does the Commutative Property apply to subtraction? Is $2 - 7$ equal to $7 - 2$? Explain.

   b. Using the Associative Property, $9 + (6 + 3) = (9 + 6) + 3$.

   Is $9 - (6 - 3)$ equal to $(9 - 6) - 3$? Explain.

16. Evaluate True or False? When n is a negative integer, $n - n = 0$. Justify your response.

17. Create Write a real-world problem in which two negative integers are subtracted.

Multi-Step Problem Solving

18. On the first play of a football game, the quarterback ran with the football and gained 4 yards. On the next play, he lost 7 yards. The two plays are illustrated on the number line. Write a subtraction equation that represents the two consecutive plays and the net yardage.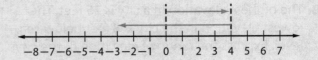

Ⓐ $-4 - 7 = -3$ yards   Ⓒ $7 - 3 = 4$ yards

Ⓑ $4 - 7 = -3$ yards   Ⓓ $3 - 7 = -4$ yards

Use a problem-solving model to solve this problem.

1 Analyze

Read the problem. Circle the information you know.
Underline what the problem is asking you to find.

2 Plan

What will you need to do to solve the problem? Write your plan in steps.

Step 1 Determine the integer that represents the yards after the first play.

Step 2 Determine the integer that represents the yards after the second play.

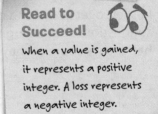

Read to Succeed!

When a value is gained, it represents a positive integer. A loss represents a negative integer.

3 Solve

Use your plan to solve the problem. Show your steps.

The quarterback gained 4 yards, so the first arrow ends at 4. He then lost 7 yards, so the second arrow goes to the left 7 units. The arrow ends at −3.

So, the subtraction equation is _____. Choice ____ is correct.

4 Justify and Evaluate

How do you know your solution is accurate?

_____

_____

_____

Ⓝ = Number and Operations   ⓂⓅ = Mathematical Processes

More Multi-Step Problem Solving

Use a problem-solving model to solve each problem.

19. The highest elevation in a city is 25 feet. The lowest elevation in the city is 8 feet below sea level. Express the range of elevation of the city as an addition expression and a subtraction expression.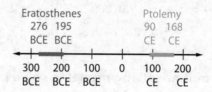

    Ⓐ $25 + (-8)$; $25 - 8$

    Ⓑ $8 - 25$; $-25 + 8$

    Ⓒ $-8 + 25$; $-8 - (-25)$

    Ⓓ $25 + 8$; $25 - (-8)$

20. Eratosthenes and Ptolemy were both mathematicians that made significant contributions in the areas of mathematics, as well as astronomy and geography. The time line below shows the estimated times they lived. Find the difference between the number of years they lived.

Eratosthenes		Ptolemy	
276	195	90	168
BCE	BCE	CE	CE

300 BCE	200 BCE	100 BCE	0	100 CE	200 CE

21. Alisha is working on her budget. The table below is her budget for a month. Find the amount of money Alisha has left over at the end of the month. Make three suggestions that change Alisha's budget and allow her to save more money each month.

Description	Amount ($)
Net pay	2,000
Cable TV	220
Car insurance	74
Cell phone	175
Credit card payment	125
Electric	135
Food	400
Gym membership	90
Rent	800
Savings	50

Ⓝ = Number and Operations   🄴🄴 = Expressions, Equations, and Relationships   🄼🄿 = Mathematical Processes   🄵🄻 = Personal Financial Literacy

222 **Chapter 3** Operations with integers

Mathematical Process
6.1(B) Use a problem-solving model that incorporates analyzing given information, formulating a plan or strategy, determining a solution, justifying the solution, and evaluating the problem-solving process and the reasonableness of the solution.

Targeted TEKS 6.3(D)

Hit the Slopes!

Marissa and her family are on a ski trip at Mount Washington in New Hampshire. At noon, the temperature had risen 5°F. At 3 P.M. the temperature rose another 3°F. They returned from the slopes at 6 P.M. By 9 P.M., the temperature had fallen 18° since 3 P.M. to the day's low temperature of −8°F.

What was the temperature before noon?

Analyze *What are the facts?*

• At noon, the temperature rose 5°.

• At 3 P.M, the temperature rose 3°.

• By 9 P.M., the temperature had fallen 18°.

• The day's low temperature was −8°F.

Plan *What is your strategy to solve this problem?*

Work backward from the low temperature at 9 P.M. Use a thermometer diagram to find the temperature before noon.

Solve *How can you apply the strategy?*

Start at [   ] °F. Shade the thermometer [   ] degrees to find the temperature at 3 P.M.

So, the temperature at 3 P.M. was _____.

Since the temperature rose twice before 3 P.M., subtract to find the previous temperatures.

10°F − 3°F = [   ] °F

[   ] °F − 5°F = [   ] °F

So, the temperature before noon was _____.

°Fahrenheit

50°
40°
30°
20°
10°
0°
−10°

Justify and Evaluate *Does the answer make sense?*

Start with 2°F before noon. Add 5°F and 3°F.

2°F + 5°F + 3°F = [   ] °F.

Then subtract 18°F. 10°F − 18°F = [   ] °F

Get Ready, Get Set, Go

The table shows the amount of time it takes Henry to do different activities before going to soccer practice.

If he needs to be at practice at 8:15 A.M., what time should he wake up in the morning to get to the soccer field?

Activity	Time (hr)
Travel to field from home	0.25
Eating breakfast	$\frac{1}{5}$
Changing into uniform	$\frac{1}{6}$
Checking E-mail messages	0.35

Analyze

Read the problem. Circle the information you know.
Underline what the problem is asking you to find.

Plan

Choose a problem-solving strategy.

I will use the _____ strategy.

Solve

Use your problem-solving strategy to solve the problem.

So, Henry should wake up at _____.

Justify and Evaluate

How do you know your solution is accurate?

_____

_____

Multi-Step Problem Solving

Work with a small group to solve the following problems. Show your work on a separate piece of paper.

1. Sea Level

Mr. Ignacio went diving along the coral reef in Oahu. He descended 12 meters below sea level. The difference between this point on the coral reef and the highest point on the island, Mount Ka'ala, is 1,232 meters. Two-fifths of the way up the mountain is a ranger station.

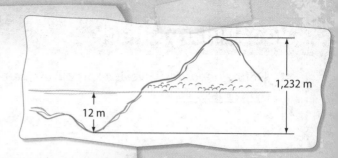

How far above sea level is the ranger station?

_____

2. Cameras

Adamo saved 13 pictures on his digital camera for a total of 12,021.1 kB. He deleted 32 pictures for a total of 29,590.4 kB.

If there are now 108 pictures, how many kilobytes of storage did he use at the beginning?

_____

3. Mystery Number

A number is multiplied by 4, and then −6 is added to the product. The result is 18.

What is the number?

_____

Use any strategy!

4. Ladders

You are standing on the middle rung of a ladder.

If you first climb up 3 rungs, then down 5 rungs, and then up 10 rungs to get onto the top rung, how many rungs are on the ladder?

_____

TEKS Mid-Chapter Check

Vocabulary Check

1. Define *opposites*. Give an example of a number and its opposite.
TEKS 6.3(D), 6.1(G)

_____

_____

Key Concept Check

2. Complete the graphic organizer by writing a real-world problem for each type of addition problem. Give the addition equation and solution to your problem. Write a rule you can use for each type of addition problem. **TEKS** 6.3(D), 6.1(E)

	Positive + Positive	Positive + Negative	Negative + Negative
Real-World Problem			
Solution			
Rule			

3. The melting point of mercury is −36°F and its boiling point is 672°F. What is the difference between the boiling point and the melting point? **TEKS** 6.3(D), 6.1(B) _____

Multi-Step Problem Solving

4. Patrick starts hiking at an elevation of −418 feet. He ascends to an elevation of 387 feet and then descends to an elevation 94 feet higher than where he began. He descended 132 feet. What is the elevation of where he stops hiking? Ⓝ ⓂⓅ

Ⓐ −482 ft   Ⓒ −324 ft

Ⓑ −456 ft   Ⓓ −31 ft

 **N** = Number and Operations   **MP** = Mathematical Processes

Use Models to Multiply Integers

INQUIRY HOW can I select tools and techniques to determine when the product of two integers will be positive or negative?

The number of students who bring their lunch to Phoenix Middle School had been decreasing at a rate of 4 students each month. What integer represents the total change in the number of students bringing their lunch after three months?

What do you know? _____

_____

What do you need to find? _____

_____

Texas Essential Knowledge and Skills

Targeted TEKS
6.3(C) Represent integer operations with concrete models and connect the actions with the models to standardized algorithms.

Mathematical Processes
6.1(C), 6.1(D), 6.1(E)

Hands-On Activity 1

Tools

The integer [ ] represents a decrease of 4 students each month. After three months, the total change will be $3 \times (-4)$.

$$3 \times (-4)$$

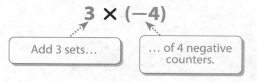

Add 3 sets…   … of 4 negative counters.

Step 1   Add 3 sets of 4 negative counters to the mat.

Step 2   Count the number of negative counters.

There are [ ] negative counters.

So, $3 \times (-4) =$ [ ]. After three months, the total change in the number of students bringing their lunch will be [ ].

The model shows that *adding* sets of *negative* counters results in *negative* counters on the mat.

Hands-On Activity 2

Use counters to find −2 × 3.

If the first factor is negative, you need to *remove* counters from the mat.

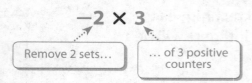

−2 × 3

Remove 2 sets... ... of 3 positive counters

Step 1   There are no counters on the mat, so add 2 sets of 3 zero pairs on the mat. The value on the mat is zero.

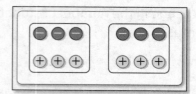

Step 2   Remove 2 sets of 3 positive counters from the mat.

There are [ ] negative counters remaining.

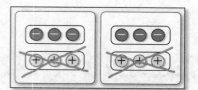

So, −2 × 3 = [ ]. The model shows that *removing* sets of *positive* counters results in sets of *negative* counters that are remaining.

Hands-On Activity 3

Use counters to find −2 × (−4).

Both factors are negative. Remove [ ] sets of [ ] negative counters from the mat.

Step 1   There are no counters on the mat, so draw 2 sets of 4 zero pairs on the mat.

Step 2   Cross out 2 sets of 4 negative counters from the mat.

There are [ ] positive counters remaining.

So, −2 × (−4) = [ ]. The model shows that *removing* sets of *negative* counters results in sets of *positive* counters that are remaining.

Investigate

Work with a partner. Determine each product. Show your work using drawings.

1. $2 \times (-3) =$ _____

2. $6 \times (-1) =$ _____

Show your work.

3. $-2 \times 4 =$ _____

4. $-1 \times 5 =$ _____

5. $-4 \times 2 =$ _____

6. $-2 \times (-4) =$ _____

7. $-3 \times (-1) =$ _____

8. $-6 \times (-2) =$ _____

9. What do your models show about removing sets of positive counters?

removing sets of negative counters? _____

_____

_____

Work with a partner to complete the table. Use counters if needed. The first one is already done for you.

	Multiplication Expression	Same Signs or Different Signs?	Product	Positive or Negative?
	2×6	Same signs	12	Positive
10.	$7 \times (-2)$			
11.	$-3 \times (-4)$			
12.	$5 \times (-3)$			
13.	2×8			
14.	$-4 \times (-1)$			
15.	-3×6			
16.	-2×5			

17. Connect Models to Rules Study the pattern in the table. Write a rule you can use to find the product of two integers without using counters. Test your rule by finding $3 \times (-7)$ using counters.

_____

_____

_____

Create
On Your Own

18. MP Apply Math to the Real World Write a real-world problem that could be represented by the expression -5×4.

_____

_____

19. INQUIRY HOW can I select tools and techniques to determine when the product of two integers will be positive or negative? _____

_____

_____

Multiply Integers

 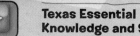

Once a parachute is deployed, a skydiver descends at a rate of about 5 meters per second. Where will the skydiver be in relation to where the parachute deployed after 4 seconds?

Texas Essential Knowledge and Skills

Targeted TEKS
6.3(D) Add, subtract, multiply, and divide integers fluently. *Also addresses 6.3(C).*

Mathematical Processes
6.1(A), 6.1(B), 6.1(D), 6.1(F)

Essential Question
WHAT happens when you add, subtract, multiply, and divide integers?

1. What integer should you use to represent the position of the skydiver in relation to the parachute's deployment after 1 second? ☐

2. The repeated addition expression $(-5) + (-5) + (-5) + (-5)$ can be used to represent the situation. What is the sum? _____

3. What is the skydiver's position after 2, 3, and 4 seconds?

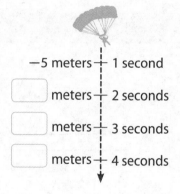

−5 meters ┼ 1 second

☐ meters ┼ 2 seconds

☐ meters ┼ 3 seconds

☐ meters ┼ 4 seconds

4. Write a multiplication sentence to represent the skydiver's position after 4 seconds. _____

5. Write a multiplication sentence to represent the skydiver's position after 5 seconds.

_____

Look Mom, no hands!

Which MP Mathematical Processes did you use?
Shade the circle(s) that applies.

Ⓐ Apply Math to the Real World.

Ⓑ Use a Problem-Solving Model.

Ⓒ Select Tools and Techniques.

Ⓓ Use Multiple Representations.

Ⓔ Organize Ideas.

Ⓕ Analyze Relationships.

Ⓖ Justify Arguments.

Multiply Integers with Different Signs

Words   The product of two integers with different signs is negative.

Examples $6(-4) = -24$ $-5(7) = -35$

The model below illustrates this rule. Remember that multiplication is the same as repeated addition.

$4(-3) = (-3) + (-3) + (-3) + (-3)$ -3 is used as an
$$= -12$$ addend four times.

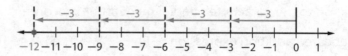

The Commutative Property of Multiplication states that you can multiply in any order. So, $4(-3) = -3(4)$.

Tutor

Examples

1. **Determine 3(−5).**

$3(-5) = -15$ The integers have different signs. The product is negative.

Check $(-5) + (-5) + (-5) = -15$ ✓

2. **Determine −6(8).**

$-6(8) = -48$ The integers have different signs. The product is negative.

Show your work.

Got It? Do these problems to find out.

a. _____

a. $9(-2)$ **b.** $-7(4)$

b. _____

Multiply Integers with Same Signs

Words   The product of two integers with the same sign is positive.

Examples $2(6) = 12$ $-10(-6) = 60$

The product of two positive integers is positive. You can use a pattern to find the sign of the product of two negative integers. Start with $(2)(-3) = -6$ and $(1)(-3) = -3$.

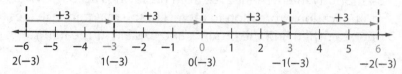

positive × negative = negative $(2)(-3) = -6$
The Multiplicative Property of Zero $(1)(-3) = -3$ +3
    $(0)(-3) = 0$ +3
negative × negative = positive $(-1)(-3) = 3$ +3
    $(-2)(-3) = 6$ +3

Each product is 3 more than the previous product. The model below illustrates this pattern.

If you extend the pattern, the next two products are $(-3)(-3) = 9$ and $(-4)(-3) = 12$. So, the product of two negative integers is positive.

Examples

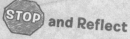
Tutor

3. Determine $-11(-9)$.

$-11(-9) = 99$ The integers have the same sign. The product is positive.

4. Determine $(-4)(-4)$.

$(-4)(-4) = 16$ The product is positive.

5. Determine $-3(-4)(-2)$.

$-3(-4)(-2) = [-3(-4)](-2)$ Associative Property

$= 12(-2)$ $-3(-4) = 12$

$= -24$ $12(-2) = -24$

Got It? Do these problems to find out.

c. $-12(-4)$ **d.** $(-5)(-5)$ **e.** $-7(-5)(-3)$

STOP and Reflect

Write three integers with a positive product. At least one of them must be a negative integer. Show your work below.

Show your work.

c. _____

d. _____

e. _____

Example

6. A submersible is diving from the surface of the water at a rate of 90 feet per minute. What is the depth of the submersible after 7 minutes?

The submersible descends 90 feet per minute. After 7 minutes, the vessel will be at 7(−90) or −630 feet. The submersible will descend to 630 feet below the surface.

Show your work.

Got It? Do this problem to find out.

    f. Financial Literacy Mr. Simon's bank automatically deducts a $4 monthly maintenance fee from his savings account. Write a multiplication expression to represent the maintenance fees for one year. Then find the product and explain its meaning.

f. _____

Guided Practice

Multiply. (Examples 1–5)

Show your work.

1. 6(−10) = _____

2. (−3)(−3)(−3) = _____

3. (−1)(−3)(−4) = _____

4. Financial Literacy Tamera owns 100 shares of a certain stock. Suppose the price of the stock drops by $3 per share. Write a multiplication expression to determine the change in her investment. Represent the integer operation on a number line. (Example 6)

_____

5. **?** **Building on the Essential Question** How is the rule for multiplying a positive integer by a negative integer represented using a model?

_____

_____

_____

Rate Yourself!

Are you ready to move on?
Shade the section that applies.

I have a few questions. | I'm ready to move on.

I have a lot of questions.

Find out online. Use the Self-Check Quiz.

Check ✓

FOLDABLES Time to update your Foldable!

Independent Practice

Multiply. (Examples 1–5)

1. $8(-12) =$ _____

Show your work.

2. $-15(-4) =$ _____

3. $(-6)(-6) =$ _____

4. $(-5)(-5)(-5) =$ _____

5. $-4(-2)(-8) =$ _____

6. $-3(-2)(1) =$ _____

Write a multiplication expression to represent each situation. Then find each product and explain its meaning. (Example 6)

7. Ethan burns 650 Calories when he runs for 1 hour. Suppose he runs 5 hours in one week.

_____

_____

8. Wave erosion causes a certain coastline to recede at a rate of 3 centimeters each year. This occurs uninterrupted for a period of 8 years.

_____

_____

_____

9. **MP** **Apply Math to the Real World** Refer to the graphic novel frame below. How many black T-shirts would Hannah and Dario need to sell to make up the loss in profit?

_____

10. **Use Multiple Representations** When a movie is rented it has a due date. If the movie is not returned on time, a late fee is assessed. Kaitlyn is charged $5 each day for a movie that is 4 days late.

   a. Words Explain why $4 \times (-5) = -20$ describes the situation. _____

   _____

   b. Numbers Write an expression to represent the fee when the movie is 3 days late. _____

11. **Use Multiple Representations** Explain why multiplying two negative numbers results in a positive product using a model. _____

   _____

   _____

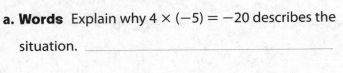 **Problems** Higher-Order Thinking

12. **Create** Write a multiplication sentence with a product of −18.

   _____

13. **Analyze** Explain how to evaluate $(-9)(-6)(15)(-7 + 7)$ as simply as possible.

   _____

   _____

14. **Analyze** Find values of a, b, and c that make each statement true. If no values exist, write *not possible*.
   a. $a < b$ and $a + c < b + c$

   _____

   b. $a < b$ and $a + c > b + c$

   _____

   c. $a < b$ and $ac < bc$

   _____

   d. $a < b$ and $ac > bc$

   _____

   e. $a < b$ and $ac = bc$

   _____

15. **Analyze** The product of two integers is −21. The difference between the integers is −10. The sum of the two integers is 4. What are the two integers?

   _____

Name _____

16. Each time Min uses an ATM that belongs to a bank other than the one she has a checking account with, she is charged a fee. The number line shows her ATM fees for one month. Write a numerical expression that represents her ATM fees and explain the meaning.

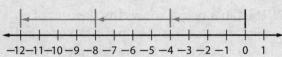

Ⓐ (−3)4; Min uses an ATM 4 times and is charged $3 for each use.

Ⓑ (−12)1; Min is charged $12 for 1 ATM use.

Ⓒ (−4)3; Min uses an ATM 3 times and is charged $4 for each use.

Ⓓ (−4)12; Min uses the ATM 12 times and is charged $4 for each use.

Use a problem-solving model to solve this problem.

1 Analyze

Read the problem. Circle the information you know. Underline what the problem is asking you to find.

2 Plan

What will you need to do to solve the problem? Write your plan in steps.

| Step 1 | Determine the direction of the arrows. |

| Step 2 | Determine the integer for each arrow. |

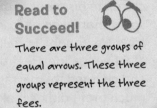

Read to Succeed!
There are three groups of equal arrows. These three groups represent the three fees.

3 Solve

Use your plan to solve the problem. Show your steps.

Since the arrows are going to the _____ the integers represented

are _____. There are three arrows that each represent _____.

(−4) • 3 = _____

So, Min used the ATM 3 times and was charged $4 each time.

The correct answer is _____. Fill in that answer choice.

4 Justify and Evaluate

How do you know your solution is accurate?

_____

_____

Ⓝ = Number and Operations   Ⓜ︎Ⓟ = Mathematical Processes

Use a problem-solving model to solve each problem.

17. The table below shows the descent of an airplane. Use the data in the table to find the rate of descent in feet per minute. Assume the plane continues to descend at a constant rate. Write a multiplication expression that represents how far the plane has descended in 7 minutes and find the product. **N** **EE** **MP**

Distance (ft)	Minutes
−1,200	1
−2,400	2
−3,600	3
−4,800	4

Ⓐ (−1,200)7; −8,400 feet

Ⓑ (−2,400)7; −16,800 feet

Ⓒ (−1,400)7; −9,800 feet

Ⓓ (−1,371)7; −9,600 feet

18. Olivia is playing a trivia game where you gain a certain amount of points for each right answer and lose a certain amount of points for each wrong answer. Some questions are worth 3 points, and some questions are worth 5 points. Olivia gets four 3-point questions right and three 3-point questions wrong. She gets three 5-point questions right and two 5-point questions wrong. How many points does she have? **N** **EE** **MP**

19. Jose drives a limousine and he wants to calculate his profit at the end of the day. He spent money on gasoline but made money on trips. He bought 14 gallons worth of gasoline at $4 per gallon. He drove customers 75 miles and charged them a rate of $5 per mile. How much profit did he make, in dollars, at the end of the day? **N** **P** **EE** **MP**

20. Tom multiplies 5 negative integers. Is the product positive, negative, or zero? Explain. **N** **MP**

N = Number and Operations   **P** = Proportionality   **EE** = Expressions, Equations, and Relationships   **MP** = Mathematical Processes

238   **Chapter 3** Operations with Integers

Use Models to Divide Integers

INQUIRY HOW can I select tools and techniques to determine when the quotient of two integers is negative?

The temperature in Galveston, Texas dropped 10 degrees over several days, with the temperature dropping 5 degrees each day. What integer represents the number of days the temperature dropped?

Texas Essential Knowledge and Skills TEKS

Targeted TEKS
6.3(C) Represent integer operations with concrete models and connect the actions with the models to standardized algorithms.

Mathematical Processes
6.1(C), 6.1(D), 6.1(E), 6.1(F), 6.1(G)

Hands-On Activity 1

The integer _____ represents a decrease of 10 degrees. To find the number of days the temperature dropped, divide by −5.

$$-10 \div (-5) = ?$$

How many groups of 5 negative counters would you have to add to get 10 negative counters?

Step 1 Start with an empty mat.

Step 2 Add two groups of 5 negative counters. Since you *added* 2 groups, the quotient is 2.

So, $-10 \div (-5) =$ _____. The temperature dropped over _____ days.

Hands-On Activity 2

Determine $10 \div (-5)$.

How many groups of 5 negative counters would you have to take away to get 10 positive counters?

Step 1 There are no negative counters to remove, so add 10 zero pairs to an empty mat.

Step 2 Remove two groups of 5 negative counters.

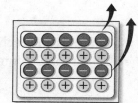

You would have to take away _____ groups of 5 negative counters. Since you are *taking away* 2 groups, the quotient is −2.

So, $10 \div (-5) = -2$.

Investigate

Collaborate

Work with a partner. Determine each quotient using models.

1. $-12 \div 3 =$ _____

2. $-8 \div 4 =$ _____

 **Analyze and Reflect**

Collaborate

Work with a partner to complete the table. The first one is already done for you.

	Multiplication Sentence	Related Division Sentence	Sign of Dividend	Sign of Divisor	Sign of Quotient
	$-5 \times 2 = -10$	$-10 \div 2 = -5$	negative	positive	negative
3.	$5 \times 2 = 10$				
4.	$5 \times (-2) = -10$				
5.	$-5 \times (-2) = 10$				
6.	$-2 \times 4 = -8$				
7.	$2 \times 4 = 8$				
8.	$2 \times (-4) = -8$				
9.	$-2 \times (-4) = 8$				

10. **MP** **Analyze Relationships** Use the table. What patterns can you find among the signs of the dividend, divisor, and quotient? _____

_____

_____

 Create

On Your Own

11. **MP** **Select Tools and Techniques** Draw a model to show $-9 \div 3$.

12. **INQUIRY** HOW can I select tools and techniques to determine when the quotient of two integers is negative?

_____

_____

Divide Integers

Launch the Lesson: Real World

A Great White shark has 3,000 teeth! It gains and loses teeth often in its lifetime. Suppose a Great White loses 3 teeth each day for 5 days without gaining any. The shark has lost 15 teeth in all.

1. Write a multiplication sentence for this situation. _____

2. Division is related to multiplication. Write two division sentences related to the multiplication sentence you wrote for Exercise 1.

Texas Essential Knowledge and Skills

Targeted TEKS
6.3(D) Add, subtract, multiply, and divide integers fluently.

Mathematical Processes
6.1(A), 6.1(B), 6.1(D), 6.1(F)

Essential Question
WHAT happens when you add, subtract, multiply, and divide integers?

Investigate Work with a partner to complete the table. The first one is done for you.

Multiplication Sentence	Division Sentences	Same Signs or Different Signs	Quotient	Positive or Negative?
$2 \times 6 = 12$	$12 \div 6 = 2$	Same signs	2	Positive
	$12 \div 2 = 6$	Same signs	6	Positive
3. $2 \times (-4) = -8$				
4. $-3 \times 5 = -15$				
5. $-2 \times (-5) = 10$				

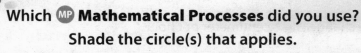

Which ⓂⓅ **Mathematical Processes** did you use?
Shade the circle(s) that applies.

Ⓐ Apply Math to the Real World.

Ⓑ Use a Problem-Solving Model.

Ⓒ Select Tools and Techniques.

Ⓓ Use Multiple Representations.

Ⓔ Organize Ideas.

Ⓕ Analyze Relationships.

Ⓖ Justify Arguments.

Key Concept

Divide Integers with Different Signs

Words The quotient of two integers with different signs is negative.

Examples $33 \div (-11) = -3$ $\qquad$ $-64 \div 8 = -8$

You can divide integers provided that the divisor is not zero. Since multiplication and division sentences are related, you can use them to find the quotient of integers with different signs.

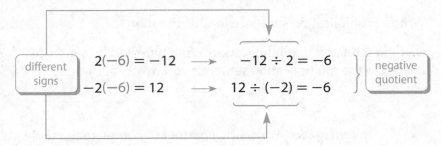

Work Zone

Examples

1. **Determine $80 \div (-10)$.** The integers have different signs.

$80 \div (-10) = -8$ $\qquad$ The quotient is negative.

Dividing Integers

If p and q are integers and q does not equal 0,
then $-\dfrac{p}{q} = \dfrac{-p}{q} = \dfrac{p}{-q}$.

In Example 2, $-\dfrac{55}{11} = \dfrac{-55}{11} = \dfrac{55}{-11}$.

2. **Determine $\dfrac{-55}{11}$.** The integers have different signs.

$\dfrac{-55}{11} = -5$ $\qquad$ The quotient is negative.

3. **Use the table to find how much the height changed each hour.**

The height of the candle decreases by 2 centimeters every two hours.

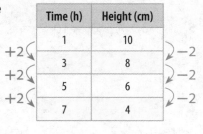

$\dfrac{\text{change in height}}{\text{change in hours}} = \dfrac{-2}{2}$

So, the change is -1 centimeter per hour.

Show your work.

a. _____

b. _____

c. _____

Got It? Do these problems to find out.

a. $20 \div (-4)$ $\qquad$ **b.** $\dfrac{-81}{9}$ $\qquad$ **c.** $-45 \div 9$

242 **Chapter 3** Operations with Integers

Divide Integers with the Same Signs

Words   The quotient of two integers with the same sign is positive.

Examples $15 \div 5 = 3$ $-64 \div (-8) = 8$

You can also use multiplication and division sentences to find the quotient of integers with the same sign.

same signs

$4(5) = 20 \longrightarrow 20 \div 4 = 5$

$-4(5) = -20 \longrightarrow -20 \div (-4) = 5$

positive quotient

Examples

Tutor

4. **Determine $-14 \div (-7)$.**   The integers have the same sign.

$-14 \div (-7) = 2$ The quotient is positive.

5. **Determine $\dfrac{-27}{-3}$.**   The integers have the same sign.

$\dfrac{-27}{-3} = 9$ The quotient is positive.

6. **Financial Literacy** **A bank charges $20 per month for every month that a checking account balance is below zero. Kendall has a balance of $-\$100$. He wants to deposit $40 each month to bring his balance to zero. How many months will it take to bring the account balance to zero?**

Each month, he deposits $40 and the bank charges $20. So, the change in his account balance is $+\$20$ each month.

Divide the current balance by the monthly change.

$-100 \div 20 = -5$ The signs are different.

It will take 5 months to bring the account balance to zero.

Got It? Do these problems to find out.

d. $-24 \div (-4)$ **e.** $-9 \div (-3)$ **f.** $\dfrac{-28}{-7}$

Show your work.

d. _____

e. _____

f. _____

Multi-Step Example

7. **STEM** One year, the estimated Australian koala population was 1,000,000. After 10 years, there were about 100,000 koalas. Determine the average change in the koala population per year. Then explain its meaning.

Step 1 100,000 − 1,000,000
= −900,000   Subtract to determine the change.

Step 2 −900,000 ÷ 10
= −90,000   Divide to find the change for each year.

The koala population has changed by −90,000 per year.

Guided Practice

Divide. (Examples 1, 2, 4 and 5)

1. −16 ÷ 2 = _____

2. $\frac{42}{-7}$ = _____

3. −30 ÷ (−5) = _____

Show your work.

4. 15 ÷ (−5) = _____

5. −8 ÷ (−2) = _____

6. −7 ÷ 7 = _____

7. A coastline has receded 450 centimeters in 9 years. Each year, the coastline recedes the same distance. One meter is equal to 100 centimeters. How far does the coastline recede each year, in meters? (Examples 6 and 7) _____

8. **Building on the Essential Question** How is dividing integers similar to multiplying integers?

_____

_____

Rate Yourself!

How confident are you about dividing integers? Check the box that applies.

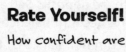

Find out online. Use the Self-Check Quiz.

Check

FOLDABLES Time to update your Foldable!

Independent Practice

Divide (Examples 1, 2, 4, and 5)

1. $50 \div (-5) =$ _____

2. $-18 \div 9 =$ _____

3. $-15 \div (-3) =$ _____

4. $-100 \div (-10) =$ _____

Show your work.

5. $\dfrac{22}{-2} =$ _____

6. $\dfrac{84}{-12} =$ _____

7. $\dfrac{-26}{13} =$ _____

8. $\dfrac{-21}{-7} =$ _____

9. $12 \div (-4) =$ _____

10. $-48 \div 16 =$ _____

11. $\dfrac{-18}{3} =$ _____

12. $\dfrac{-4}{-2} =$ _____

13. The distance remaining for a road trip over several hours is shown in the table. Use the information to find how much the distance remaining changed each hour. (Example 3) _____

Time (h)	Distance Remaining (mi)
2	480
4	360
6	240
8	120

14. **MP** **Justify Arguments** Last year, Mr. Engle's total income was $52,000, while his total expenses were $53,800. Determine the average difference between his income and expenses each month.

Then explain its meaning. (Examples 6 and 7) _____

_____

15. **MP** **Use Multiple Representations** Recall that division is repeated subtraction.

a. **Numbers** Write a division sentence that is represented by

the model. _____

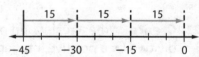

b. **Connect Models to Rules** How does the model illustrate the rule for dividing -45 by -15?

_____

_____

_____

c. **Models** How would the model change if the division problem was $-40 \div (-8)$?

_____

_____

_____

Determine the value of each expression.

16. $\dfrac{-(-36)}{-9} =$ _____

17. $\dfrac{-|-9|}{|-3|} =$ _____

18. $\dfrac{-8}{-|4|} =$ _____

19. **STEM** The temperature on Mars ranges widely from −207°F to 80°F. Divide the difference by 2 to find the average of the temperature extremes on Mars. _____

 H.O.T. Problems Higher-Order Thinking

20. **Analyze** You know that multiplication is commutative because $9 \times 3 = 3 \times 9$. Is division commutative? Explain.

_____

_____

21. **Evaluate** Addition, subtraction, and multiplication are said to be *closed* for integers. That is, when you add, subtract, or multiply integers, the result is also an integer. Is division closed for integers? Explain.

_____

_____

_____

22. **Analyze** Find two integers whose product is −32 and whose quotient is −2.

_____

23. **Create** Write a real-world problem in which a negative integer must be divided by a positive integer.

_____

_____

_____

24. **Analyze** The table shows the population change for each of 5 years. Find the average change by adding the changes and dividing by the number of changes. _____

Year	Population Change
2012	3,088
2013	−3,297
2014	1,340
2015	2,933
2016	−4,816

Name _____

Multi-Step Problem Solving

25. The table shows the distance and time for each phase of a submersible's exhibition. Which of the following represents the average speed throughout the exhibition?

Distance (m)	Time (sec)
−15	5
−30	6
+5	5
−50	10

- Ⓐ 3 m/s
- Ⓑ −3 m/s
- Ⓒ −3.5 m/s
- Ⓓ 3.5 m/s

Use a problem-solving model to solve this problem.

1 Analyze

Read the problem. Circle the information you know.
Underline what the problem is asking you to find.

2 Plan

What will you need to do to solve the problem? Write your plan in steps.

Step 1 Determine the speed for each phase of the exhibition.

Step 2 Add the speeds and divide to find the average speed.

3 Solve

Use your plan to solve the problem. Show your steps.

Phase 1: $-15 \div 5 = -3$ Phase 2: $-30 \div 6 = -5$
Phase 3: $5 \div 5 = 1$ Phase 4: $-50 \div 10 = -5$

The average speed is $\dfrac{(-3) + (-5) + (1) + (-5)}{4}$ or -3.

So, the average speed of the submersible is _____ meters per second.

The correct answer is _____.

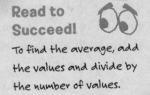

Read to Succeed!
To find the average, add the values and divide by the number of values.

4 Justify and Evaluate

How do you know your solution is accurate?

_____

_____

Ⓝ = Number and Operations   Ⓟ = Proportionality   ⓂⓅ = Mathematical Processes

More Multi-Step Problem Solving

Use a problem-solving model to solve each problem.

26. Dakota earns the money shown in the table. After buying 4 chairs, she has $30 left. How much did Dakota pay for each chair? Ⓝ Ⓔ Ⓜ

Job	Amount Earned
Babysitting	$120
Pet sitting	$65
Dog walking	$45

Ⓐ $22.50

Ⓑ $50

Ⓒ $47.50

Ⓓ $200

27. The table below shows the temperature for a town over 5 consecutive days. Use the data to find the average temperature. Convert the average to degrees Fahrenheit using the formula below. Ⓝ Ⓔ Ⓟ Ⓜ

$$F = \frac{9C + 160}{5}$$

Day	Temperature (C)
1	−19°C
2	−18°C
3	−15°C
4	−15°C
5	−18°C

28. Julian played a game, starting with a certain number of points. He lost 6 points each of the first three rounds. He gained 3 points and then gained 7 points the next two rounds. Then he lost 8 points each of two rounds. His final score is −9. How many points did he have in the beginning of the game? Ⓝ Ⓔ Ⓜ

29. Frank divides two negative integers. He divides the quotient by a positive integer and multiplies the quotient by a negative integer. Is the result positive or negative? Explain. Ⓝ Ⓜ Ⓜ

Ⓝ = Number and Operations   Ⓟ = Proportionality   Ⓔ = Expressions, Equations, and Relationships   Ⓜ = Measurement and Data   Ⓜ = Mathematical Processes

248   Chapter 3 Operations with Integers

Mixed Problem Solving with Integers

Texas Essential Knowledge and Skills

Targeted TEKS
6.3(D) Add, subtract, multiply, and divide integers fluently.

Mathematical Processes
6.1(A), 6.1(B), 6.1(C), 6.1(G)

  Launch the Lesson: Real World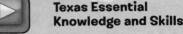

Watch

Lake Bridgeport has a maximum depth of −85 feet. Cascade Cavern reaches a depth of −132 feet. A diver descended to the maximum depth of Lake Bridgeport four times and a hiker descended to the deepest part of Cascade Cavern three times. How much farther did the hiker travel than the diver?

Essential Question

WHAT happens when you add, subtract, multiply, and divide integers?

1. Write a multiplication sentence to represent the total depth of

    the dives. _____

    Represent your multiplication sentence on the number line at the right.

2. Write a multiplication sentence to represent the total depth hiked.

    _____

    Represent your multiplication sentence on the number line at the right.

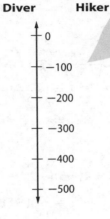

3. How much farther did the hiker travel

    than the diver? _____

Which MP Mathematical Processes did you use?
Shade the circle(s) that applies.

Ⓐ Apply Math to the Real World.   Ⓔ Organize Ideas.

Ⓑ Use a Problem-Solving Model.   Ⓕ Analyze Relationships.

Ⓒ Select Tools and Techniques.   Ⓖ Justify Arguments.

Ⓓ Use Multiple Representations.

Expressions with Integers

You can find the value of numerical expressions that include integers.

Examples

Tutor

Determine the value of each expression.

1. $-4(3) + 8$

$= -4(3) + 8$ Write the expression.

$= -12 + 8$ Multiply.

$= \boxed{}$ Add.

2. $\left(\dfrac{-25}{5}\right) - 3$

$= \left(\dfrac{-25}{5}\right) - 3$ Write the expression.

$= \boxed{} - 3$ Divide.

$= \boxed{}$ Subtract.

3. $-4(-5)(-2) - (-8)$

$= -4(-5)(-2) - (-8)$ Write the expression.

$= \left(\boxed{}\right)(-2) - (-8)$ Multiply.

$= \boxed{} - (-8)$ Multiply.

$= -40 + \boxed{}$ Add the opposite.

$= \boxed{}$ Subtract.

4. $\left(\dfrac{36}{-12}\right)(-1) + (-7)$

$= \left(\dfrac{36}{-12}\right)(-1) + (-7)$ Write the expression.

$= \left(\boxed{}\right)(-1) + (-7)$ Divide.

$= \boxed{} + \left(\boxed{}\right)$ Multiply.

$= \boxed{}$ Add.

Show your work.

Got It? Do these problems to find out.

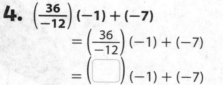

a. $-7(-8) + 11$

b. $\left(\dfrac{-48}{-6}\right) + 5$

c. $(-3)(7)(-2) + (-1)$

d. $\left(\dfrac{55}{-5}\right)(-1)(3) - (-9)$

a. _____

b. _____

c. _____

d. _____

Solve Multi-Step Problems with Integers

You can use the four-step plan when solving multi-step problems with integers. First, analyze the given information. Then, decide on a plan. Third, use the plan to find the solution. Finally, justify the solution.

Multi-Step Example

Tutor

5. The table shows the minimum and maximum temperatures on various planets. Which planet has the greatest variation in temperature? the least?

Planet	Maximum Temperature (°C)	Minimum Temperature (°C)
Earth	58	−88
Mars	36	−123
Mercury	465	−184
Jupiter	−148	−180

Step 1 To find each variation, subtract the minimum from the maximum.

Earth: $58 - (-88) = 146$

Mars: $36 - (-123) = 159$

Mercury: $465 - (-184) = 649$

Jupiter: $-148 - (-180) = 32$

Step 2 Analyze the results.

The difference between the minimum and maximum temperatures on Mercury is the highest of the four planets at 649°C, so it has the greatest variation of temperatures.

Of the four planets, Jupiter has the least variation between minimum and maximum temperatures at 32°C.

Got It? Do this problem to find out.

e. Financial Literacy At the beginning of the month, the balance of an account was −$72. During the month, the following deposits and withdrawals were made: $55, −$20, $82, −$10. What was the account balance at the end of the month?

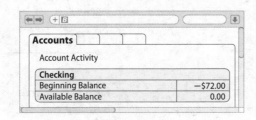

Show your work.

e. _____

Multi-Step Example

Tutor

6. An airplane descends 125 feet each minute after having reached an altitude of 28,525 feet. What is the airplane's altitude after 15 minutes?

Step 1 $15 \times (-125) = -1,875$ Multiply to find the change in altitude.

The change in altitude is −1,875 feet.

Step 2 $28,525 - 1,875 = 26,650$ Find the current altitude.

So, the airplane's altitude is 28,525 − 1,875 or 26,650 feet.

Guided Practice

Determine the value of each expression. (Examples 1 and 2)

1. $-11(-8) + 9 =$ _____

2. $\left(\dfrac{-90}{-9}\right)(3)(-2) + 4 =$ _____

3. The temperature dropped a total of 32°F over a 4-day period. The temperature on the first day started out at 65°F. What was the temperature on Day 3 if it

dropped the same amount each day? Explain. (Example 3) _____

_____

_____

4. A contestant on a game show has −$1,200. He earns $800 then loses another $550. By how much did the contestant's earnings change after this if he ended the game with $350?

(Example 4) _____

5. (?) **Building on the Essential Question** Explain how the four-step plan is used in solving multi-step problems with

integers. _____

_____

_____

_____

Rate Yourself!

How confident are you about solving multi-step problems with integers? Check the box that applies.

☹ ☺ ☺

☐ ☐ ☐ ☐ ☐

Find out online. Use the Self-Check Quiz.

Check

Independent Practice

6.3(D), 6.1(A) TEKS

Determine the value of each expression. (Examples 1 and 2)

1. $-7(3) - 9 =$ _____

2. $5(-20) + 14 =$ _____

3. $\left(\dfrac{39}{-3}\right) + 5 =$ _____

4. $\left(\dfrac{-63}{-7}\right) - 3 =$ _____

5. $(11)(-2)(-4) - (-10) =$ _____

6. $\left(\dfrac{25}{-5}\right)(-4)(5) + (-37) =$ _____

7. The erosion rate of a coastline is about 3 feet per year. If erosion continues at the current rate, how many years will it take for the coastline to erode 15 feet to a grass line and then another 24 feet to a tree line? Explain. (Example 3)

_____

_____

8. For every 1,000 feet above sea level, the air temperature decreases by 4°F. The highest natural point in Texas is Guadalupe Peak at 8,751 feet. If the temperature at sea level is 76°F, what is the temperature near the summit at

8,000 feet? (Example 4) _____

9. The scores for a nine-hole game of golf are shown in the table. The player with the lower total score wins. Who won the golf game? Explain.

	Hole								
Player	1	2	3	4	5	6	7	8	9
Tom	1	−2	0	0	1	−1	−1	2	−2
Paida	0	0	1	−2	−1	−1	2	1	1

_____

_____

_____

10. Financial Literacy A flat-screen television costs $1,306.62. A monthly fee of $5.50 is added if it is paid in installments. Marisa will pay for

the television over 18 months. How much will she pay each month? _____

11. The wind outside makes the outside temperature feel colder than the actual temperature. This is called the *wind chill*. What is the difference in wind chill when it is 5°F and the wind increases from 10 miles per hour to 30 miles per hour than when it is −5°F and the wind increases from

10 miles per hour to 30 miles per hour? _____

	Temperature (°F)			
Wind speed (mph)	calm	5°	0°	−5°
10		−10	−16	−22
20		−15	−22	−29
30		−19	−26	−33

12. Financial Literacy The profit of a company is found by subtracting the expenses from the income. The table shows the expenses and income for a company for four months. What was the company's total profit after the four months? What does a negative profit mean?

Month	Expenses	Income
January	$13,090	$3,575
February	$14,129	$4,311
March	$13,877	$10,298
April	$15,624	$14,382

_____

_____

 H.O.T. Problems Higher-Order Thinking

13. Create Write a real-world problem that can be solved by multiplying, then subtracting integers.

_____

_____

_____

14. Analyze Factors can be written with exponents. For example, $(-1)^2 = (-1)(-1) = 1$ and $(-1)^3 = (-1)(-1)(-1) = -1$. For each exponent, determine if the product is positive or negative. Explain the pattern.

_____

_____

a. $(-1)^4$ _____   **c.** $(-1)^{10}$ _____

b. $(-1)^5$ _____   **d.** $(-1)^{101}$ _____

15. Financial Literacy The balance of a savings account after four transactions was $245. The original balance was $280. Give a sample set of what the four

deposits and/or withdrawals might have been. _____

_____

Evaluate Determine the value of each expression. How are these expressions different from the ones throughout the rest of the lesson?

16. $-12\left(\dfrac{-3}{4}\right) + 2 =$ _____

17. $\left(\dfrac{9}{4}\right)\left(\dfrac{-8}{3}\right) - 3 =$ _____

_____

_____

Multi-Step Problem Solving

18. The table shows the cost per acre for a farm to grow corn. Suppose a farm yields 150 bushels of corn per acre. How much is the cost per bushel of corn, in dollars?

Description	Cost ($)
Seed	80
Pesticides	45
Labor	50
Machine repair and gas	70
Taxes	30
Storage	25

Use a problem-solving model to solve this problem.

1 Analyze

**Read the problem. Circle the information you know.
Underline what the problem is asking you to find.**

2 Plan

**What will you need to do to solve the problem? Write your
plan in steps.**

Step 1   Determine the total cost per acre.

Step 2   Divide by the number of bushels of corn per acre.

> **Read to Succeed!**
> When placing answers in an answer grid, keep in mind the placement of the decimal point.

3 Solve

Use your plan to solve the problem. Show your steps.

The total cost per acre is 80 + 45 + 50 + 70 + 30 + 25 or _____ .

The cost per bushel of corn is $ _____ ÷ _____ or $ ____ per bushel.

So, the cost is $ ____ per bushel. Place ____ in the grid.

4 Justify and Evaluate

How do you know your solution is accurate?

_____

_____

_____

N = Number and Operations   MP = Mathematical Processes

More Multi-Step Problem Solving

Use a problem-solving model to solve each problem.

19. Vincent stopped to get gas and noted the mileage on his truck was 10,120. The next time he stopped to get gas, the mileage was 10,870. If his truck has a 30-gallon gas tank, how many miles per gallon is the truck getting? Assume the truck was on empty both times he stopped to get gas. **N EE MP**

20. Profit is the amount of money earned after expenses are paid. The revenue, or amount of money earned, during a 5-day period for an ice cream shop is shown in the table. Determine the average daily profit, assuming that it costs $425 a day to operate the ice cream shop. **N FL EE MP**

Day	Revenue ($)
Tuesday	350
Wednesday	380
Thursday	620
Friday	680
Saturday	700

21. Last week, Lamont deposited three checks and paid four bills as shown in the check register below. If the starting balance in his checking account was −$45, what is his current balance? **N FL EE MP**

Description	Amount ($)
Check #123 - cable	124
Check #124 - phone	140
Deposit	250
Check #125 - groceries	225
Deposit	350
Check #126 - electric	166
Deposit	325

22. Vanesa multiplies two integers. When she adds the product to 4, the sum is 0. What can you say about the two integers? **N MP**

N = Number and Operations   **EE** = Expressions, Equations, and Relationships   **MP** = Mathematical Processes   **FL** = Personal Financial Literacy

256   Chapter 3 Operations with Integers

Space Weather Forecaster

Did you know that space weather, or the conditions on the Sun and in space, can directly affect communication systems and power grids here on Earth? If you enjoy learning about the mysteries of space, then you should consider a career involving space weather. A space weather forecaster uses spacecraft, telescopes, radar, and supercomputers to monitor the sun, solar winds, and the space environment in order to forecast the weather in space.

Mathematical Process
6.1(A) Apply mathematics to problems arising in everyday life, society, and the workplace.
Targeted TEKS 6.3(D)

Is This the Career for You?

Are you interested in a career as a space weather forecaster? Take some of the following courses in high school.

◆ Astronomy
◆ Calculus
◆ Chemistry
◆ Earth Science
◆ Physics

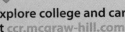

Explore college and careers at ccr.mcgraw-hill.com

Predicting Space Storms!

Use the information in the table to solve each problem.

1. Locate the average temperatures for Earth, Jupiter, Mars, Mercury, Neptune, and Saturn on a number line. Label the points.

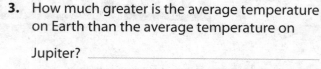

2. The temperatures on Mercury range from −279°F to 800°F. What is the difference between the highest and lowest temperatures? _____

3. How much greater is the average temperature on Earth than the average temperature on Jupiter? _____

4. One of Neptune's moons, Triton, has a surface temperature that is 61°F less than Neptune's average temperature. What is Triton's surface temperature? _____

5. The temperature on Mars can reach a low of −304°F. What is the difference between the low and the average temperature? _____

Average Temperature of Planets			
Planet	Average Temperature (°F)	Planet	Average Temperature (°F)
Earth	59	Neptune	−330
Jupiter	−166	Saturn	−220
Mars	−85	Uranus	−320
Mercury	333	Venus	867

 TEKS Career Project

It's time to update your career portfolio! Investigate the education and training requirements for a career as a space weather forecaster. Prepare a brief oral presentation and present it to your classmates. As others are presenting, listen carefully to their presentations. At the end, ask any clarifying questions.

Collaborate

_____

_____

_____

List other careers that someone with an interest in astronomy could pursue.

• _____

• _____

• _____

• _____

• _____

Chapter Review

Vocabulary Check

Work with a partner to complete each sentence using the vocabulary list at the beginning of the chapter. Seek clarification of each term as needed.

1. The sum of an integer and its _____ inverse is 0.

2. A(n) _____ integer is greater than 0.

3. The set of _____ contains all the whole numbers and their opposites.

4. The _____ value of a number is the distance it is from 0 on a number line.

5. 5 and −5 are _____.

6. The result when one positive counter is paired with one negative counter is a _____ pair.

Reconstruct the vocabulary word and definition from the letters under the grid. The letters for each column are scrambled directly under that column.

| N | E | G | A | T | I | V | E | | I | N | T | E | G | E | R | : | | | |

			E		E	R								W	G				E
I	E	A	N	T	I	V				E		I	R	N				E	
N	N	T	E	G	E	E	S	A	H	N	N	E	G	E	I	I	E	A	N
T	N	T	A	G	Z	R	R	T	A	A	T	E	I	A	T	L	T	E	N
I	H	G	W	I	T	H	E	O	X	R	T	S	G	S	R	T	V	S	S

Use Your FOLDABLES

Collaborate

Use your Foldable to help review the chapter. Share your Foldable with a partner and take turns summarizing what you learned in this chapter, while the other partner listens carefully. Seek clarificiation of any concepts, as needed. TEKS 6.1(D)

Tape here

Operations with Integers

How do I add integers with different signs?

How do I subtract integers with different signs?

How do I multiply integers with different signs?

How do I divide integers with different signs?

Got it?

Find the Error The problems below may or may not contain an error. If the problem is correct, write a "✓" by the answer. If the problem is not correct, write an "X" over the answer and correct the problem. TEKS 6.3(D)

1. $|-5| + |2| = -\cancel{3}$

$|-5| + |2| = 5 + 2$ or 7

The first one is done for you.

2. $3|-6| = 18$

3. $-24 \div |-2| = 12$

4. In a trivia game, a correct answer is worth 2 points and an incorrect answer is worth −3 points. Jay answered a total of 26 questions in the game. If he answered 4 more questions correctly than incorrectly, how many points did he earn in the game? Justify your response.

1 Analyze

2 Plan

3 Solve

4 Justify and Evaluate

_____

_____

Got it?

5. A golfer's score is compared to par. For example, a score of −2 means 2 under par and is a better score than +3 or 3 over par. The table below shows the scores for three golfers. Order the golfers from first place to third place. Justify your response. N MP

Golfer	Round 1	Round 2	Round 3	Round 4	Round 5	Round 6
Thorne	−1	+1	−2	−2	+4	−3
Hollern	+1	−2	0	−3	+1	−1
Brigham	+2	−4	+3	−1	+2	−3

_____

_____

_____

_____

N = Number and Operations   MP = Mathematical Processes

Reflect

 Answering the Essential Question

Use what you learned about integers to complete the graphic organizer. Explain how to determine the sign of the result when performing each operation. **TEKS** 6.1(D), 6.1(F), 6.1(G)

Addition and Subtraction

? **Essential Question**

WHAT happens when you add, subtract, multiply, and divide integers?

Multiply and Divide

 ? **Answer the Essential Question.** WHAT happens when you add, subtract, multiply, and divide integers? Verbally share your response with a partner, seeking and providing clarification as needed.

Chapter 4
Understand Proportions

Texas Essential Knowledge and Skills

Targeted TEKS
6.4 The student applies mathematical process standards to develop an understanding of proportional relationships in problem situations.

Mathematical Processes
6.1, 6.1(A), 6.1(B), 6.1(C), 6.1(D), 6.1(E), 6.1(F), 6.1(G)

Essential Question

HOW do you use equivalent ratios and rates in the real world?

Math in the Real World

American Pronghorn used to roam in the western $\frac{2}{3}$ of the United States. They are now limited to areas from the Panhandle to the Trans-Pecos. They are the second fastest land animals. They can run at speeds of 50 miles per hour.

If a pronghorn antelope runs 1 mile in 50 seconds, fill in the diagram to show how far it will run in 150 seconds.

Vocabulary ELL ELPS c.4.C(1)

dimensional analysis   ratio   unit price

equivalent ratio   ratio table   unit rate

proportion   scale factor

rate   scaling

Studying Math ELL ELPS c.2.E(3), c.3.H(3), c.4.C(3), c.4.D, c.4.F(1), c.4.F(2)

New Vocabulary New vocabulary terms are clues about important concepts. Learning new vocabulary words is more than just memorizing the definition. Whenever you see a new vocabulary word, ask yourself:

- How does this fit with what I already know?

- How is this alike or different from something I learned earlier?

Organize your answers in a word map like the one shown.

Make a word map for *proper fraction*.

Definition from Text

A rate is a comparison by division of two quantities with different kinds of units.

In Your Own Words

A rate compares two amounts with different units using division.

rate

Examples

- 45 miles per hour

- 16 books for 8 students

Nonexamples

- 5 black cats out of 15 cats

- 3 sugar cookies to 9 cookies

Definition

_____

_____

In Your Own Words

_____

_____

proper fraction

Examples

- _____

- _____

Nonexamples

- _____

- _____

6.1(A), 6.4(B)

Your Turn! You will solve this problem in the chapter.

Quick Review

Review 5.3(C), 4.3(C) TEKS

Example 1

Determine $6\overline{)348}$.

$$
\begin{array}{r}
58 \\
6\overline{)348} \\
-30 \\
\hline
48 \\
-48 \\
\hline
0
\end{array}
$$

Divide each place-value position from left to right.

Since $48 - 48 = 0$, there is no remainder.

Example 2

Express $\frac{40}{64}$ in simplest form.

$$\frac{40}{64} = \frac{5}{8}$$ (÷8, ÷8)

Divide the numerator and denominator by the greatest common factor (GCF), 8.

Since the GCF of 5 and 8 is 1, the fraction $\frac{5}{8}$ is in simplest form.

Quick Check

Check ✓

Divide Whole Numbers Determine each quotient.

1. $3\overline{)87}$

2. $8\overline{)584}$

3. $52\overline{)312}$

 Show your work.

Simplify Fractions Express each fraction in simplest form.

4. $\frac{32}{48} = $ _____

5. $\frac{7}{28} = $ _____

6. $\frac{15}{25} = $ _____

7. An airplane has flown 260 miles out of a total trip of 500 miles. What fraction, in simplest form, of the trip has been completed?

_____

How Did You Do?

Which problems did you answer correctly in the Quick Check? Shade those exercise numbers below.

① ② ③ ④ ⑤ ⑥ ⑦

   Use the Foldable throughout this chapter to help you learn about ratios and rates.

✂ cut on all dashed lines   ⬜ fold on all solid lines   tape to page 344

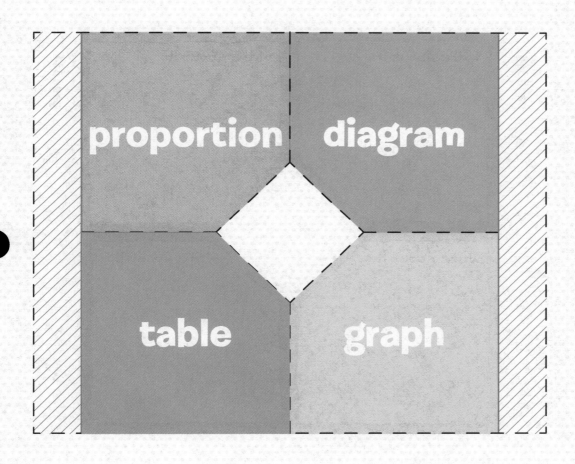

 Use the Foldable throughout this chapter to help you learn about ratios and rates.

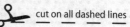 cut on all dashed lines · fold on all solid lines · tape to page 344

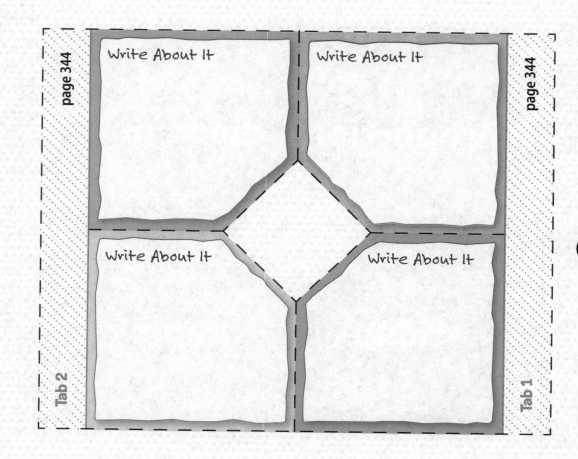

page 344

page 344

Write About It

Write About It

Write About It

Write About It

Tab 2

Tab 1

INQUIRY HOW can I select tools to relate quantities?

Max has 3 fiction books and 6 nonfiction books to donate to the community center. He wants to package them so that there are an equal number of fiction and nonfiction books in each group. He also wants to have as many packages as possible. How many books are in each group?

What do you know? _____

_____

_____

What do you need to find? _____

_____

Hands-On Activity 1

Step 1 Use 3 red counters to represent the fiction books.
Use 6 yellow counters to represent the nonfiction books.

Step 2 Determine the smallest possible equal-size groups.
Use mats to divide the counters into the groups.

Each group has an equal number of fiction books and an equal number of nonfiction books.

Each group has ☐ fiction book and ☐ nonfiction books.

Hands-On Activity 2

Maria is also collecting books. She wants to make packages that have 3 fiction books and 4 nonfiction books. She already has 9 fiction books. How many nonfiction books will she need?

Use a multiplication table to compare the numbers.

Step 1 Compare the rows for 3 and 4 on a multiplication table.

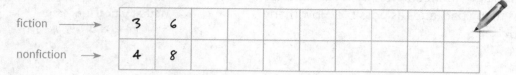

fiction ⟶

3	6								
4	8								

nonfiction ⟶

Step 2 Read across the top until you reach 9. Find the corresponding number in the bottom row and circle the 2 numbers.

Maria needs ⬚ nonfiction books.

Hands-On Activity 3

Sanjay has 27 red and blue jerseys. Divide them into two groups so that for every 4 red jerseys, there are 5 blue jerseys.

Step 1 Complete the rows for 4 and 5 on a multiplication table.

red ⟶

4	8								
5	10								

blue ⟶

Step 2 Read across both rows until you find two numbers with a sum of 27.

There are ⬚ red jerseys and ⬚ blue jerseys.

Check Draw a picture to check your answer.

Investigate

Collaborate

Work with a partner. Determine the number of pieces of fruit that should be put in each group. Make as many equal-size groups as possible using all the fruit. Draw counters to represent the fruit.

1. 3 apples and 9 pears

2. 4 peaches and 6 oranges

Show your work.

3. 4 plums and 7 bananas

4. 6 apricots and 9 mangos

Work with a partner. Use a multiplication table to solve the following problems.

5. Evie wants groups of 3 notebooks and 5 pens. She already has 12 notebooks.

How many pens will she need? _____

notebooks ⟶

pens ⟶

6. Louis wants groups of 6 daisies and 8 tulips for flower arrangements.

He already has 24 daisies. How many tulips will he need? _____

daisies ⟶

tulips ⟶

7. Selma has 77 strawberries. Divide them into two groups so that for every 4 strawberries in Group 1 there are 7 strawberries in Group 2.

_____

Group 1 ⟶

Group 2 ⟶

8. **MP** **Analyze Relationships** Describe the patterns used in the tables in Activities 2 and 3.

_____

_____

_____

9. **MP** **Analyze Relationships** How would finding the least common multiple help you when dividing items into equal groups?

_____

_____

Create

On Your Own

10. **MP** **Apply Math to the Real World** Write and solve a word problem in which there are 3 yellow beads for every 2 blue beads.

_____

_____

11. **MP** **Apply Math to the Real World** Write and solve a real-world word problem in which there are 3 tables for every 8 chairs.

_____

_____

_____

12. **MP** **Apply Math to the Real World** Write and solve a real-world word problem in which there are 3 pancakes for every person.

_____

_____

_____

13. **INQUIRY** How can I select tools to relate quantities?

_____

_____

_____

Launch the Lesson: Real World Watch

In her dog-walking business, Mrs. DeCarbo walks 2 large dogs and 8 small dogs. How can we compare these quantities?

Compare the number of small dogs to large dogs. Use yellow counters to represent the large dogs. Use red counters to represent the small dogs. Draw the counters in the box.

Texas Essential Knowledge and Skills TEKS

Targeted TEKS
6.4(C) Give examples of ratios as multiplicative comparisons of two quantities describing the same attribute. *Also addresses 6.4(B), 6.4(E).*

Mathematical Processes
6.1(A), 6.1(B), 6.1(C), 6.1(D), 6.1(F)

Vocab

Vocabulary
ratio

Essential Question
HOW do you use equivalent ratios and rates in the real world?

1. $2 + \boxed{} = 8$ There are $\boxed{}$ *more* small dogs than large dogs.

2. $2 \times \boxed{} = 8$ There are $\boxed{}$ *times* as many small dogs as large dogs.

3. $8 - \boxed{} = 2$ There are $\boxed{}$ *fewer* large dogs than small dogs.

4. $8 \div \boxed{} = 2$ The number of large dogs is $\dfrac{\boxed{}}{\boxed{}}$ the number of small dogs.

5. Which comparison(s) above was a multiplicative comparison? Circle it.

Which MP **Mathematical Processes** did you use?
Shade the circle(s) that applies.

Ⓐ Apply Math to the Real World.   Ⓔ Organize Ideas.

Ⓑ Use a Problem-Solving Model.   Ⓕ Analyze Relationships.

Ⓒ Select Tools and Techniques.   Ⓖ Justify Arguments.

Ⓓ Use Multiple Representations.

Ratios as Multiplicative Comparisons

There are many ways to compare amounts or quantities. A **ratio** is a multiplicative comparison of two quantities describing the same attribute. A ratio of 3 hammers to 12 nails can be written in three ways.

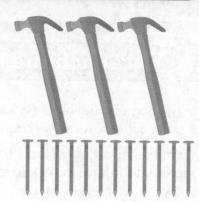

3 to 12   3:12 $\frac{3}{12}$

As with fractions, ratios are often expressed in simplest form. Ratios can also be expressed as decimals.

Example

Tutor

1. **Express the ratio in simplest form that compares the number of hammers to the number of nails. Then explain its meaning.**

Express the ratio as a fraction. Then simplify.

hammers ····▶
nails ····▶
$$\frac{3}{12} = \frac{1}{4}$$

The GCF of 3 and 12 is 3.

The ratio of hammers to nails is $\frac{1}{4}$ or 0.25, 1 to 4, or 1:4. This means that for every 1 hammer, there are 4 nails. By using a multiplicative comparison, there are four times as many nails as hammers or $\frac{1}{4}$ as many hammers as nails.

Show your work.

Got It? Do this problem to find out.

a. Express the ratio in simplest form and as a decimal that compares the number of suns to the number of moons. Then explain its meaning.

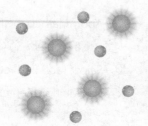

a. _____

Use Ratios to Compare Categorical Data

Each piece of categorical data can only be assigned to one group. Bar diagrams (or strip diagrams) and frequency tables can be used to represent categorical data. Ratios can be used to compare the data.

Examples

Watch Tutor

2. Several students named their favorite way to exercise. Write the ratio that compares the number who chose running to the total number of students.

Favorite Form of Exercise	
Exercise	Number of Responses
Running	8
Sports	13
Swimming	3

Running: 8

Total: 8 + 13 + 3, or 24

running responses ····▶
total responses ····▶

$$\frac{8}{24} = \frac{1}{3}$$ ÷8 ÷8

The GCF of 8 and 24 is 8.

The ratio is $\frac{1}{3}$, 1 to 3, or 1:3. As a decimal, the ratio is $0.\overline{3}$.

So, 1 out of every 3 students chose running as their favorite form of exercise. By using a multiplicative comparison, there were three times as many total students as students who chose running, or $\frac{1}{3}$ as many that chose running as the total number of students.

3. Monday's yogurt sales are recorded in the table. Write the ratio that compares the sales of strawberry yogurt to the total sales. Then explain its meaning.

Flavor	Number Sold
Peach	3
Blueberry	6
Vanilla	7
Strawberry	8

Strawberry: 8

Total: 8 + 3 + 6 + 7, or 24

strawberry yogurt sold ····▶
total sold ····▶

$$\frac{8}{24} \div \frac{8}{8} = \frac{1}{3} \text{ or 1 to 3}$$

Show your work.

So, ☐ out of every ☐ yogurt cups sold were strawberry.

Got It? Do this problem to find out.

b. A pet store sold the animals listed in the table in one week. Write the ratio of goldfish to pets sold that week. Then explain its meaning.

Pet	Number Sold
Goldfish	27
Hamster	11
Iguana	4

b. _____

Example

4. Katy wants to divide her 30 flowers into two groups, so that the ratio is 2 to 3.

Step 1 Use a bar diagram to show a ratio of 2 to 3.

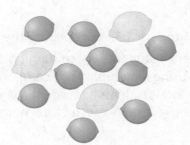

30 flowers

Step 2 There are 5 equal sections. So, each section represents 30 ÷ 5 or 6 flowers.

There are 12 flowers in one group and 18 in the other.

Guided Practice

Write each ratio as a fraction in simplest form and as a decimal. Round to the nearest hundredth. Then explain its meaning. (Example 1)

1. candles to matches

Show your work. ➡

_____

_____

2. lemons:limes

_____

_____

3. Last week, William ate 15 grapes, 2 bananas, and 3 apples. Determine the ratio of grapes to the total number of fruit in simplest form. Use a multiplicative comparison to

explain its meaning. (Examples 2 and 3) _____

_____

4. Divide 28 cans of soda into two groups so the ratio is 3 to 4.

(Example 4) _____

5. ? **Building on the Essential Question** How can you use mental math to determine if a ratio is simplified?

_____

_____

Rate Yourself!

How confident are you about ratios? Shade the ring on the target.

I'm on target.

I need help.

Find out online. Use the Self-Check Quiz.

Check ✓

FOLDABLES Time to update your Foldable!

Independent Practice

6.4(B), 6.4(C), 6.4(E), 6.1(A), 6.1(D)

Write each ratio as a fraction in simplest form and as a decimal. Round to the nearest hundredth. Then explain its meaning. (Example 1)

1. goggles:snorkels

Show your work.

2. cans of soup to soup bowls

3. A kennel has 8 adult dogs and 14 puppies. What is the ratio of adult dogs to puppies? Use a multiplicative comparison to explain its meaning. (Example 2)

4. The table shows the number of movies Patrick has seen this year. Determine the ratio of comedies to the total. Use a multiplicative comparison to explain its meaning. (Example 3) _____

Type	Number of Movies
Action	4
Animated	1
Comedy	3
Drama	2

5. Divide 33 photos into two groups so the ratio is 4 to 7. (Example 4)

6. **(MP) Apply Math to the Real World** Refer to the graphic novel frame below for Exercises a–b.

a. For each store, what is the ratio of the number of cans to the price?

_____

b. What would be the ratio of the number of cans to the price at Super Saver and Price Busters if a coupon for $1 off the total purchase is used? _____

7. **MP** **Select Tools and Techniques** The graph shows the number of Wimbledon championships of several countries.

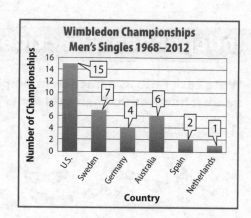

Wimbledon Championships Men's Singles 1968–2012

a. Write the ratio that compares the championships won by Australia to the total number won by the United States in simplest form. Then explain its meaning.

_____

_____

b. Write the ratio that compares the championships won by Australia to the total number of championships. Then explain its meaning.

_____

_____

H.O.T. Problems Higher-Order Thinking

8. Create Create three different drawings showing a number of rectangles and circles in which the ratio of rectangles to circles is 3:1.

Show your work.

9. Analyze Determine the missing number in the following pattern. Explain your reasoning.

12, 24, 72, 288, ⬚

_____

_____

10. Analyze The table shows how Levon spends his time at the gym. Over the course of a week, he wants to spend 600 minutes at the gym keeping the same ratio of activities. How much more time will he spend lifting weights than on the treadmill? Explain your reasoning.

Activity	Time (min)
Treadmill	25
Lifting weights	35

_____

_____

_____

_____

Multi-Step Problem Solving

11. The table shows the types of sandwiches sold on Friday. What is the denominator when the ratio of veggie to the total number of sandwiches is written as a fraction in simplest form? **P** **MP**

Sandwich	Number Sold
Turkey	9
Tuna	11
Veggie	6
Chicken	14

Use a problem-solving model to solve this problem.

1 Analyze

Read the problem. Circle the information you know.
Underline what the problem is asking you to find.

2 Plan

What will you need to do to solve the problem?
Write your plan in steps.

Step 1   Determine the total number of sandwiches sold.

Step 2   Express the ratio of veggie sandwiches to total sandwiches as a fraction in simplest form.

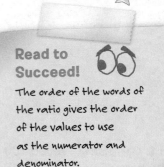

Read to Succeed!

The order of the words of the ratio gives the order of the values to use as the numerator and denominator.

3 Solve

Use your plan to solve the problem. Show your steps.

The total number of sandwiches sold is ☐ + ☐ + ☐ + ☐

or ☐ sandwiches.

The ratio of veggie to total sandwiches is ☐/☐ or ☐/☐.

So, the simplified denominator is ☐. Complete the grid.

4 Justify and Evaluate

How do you know your solution is accurate?

_____

_____

More Multi-Step Problem Solving

Use a problem-solving model to solve each problem.

12. The table shows the types of breakfasts sold on Thursday. What is the denominator of the simplified ratio of oatmeal orders to total orders? **P** **MP**

Breakfast	Number Sold
Omelets	14
Pancakes	17
Waffles	11
Oatmeal	8

13. How many blue counters must be added so that the ratio of yellow counters to total counters is 1:6? **P** **MP**

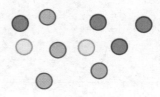

_____

14. Cantrise surveyed 100 students about their favorite type of music. After she makes the graph, she receives two more votes for rap. What is the new ratio of rap to total types of music? **N** **P** **MP**

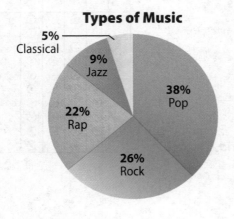

Types of Music

- 5% Classical
- 9% Jazz
- 38% Pop
- 22% Rap
- 26% Rock

15. The ratio of blue circles to total circles is 4 to 5. There are more than 10 circles. Describe what this group of circles might look like. Explain. **P** **MP**

_____

_____

_____

_____

 N = Number and Operations   **P** = Proportionality   **MP** = Mathematical Processes

INQUIRY HOW can I select tools to compare quantities in real-world situations?

Jamila and Anica were rollerblading. They skated 14 miles in 2 hours. If they skated at a constant rate, how many miles did they skate in 1 hour?

What do you know? _____

_____

What do you need to find? _____

_____

Texas Essential Knowledge and Skills TEKS

Targeted TEKS
6.4(D) Give examples of rates as the comparison by division of two quantities having different attributes, including rates as quotients.

Mathematical Processes
6.1(C), 6.1(D), 6.1(E), 6.1(F), 6.1(G)

Hands-On Activity 1

Step 1 Use a bar diagram to represent 14 miles. The box is separated into two equal sections to represent 2 hours.

```
|------------------ 14 miles ------------------|
|     1 hour      |     1 hour      |
```

Step 2 Each section represents one hour. Determine the number of miles skated in one hour.

```
|------------------ 14 miles ------------------|
|     1 hour      |     1 hour      |
|---- 7 miles ----|
```

So, they skated 14 ÷ 2 or ☐ miles in one hour.

1. What operation did you use to find the answer?

_____

2. Do the quantities 14 miles and 2 hours have the same or different attributes?

_____

Hands-On Activity 2

A package of 5 crackers contains 205 Calories. How many Calories are in one cracker?

Step 1   Draw a bar diagram to represent 205 Calories. Divide the bar diagram into 5 equal sections to represent 5 crackers.

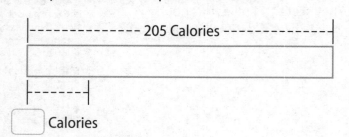

|-------------- 205 Calories --------------|

▢ Calories

Step 2   Label the first section "1 cracker." Determine the number of Calories in 1 cracker.

So, one cracker contains 205 ÷ 5 or ▢ Calories.

Hands-On Activity 3

A bottle of body wash costs $2.88 and contains 12 ounces. How much does it cost per ounce?

Step 1   Draw a bar diagram to represent _____. Divide the bar

diagram into ▢ equal sections to represent ▢ ounces.

▢

Step 2   Label the first section "_____." Determine the cost for 1 ounce of body wash.

So, one ounce of body wash costs $2.88 ÷ 12 or $ ▢ .

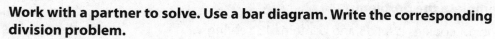

Investigate

Work with a partner to solve. Use a bar diagram. Write the corresponding division problem.

3. Travis drove 129 miles in 3 hours. He drove at a constant speed.

   How many miles did he drive in 1 hour? _____

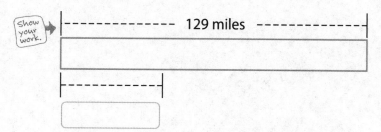

4. Six oranges cost $5.34. How much does 1 orange cost? _____

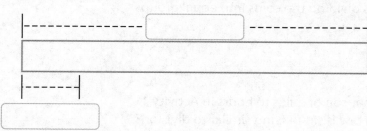

5. Doug read 231 pages in 7 hours. He read the same number of pages each

   hour. How many pages did he read in 1 hour? _____

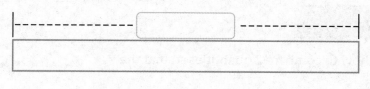

   [ ] pages

6. Mariah has 72 flowers in 4 vases. She put the same number of flowers in

   each vase. How many flowers are in 1 vase? _____

   [ ] flowers

Analyze and Reflect

Collaborate

Work with a partner to complete the problem.

7. In the bakery, a container of cookies is $4.55 and contains 13 servings. The coins below equal $4.55. Divide the coins into 13 equal groups to determine the cost per serving. Circle each group. _____

8. **MP Analyze Relationships** How does dividing the coins into equal groups help solve the problem? _____

_____

9. **MP Analyze Relationships** The comparison of miles to hours in Activity 1 is 14:2, which can be reduced to 7:1. How is simplifying similar to division?

_____

_____

Create

On Your Own

10. **MP Organize Ideas** Write a rule for how to compare 2 quantities so that the second quantity has a value of 1.

_____

_____

11. **MP Analyze Relationships** Write and solve a real-world word problem in which the unit rate is 7 miles per hour.

_____

_____

_____

12. **INQUIRY** HOW can I select tools to compare quantities in real-world situations?

_____

_____

Rates

 Launch the Lesson: Vocabulary

Texas Essential Knowledge and Skills

Targeted TEKS
6.4(D) Give examples of rates as the comparison by division of two quantities having different attributes, including rates as quotients. *Also addresses 6.4(B).*

Mathematical Processes
6.1(A), 6.1(B), 6.1(C), 6.1(D), 6.1(F)

Use your glossary to complete the definitions of the vocabulary words in the table.

Definition	Examples
ratio: A multiplicative comparison of two _____.	2 out of 3, 2 to 3, 2:3, $\frac{2}{3}$
rate: A comparison by _____ of two quantities having different _____.	$\dfrac{36 \text{ miles}}{3 \text{ hours}}$ 36 miles for every 3 hours $26 for 5 bags 19 songs in 5 minutes
unit rate: A _____ that is _____ so that it has a denominator of _____.	$\dfrac{12 \text{ miles}}{1 \text{ hour}}$, 12 miles per hour $5.20 for 1 bag 3.8 songs in 1 minute

Vocab

Vocabulary
rate
unit rate
unit price

Essential Question (?)
HOW do you use equivalent ratios and rates in the real world?

 Real-World Investigation

Desiree typed a 15-character text message in 5 seconds.

1. Write the rate Desiree typed as a fraction. ☐ characters / ☐ seconds

2. What operation would you use to write the fraction in simplest form?

_____

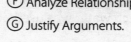 **Which ㎆ Mathematical Processes did you use?**
Shade the circle(s) that applies.

Ⓐ Apply Math to the Real World.
Ⓑ Use a Problem-Solving Model.
Ⓒ Select Tools and Techniques.
Ⓓ Use Multiple Representations.
Ⓔ Organize Ideas.
Ⓕ Analyze Relationships.
Ⓖ Justify Arguments.

Determine a Unit Rate

A **rate** is a comparison by division of two quantities having different attributes. A **unit rate** has a denominator of 1 unit when the rate is written as a fraction. To write a rate as a unit rate, find a quotient. Divide the numerator and the denominator of the rate by the denominator.

Rate	Quotient	Unit Rate

$$\frac{15 \text{ characters}}{5 \text{ seconds}} = 15 \div 5 = \frac{3 \text{ characters}}{1 \text{ second}}$$

 Examples

 Tutor

1. **Samantha picked 45 oranges in 5 minutes. Express this rate as a unit rate.**

Write the rate as a fraction. Compare the number of oranges to the number of minutes. Then divide.

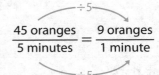
$$\frac{45 \text{ oranges}}{5 \text{ minutes}} = \frac{9 \text{ oranges}}{1 \text{ minute}}$$
÷5   ÷5

So, the unit rate is $\frac{9 \text{ oranges}}{1 \text{ minute}}$, or 9 oranges per minute.

> **Simplifying Rates**
>
> The lowest common factor of 3 and 5 is 1. To find the unit rate of the rate $\frac{3 \text{ miles}}{5 \text{ minutes}}$, divide both the numerator and denominator by 5. So, the unit rate in fraction form is $\frac{3}{5}$ mile per minute.

2. **The Australian dragonfly can travel 18 miles in 30 minutes. How far can the dragonfly travel in 1 minute?**

Write the rate as a fraction. Compare the distance to the number of minutes. Then divide.

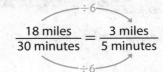
$$\frac{18 \text{ miles}}{30 \text{ minutes}} = \frac{3 \text{ miles}}{5 \text{ minutes}}$$
÷6   ÷6

The rate 3 to 5 cannot be simplified to a whole number rate.

It can be written as the quotient $\frac{3 \text{ miles}}{5 \text{ minutes}}$ or as a unit rate of $\frac{3}{5}$ mile to 1 minute.

The dragonfly can travel $\frac{3}{5}$ mile every minute.

 Show your work.

Got It? Do these problems to find out.

a. _____

a. Ama downloaded 35 songs in 5 minutes. How many songs did she download per minute?

b. Jonathan is baking several loaves of bread to sell in his bakery. He used 9 cups of water and 12 cups of whole wheat flour. How much water was used per cup of flour?

b. _____

Solve Comparison Problems Involving Rates

You can apply qualitative reasoning to solve comparison problems involving rates.

Multi-Step Example

Tutor

3. An adult's heart beats about 2,100 times every 30 minutes. A baby's heart beats about 2,600 times every 20 minutes. How many more beats does a baby's heart beat in 60 minutes than an adult's heart?

Step 1 Determine the unit rates.

Adult: $\dfrac{2,100 \text{ beats}}{30 \text{ minutes}}$ or $\dfrac{70 \text{ beats}}{1 \text{ minute}}$

Baby: $\dfrac{2,600 \text{ beats}}{20 \text{ minutes}}$ or $\dfrac{130 \text{ beats}}{1 \text{ minute}}$

Step 2 Using the unit rate for each, determine the number of beats in 60 minutes.

Adult: $70 \times 60 = 4,200$ beats
Baby: $130 \times 60 = 7,800$ beats

Step 3 Determine the difference. $7,800 - 4,200 = 3,600$

So, a baby's heart beats 3,600 more times in 60 minutes. Since the unit rate of a baby's heart rate is greater than an adult's, a baby's heart beats faster.

> **Key Phrases**
> Key phrases such as per, in, and for every are often used to describe unit rates.

Got It? Do this problem to find out.

c. A hummingbird's heart rate while resting is about 7,500 beats every 30 minutes. How many more beats does a hummingbird's heart beat in 60 minutes than a human baby's heart?

Show your work.

c. _____

Find a Unit Price

You can use what you know about unit rates to find a unit price. The **unit price** is the cost per unit. To write a price as a unit price, divide the numerator and the denominator of the rate by the denominator.

$$\overset{\div 4}{\overbrace{\dfrac{\$36.60}{4 \text{ tickets}}}} = \underset{\div 4}{\underbrace{\dfrac{\$9.15}{1 \text{ ticket}}}}$$

For example, it costs $36.60 for 4 movie tickets. So, the cost per unit, or per ticket, is $9.15.

Example

4. **Financial Literacy** Four potted plants cost $88.72. What is the price per plant?

Write the rate as a fraction. Compare the total cost to the number of plants. Then divide.

$$\frac{\$88.72}{4 \text{ plants}} = \frac{\$22.18}{1 \text{ plant}}$$

÷4 ... ÷4

So, the price per potted plant is $22.18.

Guided Practice

Express each rate as a unit rate. (Examples 1 and 2)

1. 44 points in 4 quarters = _____

2. 125 feet in 5 seconds = _____

Show your work.

3. 360 miles traveled on 12 gallons of gasoline = _____

4. 12 meters in 28 seconds = _____

5. Molly shot 20 baskets in 4 minutes. Nico shot 42 baskets in 6 minutes. How many more baskets did Nico shoot per minute? (Example 3) _____

6. For Carolina's birthday, her mom took her and 4 friends to a water park. Carolina's mom paid $42.50 for 5 student tickets. What was the price for one student ticket? (Example 4)

_____

7. ❓ **Building on the Essential Question** How are rates and ratios different? _____

_____

_____

Rate Yourself!

☐ I understand how to find a unit rate.

▶▶ Great! You're ready to move on!

☐ I still have some questions about rates.

📖 Find out online. Use the Self-Check Quiz ✓ Check

Independent Practice

6.4(D), 6.4(B), 6.1(D), 6.1(G)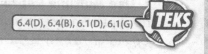

Express each rate as a unit rate. (Examples 1 and 2)

1. 72 ounces in 6 steaks = _____

 Show your work.

2. 162 water bottles in 9 cases = _____

3. Marcella divided 40.8 gallons of paint among 8 containers. How much paint is in each container? (Example 1) _____

4. Central Subs made 27 sandwiches using 12 pounds of turkey. How much turkey was used per sandwich? (Example 2)

_____

5. The results of a car race are shown. How much faster did Evans drive per lap than Loza?

Explain. (Example 3) _____

_____

_____

_____

Drivers' Times		
Driver	Laps	Time (min)
Cutwright	35	84
Evans	42	96.6
Loza	38	102.6

6. Theo's mom bought an eight-pack of juice boxes at the store for $4.

Determine the unit rate for the juice boxes. (Example 4) _____

_____

7. Joshua's cousin pledged $12 for a charity walk. If Joshua walked 3 miles,

how much did his cousin pay per mile? (Example 4) _____

8. **MP Justify Arguments** The Lovin' Lemon Company sells a 4-gallon jug of lemonade for $24. The Sweet and Sour Company sells an eight-pack of 1-quart bottles of lemonade for $16.00. Which company has a higher unit price? Explain your answer. (*Hint: There are 4 quarts in 1 gallon.*)

_____

_____

9. The Shanghai Maglev Train is one of the fastest trains in the world, traveling about 2,144 miles in 8 hours.

   a. How many miles does it travel in one hour? _____

   b. The distance between Columbus, Ohio, and New York City is about 560 miles. How many hours would it take the train to travel between the cities?

_____

10. **MP Use Multiple Representations** The table shows the approximate population and areas of five states. *Population density* is the number of people per square unit of an area.

State	Population Estimate (as of July 2007)	Area (square miles)
California	36,500,000	163,707
Florida	18,300,000	65,758
Iowa	2,990,000	56,276
New Jersey	8,690,000	8,722
Wyoming	522,000	97,818

a. **Numbers** Determine the population density of each state. Round to the nearest tenth.

_____

_____

_____

b. **Graph** Make a bar graph of the five population densities.

c. **Words** Connecticut has about the same population as Iowa, but its area is 4,875 square miles. Without calculating, compare Connecticut's population density to Iowa's. Justify your answer.

_____

_____

_____

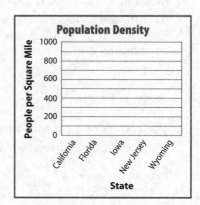

Population Density

11. **Find the Error** Julie wrote the rate $108 in 6 weeks as a unit rate. Determine her mistake and correct it.

_____

_____

_____

_____

$$\frac{\$108}{6\ weeks} = \frac{\$54}{3\ weeks}$$

 H.O.T. Problems Higher-Order Thinking

12. **Analyze** The ratio of red jelly beans to yellow jelly beans in a dish is 3:4. If Greg eats 3 red jelly beans and 6 yellow ones, the ratio is 4:5. How many yellow jelly beans were originally in the dish?

_____

13. **Analyze** If you travel at a rate of 45 miles per hour, how many minutes will it take you to travel 1 mile? Justify your response.

_____

_____

Multi-Step Problem Solving

14. Zariah is training for a 5-kilometer run, which is about 3 miles. She begins her training by running 1 mile each day for 5 days. She records the number of minutes it takes her to run a mile, as seen in the table. What is her average time in feet per second?

(A) 0.16 ft/sec

(B) 5.87 ft/sec

(C) 6.29 ft/sec

(D) 18.86 ft/sec

Day	Time (min)
1	15
2	13
3	16
4	14
5	12

Use a problem-solving model to solve this problem.

1 Analyze

Read the problem. Circle the information you know.
Underline what the problem is asking you to find.

2 Plan

What will you need to do to solve the problem? Write your plan in steps.

Step 1 Determine the average time in minutes.
Convert to seconds.

Step 2 Divide the number of feet in a mile by the seconds.

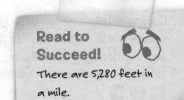

Read to Succeed!
There are 5,280 feet in a mile.

3 Solve

Use your plan to solve the problem. Show your steps.

The average time is $\frac{15 + 13 + 16 + 14 + 12}{5}$ or ⬚ minutes.

14 minutes × 60 = ⬚ seconds

So, Zariah runs an average of 5,280 ÷ 840 or about ⬚ feet per second.

Choice _____ is correct. Fill in that answer choice.

4 Justify and Evaluate

How do you know your solution is accurate?

_____

_____

_____

P = Proportionality   MP = Mathematical Processes

More Multi-Step Problem Solving

Use a problem-solving model to solve each problem.

15. Adam records his biking speed for five consecutive days in a table. There are 5,280 feet in a mile. Determine his average rate in feet per minute. Ⓟ Ⓝ Ⓜ

Day	Speed (miles per hour)
1	12
2	15
3	13
4	16
5	17

Ⓐ 1,232 ft/min

Ⓑ 1,276 ft/min

Ⓒ 1,285 ft/min

Ⓓ 1,320 ft/min

16. At a grocery store, a 24-pack of 16.9-ounce water bottles is sold for $4.99. There are 128 ounces in a gallon. Determine the price per gallon. Round to the nearest penny. Ⓟ Ⓝ Ⓜ

_____

17. Carmine is in charge of buying shirts for the senior class. She contacted three companies and recorded their pricing information in the table below. What is the best price per shirt? Ⓟ Ⓝ Ⓜ

Company	Cost
A	20 shirts for $38.40
B	25 shirts for $48.75
C	30 shirts for $57.00

18. Using the rate $\frac{y \text{ yards}}{m \text{ minutes}}$, predict what will happen to the value of the ratio for each scenario in the table below. Explain your reasoning. Ⓟ Ⓝ Ⓜ

y	m	value of ratio
increases	unchanged	
unchanged	increases	
decreases	unchanged	
unchanged	decreases	

_____
_____
_____
_____

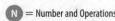 

Ratio and Rate Tables

  ## Launch the Lesson: Real World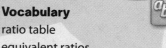

Texas Essential Knowledge and Skills

Targeted TEKS
6.5(A) Represent mathematical and real-world problems involving ratios and rates using scale factors, tables, graphs, and proportions. *Also addresses 6.4(B).*

Mathematical Processes
6.1(A), 6.1(B), 6.1(C), 6.1(D), 6.1(F)

A recipe for homemade glue includes 2 cups of flour and 3 cups of water to make one batch. Determine the ratios in simplest form of flour to water needed for 2 and 3 batches.

1. Draw red counters to show the number of cups of flour and draw yellow counters to show the number of cups of water needed to make 2 batches of glue.

flour →
water →

2. Draw red counters to show the number of cups of flour and draw yellow counters to show the number of cups of water needed to make 3 batches of glue.

flour →
water →

3. What do you notice about the simplest form of the ratios of flour to water needed for 2 and 3 batches?

Vocabulary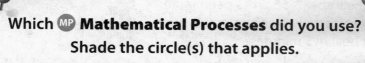
ratio table
equivalent ratios
scale factor
scaling

Essential Question
HOW do you use equivalent ratios and rates in the real world?

Which MP **Mathematical Processes** did you use?
Shade the circle(s) that applies.

Ⓐ Apply Math to the Real World.
Ⓑ Use a Problem-Solving Model.
Ⓒ Select Tools and Techniques.
Ⓓ Use Multiple Representations.
Ⓔ Organize Ideas.
Ⓕ Analyze Relationships.
Ⓖ Justify Arguments.

Equivalent Ratios

The quantities in the opening activity can be organized into a table. This table is called a **ratio table** or a rate table because the columns are filled with pairs of numbers that have the same ratio.

Flour	2	4	6
Water	3	6	9

The ratios $\frac{2}{3}$, $\frac{4}{6}$, and $\frac{6}{9}$ are equivalent since each simplifies to a ratio of $\frac{2}{3}$.

Equivalent ratios express the same relationship between quantities.

Examples

 Watch Tutor

1. **To make a cleaning solution, you mix 1 cup of bleach with 16 cups of water. How much bleach should you mix with 80 cups of water to get the same strength of cleaning solution?**

Use a ratio table. Since $16 \times 5 = 80$, multiply each quantity by ☐.

So, add ☐ cups of bleach to 80 cups of water.

	×5	
Bleach (c)	1	5
Water (c)	16	80
	×5	

2. **In a recent year, Joey Chestnut won a hot dog eating contest by eating nearly 66 hot dogs in 12 minutes. If he ate at a constant rate, determine about how many hot dogs he ate every 2 minutes.**

Divide each quantity by one or more common factors until you reach a quantity of 2 minutes.

So, Chestnut ate about 11 hot dogs every 2 minutes.

	÷2	÷3	
Hot Dogs	66	33	11
Time (min)	12	6	2
	÷2	÷3	

Check for Accuracy

To check your answer for Example 2, check to see if the ratio of the two new quantities is equivalent to the ratio of the original quantities.

$$\frac{11}{2} \times \frac{6}{6} = \frac{66}{12}$$

Got It? Do these problems to find out.

 Show your work.

a. Lily's heart beats 56 times per minute. At that rate, how many times will her heart beat in 5 minutes?

Beats	56	
Time (min)	1	5

b. Patrick can make 8 chairs in 20 hours. At this rate, how long will it take him to make 2 chairs?

Chairs	8	2
Time (h)	20	

a. _____

b. _____

Use Scaling

Multiplying or dividing two related quantities by the same number is called **scaling**. The number by which you multiply is the **scale factor**. Sometimes you may need to *scale back* and then *scale forward* to find an equivalent ratio.

Examples

Tutor

3. **Skim milk contains about 80 Calories for every 8 ounces. How many Calories do 10 ounces of skim milk contain?**

Milk (oz)	8		10
Calories	80		

There is no whole number by which you can multiply 8 to get 10. So, scale back to 1 and then scale forward to 10.

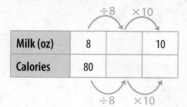

Milk (oz)	8		10
Calories	80		

Divide each quantity by a common factor, 8. Then, since 1 × 10 = 10, multiply each quantity by the scale factor, 10.

So, 10 ounces of skim milk have 100 Calories.

4. **Joe mows lawns during his summer vacation to earn money. He took 14 hours last week to mow 8 lawns. At this rate, how many lawns could he mow in 49 hours?**

Is there a whole number by which you can multiply 14 to get 49? _____

Scale back to _____, and then scale forward to _____.

÷2 ×7

Number of Hours	14	7	49
Number of Lawns	8	4	28

÷2 ×7

So, Joe can mow _____ lawns in 49 hours.

Got It? Do this problem to find out.

c. A child's height measures 105 centimeters. Estimate her height in inches.

Height (cm)	25		105
Height (in.)	10		

Show your work.

c. _____

Scale Factor

A scale *factor* is a number by which you *multiply*. So, in Example 4, 7 is the scale factor. Dividing by 2 is the same as multiplying by $\frac{1}{2}$. So, the scale factor would be $\frac{1}{2}$, not 2.

Example

5. **Paolo bought a $50 gift card for $45. Use a ratio table to find how much he would pay for a $20 gift card.**

Set up a ratio table. Use scaling to find the desired quantity.

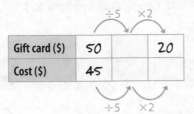

Gift card ($)	50		20
Cost ($)	45		

Divide each quantity by a common factor, 5.

Then, since $10 \times 2 = 20$, multiply each quantity by the scale factor, 2.

Paolo would spend $18 for a $20 gift card.

Guided Practice

Complete each ratio table to solve each problem.

1. Frederick earns $8 an hour tutoring. How much does he earn after tutoring for 4 hours? (Example 1) _____

Pay ($)	8			
Time (h)	1			4

2. A spider traveled 20 feet in 12 minutes. At this rate, how far could it travel in 3 minutes? (Example 2) _____

Distance (ft)	20		
Time (min)	12		3

3. Jackie bought 4 packs of hamburger that are on sale and paid a total of $16. Use a ratio table to determine how much additional she will pay to buy 3 more packs of hamburger at the same store. (Example 5) _____

Number of Packs			
Cost ($)			

4. **Building on the Essential Question** How can you determine if two ratios are equivalent?

_____

_____

_____

_____

Rate Yourself!

How well do you understand ratio tables? Circle the image that applies.

Clear   Somewhat   Not So
             Clear   Clear

Find out online. Use the Self-Check Quiz.

Check

 FOLDABLES Time to update your Foldable!

Independent Practice

6.5(A), 6.1(E) TEKS

Complete each ratio table to solve each problem.

1. To make 8 cups of beef stew, you need about 2 pounds of beef. How many pounds of beef do you need to make 24 cups of beef stew? (Example 1) _____

Stew (c)	8		24
Beef (lb)	2		

2. Ten skeins of yarn will make 4 scarves. How many scarves can be made with 25 skeins of yarn? (Examples 3 and 4) _____

Yarn (skeins)	10		25
Scarves	4		

3. Before vacation, Sophie exchanged 300 American dollars for 378 New Zealand dollars. How many New Zealand dollars will she get for 50 American dollars? (Example 2) _____

American Dollars	300		50
New Zealand Dollars	378		

4. Sophia walked 6 miles in 90 minutes at Bear Creek Park in Euless, Texas. If she continues at this rate, use a ratio table to determine how many miles she could walk in 60 minutes. (Example 5) _____

Distance (mi)			
Time (min)			

5. **MP Organize Ideas** A lasagna recipe that serves 6 people calls for 1 pound of pasta, 1.5 pounds of meat, 2 cups of cheese, and 2 cups of sauce.

   a. Complete a ratio table to represent this situation.

   b. How much of each ingredient would you need to make an identical recipe that serves 18 people?

   _____
   _____

People Served	
Pasta (lb)	
Meat (lb)	
Cheese (c)	
Sauce (c)	

   c. How much of each ingredient would you need to make an identical recipe that serves 3 people? Explain your reasoning.

   _____
   _____
   _____
   _____

6. On a typical day, flights at a local airport arrive at a rate of 10 every 15 minutes. At this rate, how many flights would you expect to arrive in 1 hour?

Number of Flights			
Minutes			

_____

7. 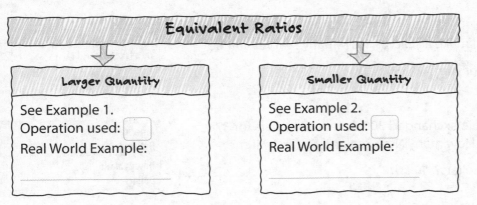 **Analyze Relationships** Complete the graphic organizer to explain how equivalent ratios are used to find larger quantities and smaller quantities.

Equivalent Ratios

Larger Quantity	Smaller Quantity
See Example 1.	See Example 2.
Operation used: ☐	Operation used: ☐
Real World Example:	Real World Example:
_____	_____

8. Find the Error Melody used the ratio table to find the number of people served with 15 pounds of ground turkey. Determine the error and correct her answer.

Pounds of Ground Turkey	2	1	15
People Served	6	5	19

_____

_____

_____

🔥 H.O.T. Problems Higher-Order Thinking

9. Evaluate There are 18 bulls and 45 cows on a ranch. If 4 more bulls and 4 more cows were added, will the ratio of bulls to cows remain the same? Justify your answer using a ratio table.

Bulls			
Cows			

_____

_____

_____

10. Create Complete the ratio table to illustrate a real-world relationship among two quantities in which the scale factor is 4.

_____

Multi-Step Problem Solving

11. Marybeth makes money babysitting. She charges a flat rate of $5 plus $5 per hour for each child. The rule $5(n) + 5$ can be used to calculate her fee per hour, where n is the number of children. Complete the table to find the ratios of the number of children to the fee. Write each ratio in simplest form.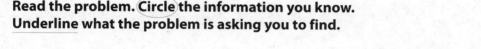

Number of children	1	2	3	4	5
Babysitting fee per hour ($)					

(A) $\dfrac{1}{10}, \dfrac{2}{15}, \dfrac{3}{20}, \dfrac{4}{25}, \dfrac{1}{6}$

(B) $\dfrac{1}{11}, \dfrac{1}{6}, \dfrac{3}{13}, \dfrac{2}{7}, \dfrac{1}{3}$

(C) $\dfrac{10}{1}, \dfrac{15}{2}, \dfrac{20}{3}, \dfrac{25}{4}, \dfrac{6}{1}$

(D) $\dfrac{1}{10}, \dfrac{2}{15}, \dfrac{3}{20}, \dfrac{4}{25}, \dfrac{1}{30}$

Use a problem-solving model to solve this problem.

1 Analyze

**Read the problem. Circle the information you know.
Underline what the problem is asking you to find.**

2 Plan

What will you need to do to solve the problem? Write your plan in steps.

Step 1   Use the rule to determine each fee.

Step 2   Express each ratio in simplest form.

Read to Succeed!

Remember to multiply first then add 5.

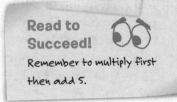

3 Solve

Use your plan to solve the problem. Show your steps.

Complete the table.

Number of children	1	2	3	4	5
Babysitting fee per hour ($)					

The number of children is the numerator and the fee is the denominator. Simplify if necessary.

The ratios are _____, _____, _____, _____, _____.

Choice _____ is correct. Fill in that answer choice.

4 Justify and Evaluate

How do you know your solution is accurate?

_____

_____

 = Number and Operations   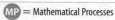 = Proportionality    = Mathematical Processes

More Multi-Step Problem Solving

Use a problem-solving model to solve each problem.

12. A rental car company charges $0.25 a mile. Use a table like the one below to find the ratios of the cost to the number of miles in simplest form. Ⓟ ⓂⓅ

Cost ($)				
Number of Miles	5	10	15	20

Ⓐ $\frac{5}{4}, \frac{5}{2}, \frac{15}{4}, \frac{5}{1}$

Ⓑ $\frac{4}{1}, \frac{4}{1}, \frac{4}{1}, \frac{4}{1}$

Ⓒ $\frac{1}{4}, \frac{1}{4}, \frac{1}{4}, \frac{1}{4}$

Ⓓ $\frac{1}{25}, \frac{2}{5}, \frac{3}{75}, \frac{5}{1}$

13. The tables below show the swimming speeds of the King penguin and the Emperor penguin. Determine which table shows a proportional relationship. Write the proportional relationship in miles per hour rounded to the hundredths place. Ⓝ Ⓟ ⓂⓅ

King Penguin				
Distance (ft)	440	860	1,300	1,740
Time (min)	1	2	3	4

Emperor Penguin				
Distance (ft)	412	824	1,236	1,648
Time (min)	1	2	3	4

14. Joshua is trying to determine the number of pizzas to order. The table below shows the number of people pizzas will feed. If each pizza costs $7, how much will it cost to feed 36 people? Ⓟ Ⓝ ⓂⓅ

Number of Pizzas	5	7	9
Number of People	15	21	27

15. On the blueprint below, 1 inch represents 2.5 feet of the house. Complete a table that shows the corresponding number of feet of the house for each length on the blueprint. Ⓟ Ⓝ ⓂⓅ

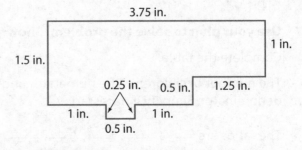

Launch the Lesson: Vocabulary

The coordinate plane is formed when two perpendicular number lines intersect at their zero points. This point is called the origin. The horizontal number line is called the *x*-axis and the vertical number line is called the *y*-axis. An ordered pair, such as (2, 3), is a pair of numbers used to locate a point on the coordinate plane.

Name each part of the coordinate plane.

_____

_____

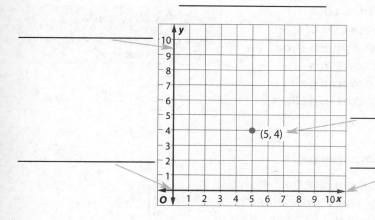

_____

_____

Texas Essential Knowledge and Skills

Targeted TEKS
6.5(A) Represent mathematical and real-world problems involving ratios and rates using scale factors, tables, graphs, and proportions. *Also addresses 6.4(B).*

Mathematical Processes
6.1(A), 6.1(B), 6.1(C), 6.1(D), 6.1(E), 6.1(F)

Essential Question

HOW do you use equivalent ratios and rates in the real world?

Real-World Link

In 3 minutes, a North American wood turtle can travel about 17 yards. If the *x*-axis represents minutes and the *y*-axis represents yards, write an ordered pair to represent this situation.

(_____ , _____)
minutes   yards

Which MP **Mathematical Processes** did you use?
Shade the circle(s) that applies.

Ⓐ Apply Math to the Real World.
Ⓑ Use a Problem-Solving Model.
Ⓒ Select Tools and Techniques.
Ⓓ Use Multiple Representations.
Ⓔ Organize Ideas.
Ⓕ Analyze Relationships.
Ⓖ Justify Arguments.

Graph Ratios and Rates

You can use an ordered pair to name any point on the coordinate plane. The first number in an ordered pair is the *x*-coordinate, and the second number is the *y*-coordinate.

| The *x*-coordinate corresponds to a number on the *x*-axis. | ⟶ **(3, 6)** ⟵ | The *y*-coordinate corresponds to a number on the *y*-axis. |

You can express information in a table as a set of ordered pairs. To see patterns, graph the ordered pairs on the coordinate plane.

 Real World

Tutor

Examples

The table shows the cost in dollars to create CDs of digital photos at a photo shop. The table also shows this information as ordered pairs (number of CDs, cost in dollars).

Cost to Create CDs		
Number of CDs, *x*	Cost in Dollars, *y*	Ordered Pair (*x, y*)
1	3	(1, 3)
2	6	(2, 6)
3	9	(3, 9)

1. **Graph the ordered pairs.**

Start at the origin. Use the *x*-coordinate and move along the *x*-axis. Then use the *y*-coordinate and move along the *y*-axis. Draw a dot at each point.

Show your work.

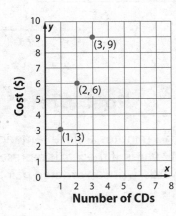

2. **Describe the pattern in the graph.**

The points appear in a line. Each point is one unit to the right and three units up from the previous point.

So, the cost increases by $3 for every CD created.

Got It? Do these problems to find out.

The table shows Gloria's earnings for 1, 2, and 3 hours. The table also lists this information as ordered pairs (hours, earnings).

a. Graph the ordered pairs.

b. Describe the pattern in the graph.

Gloria's Earnings		
Hours, *x*	Dollars Earned, *y*	Ordered Pair (*x, y*)
1	5	(1, 5)
2	10	(2, 10)
3	15	(3, 15)

a.

b. _____

Solve Prediction and Comparison Problems

You can use tables and graphs to solve prediction and comparison problems involving ratios and rates. The greater the ratio, the steeper the line will appear.

Examples

Tutor

Two friends are making scrapbooks. Renée places 4 photos on each page. Gina places 6 photos on each page.

3. Make a table for each scrapbook that shows the total number of photos placed, if each book has 1, 2, 3, or 4 pages. List the information as ordered pairs (pages, photos).

Renée's Scrapbook		
Pages, x	Photos, y	(x, y)
1	4	(1, 4)
2	8	(2, 8)
3	12	(3, 12)
4	16	(4, 16)

Gina's Scrapbook		
Pages, x	Photos, y	(x, y)
1	6	(1, 6)
2	12	(2, 12)
3	18	(3, 18)
4	24	(4, 24)

4. **Graph the ordered pairs for each friend on the same coordinate plane. How does the ratio of photos to each page compare for each person? How is this shown on the graph?**

Graph the ordered pairs for Renée's scrapbook in blue.

Graph the ordered pairs for Gina's scrapbook in red.

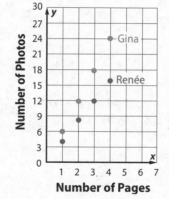

The ratio of photos to pages for Renée's scrapbook is 4:1 while the ratio for Gina's scrapbook is 6:1. On the graph, both sets of points appear to be in a straight line, but the line for Gina is steeper than the line for Renée.

5. **Predict the number of photos that each friend will use on 15 pages.**

Renée uses 4 times as many photos as pages, so she will use 15 × 4 or 60 photos. Gina uses 6 times as many photos, so she will use 15 × 6 or 90 photos. Since the line for Gina is steeper, she will use more photos.

> **STOP and Reflect**
>
> Marta is also making a scrapbook. She places 5 photos on each page. How does the ratio of photos to each page compare for her book, Gina's book, and Renée's book?

Guided Practice

Two friends are each saving money in their bank accounts. Marcus saves $10 each week while David saves $15 each week. (Examples 1–5)

1. Make a table for each friend that shows the total amount saved for 1, 2, 3, and 4 weeks. List the information as ordered pairs (weeks, total dollars saved).

Show your work.

Marcus		
Weeks, x	Total Saved ($), y	(x, y)
1		
2		
3		
4		

David		
Weeks, x	Total Saved ($), y	(x, y)
1		
2		
3		
4		

2. Graph the ordered pairs for each friend on the same coordinate plane.

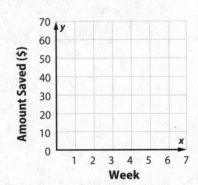

3. Predict the amount each friend will have saved after 8 weeks. Explain your reasoning.

_____

_____

_____

_____

4. How do the rates of Marcus's savings and David's savings compare? How is this shown on the graph?

_____

_____

_____

_____

_____

5.  **Building on the Essential Question** How can graphing help solve a problem involving ratios and rates?

_____

_____

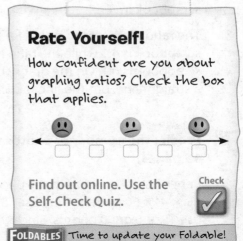

Rate Yourself!

How confident are you about graphing ratios? Check the box that applies.

Find out online. Use the Self-Check Quiz.

Check ✓

FOLDABLES Time to update your Foldable!

Independent Practice

6.4(B), 6.5(A), 6.1(G)   TEKS

The table shows the total time it took Samir to read 0, 1, 2, and 3 pages of the book. The table also lists this information as ordered pairs (number of pages, total minutes). (Examples 1–2)

Samir's Reading		
Number of Pages, x	Total Minutes, y	Ordered Pair (x, y)
0	0	(0, 0)
1	4	(1, 4)
2	8	(2, 8)
3	12	(3, 12)

1. Graph the ordered pairs and describe the pattern in the graph.

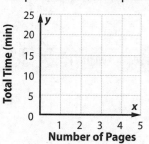

_____

_____

_____

Ken's Home Supply charges $5 for each foot of fencing. Wayne's Warehouse charges $6 for each foot of fencing. (Examples 3–5)

2. Make a table for each store that shows the total cost for 1, 2, 3, or 4 feet of fencing. List the information as ordered pairs (feet of fencing, total cost).

Ken's Home Supply		
Fencing (ft), x	Cost ($), y	(x, y)
1		
2		
3		
4		

Wayne's Warehouse		
Fencing (ft), x	Cost ($), y	(x, y)
1		
2		
3		
4		

3. Predict the cost at each store for 9 feet of fencing. Explain your reasoning.

_____

_____

_____

4. Graph the ordered pairs for each store on the same coordinate plane.

5. Using the tables and graphs, write a few sentences comparing the rates of amount charged per foot of fencing for each store.

How is this shown on the graph? _____

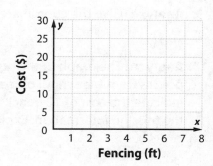

_____

_____

_____

6. **MP Justify Arguments** Patty's Pies made 2 peach pies using 10 cups of peaches. They made 3 pies using 15 cups of peaches and 4 pies using 20 cups of peaches. Predict how many cups of peaches would be needed to make 9 peach pies. Explain. _____

_____

_____

7. **MP Use Multiple Representations** The *golden rectangle* is a rectangle in which the ratio of the length to the width is approximately 1.618 to 1. This ratio is called the *golden ratio*.

Length (x)	Width (y)	(x, y)

a. **Table** Make a ratio table to show the approximate lengths of golden rectangles given widths that are 1, 2, 3, and 4 units. List the information as ordered pairs (length, width).

b. **Graph** Graph the ordered pairs on the coordinate plane.

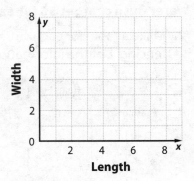

c. **Analyze** How does the area of each rectangle change as the dimensions change?

_____

_____

_____

8. **Create** Write a real-world problem using ratios or rates that could be represented on the coordinate plane. _____

_____

_____

9. **Analyze** Give the coordinates of the point located halfway between (2, 1) and (2, 4). _____

10. **Analyze** The graph to the right shows the cost of purchasing pencils from the school office. The graph is missing a point to indicate the cost of 12 pencils. Complete the graph by plotting the missing information. Explain your answer.

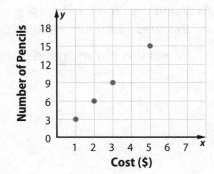

_____

_____

_____

Multi-Step Problem Solving

11. The height of a tree over time is a proportional relationship. Which statement best describes the graph of the ratio table?

Time (yr)	Height (ft)
3	4.2
5	7
8	11.2

Ⓐ For every one unit right, the line goes up three units.

Ⓑ The line appears to pass through (1, 2).

Ⓒ The line decreases from left to right.

Ⓓ The line appears to pass through the origin.

Use a problem-solving model to solve this problem.

1 Analyze

Read the problem. Circle the information you know. Underline what the problem is asking you to find.

2 Plan

What will you need to do to solve the problem? Write your plan in steps.

Step 1   Graph the ordered pairs.

Step 2   Determine which statement is true based on the graph.

Read to Succeed!

When graphing ordered pairs, the x-coordinate tells how far to the right or left. The y-coordinate tells how far up or down.

3 Solve

Use your plan to solve the problem. Show your steps.

Graph the ordered pairs.

The line appears to increase from left to right, so C is incorrect.
The line also does not pass through (1, 2), so B is incorrect.
For every unit right, the line goes up 1.4 units, so A is incorrect.

Since the line appears to pass through the origin, choice _____ is correct. Fill in that answer choice.

4 Justify and Evaluate

How do you know your solution is accurate?

_____

_____

 N = Number and Operations   **P** = Proportionality   **MP** = Mathematical Processes

More Multi-Step Problem Solving

Use a problem-solving model to solve each problem.

12. The number of bricks is proportional to the height of a wall. Which statement describes the pattern in the graph of the ordered pairs?
P MP

Number of Bricks	Height of Wall (ft)
48	4
84	7
108	9

Ⓐ As the height of the wall increases by 1 foot, there are 12 more bricks in the wall.

Ⓑ For every 48 bricks, the wall increases by 3 feet.

Ⓒ For every 36 bricks, the wall increases by 4 feet.

Ⓓ As the height of the wall increases by 2 feet, there are 48 more bricks in the wall.

13. The perimeter of an equilateral triangle is proportional to the length of the sides. An equilateral triangle with a side length of 3 cm has a perimeter of 9 cm, and an equilateral triangle with a side length of 5 cm has a perimeter of 15 cm. What is the perimeter of a triangle with a side length of 7 cm? P MP

_____

14. Five yards of material is needed to make 2 curtains. This represents a proportional relationship. If the relationship (curtains, material) were graphed, what would the y-coordinate be if the x-coordinate was 7?
P MP

_____

15. The table below shows the hours and wages for two friends who babysit. Use a graph to determine if they make the same hourly rate. Explain why or why not. P MP

	Zoe	Felix
Hours	3	5
Wages	$21	$30

_____

_____

_____

P = Proportionality   MP = Mathematical Processes

Mathematical Process
6.1(B) Use a problem-solving model that incorporates analyzing given information, formulating a plan or strategy, determining a solution, justifying the solution, and evaluating the problem-solving process and reasonableness of the solution.
Targeted TEKS 6.4(B)

Traction Action

Manuel and his friends celebrated his birthday at the FunTimes game center. He spent $\frac{4}{7}$ of his money at the fun center on go-karts and now he has $11.25 left.

How much money did he spend on go-karts?

Analyze *What are the facts?*

You know that Manuel spent $\frac{4}{7}$ of his money on go-karts. You need to determine how much money he spent on go-karts.

Plan *What is your strategy to solve this problem?*

He spent a fraction of his money. Draw a bar diagram.

Solve *How can you apply the strategy?*

Complete the bar diagram using information from the problem. Fill in the missing numbers to show the value of each section.

				3.75	3.75	3.75

—————— Amount Spent on Go-Karts —————|—————$11.25———————|

$\$\boxed{} \div \boxed{} = \$\boxed{}$

So, each section represents $\$\boxed{}$.

Manuel spent 4 × $\$\boxed{}$ or $\$\boxed{}$ on go-karts.

Justify and Evaluate *Does the answer make sense?*

Four-sevenths of $26.25 is 4 × $\boxed{}$ or $\$\boxed{}$. ✓

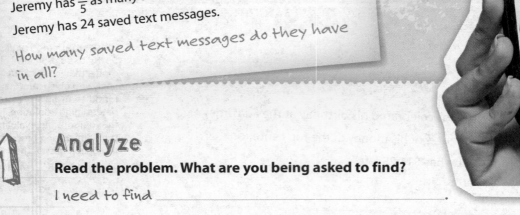

Text Tally

Jeremy has $\frac{3}{5}$ as many saved text messages as Ria.

Jeremy has 24 saved text messages.

How many saved text messages do they have in all?

1 Analyze

Read the problem. What are you being asked to find?

I need to find _____.

Underline key words and values in the problem. What information do you know?

Jeremy has $\dfrac{\boxed{}}{\boxed{}}$ as many saved texts as Ria.

Jeremy has $\boxed{}$ saved texts.

2 Plan

Choose a problem-solving strategy.

I will use the _____ strategy.

3 Solve

Use your problem-solving strategy to solve the problem.

4 Justify and Evaluate

Use information from the problem to check your answer.

_____

Work with a small group to solve the following problems. Show your work on a separate piece of paper.

1. Internet

Francesca spent 25 minutes on the Internet yesterday.

If this is $\frac{5}{6}$ of the time she spent on the computer, how long did she spend on the computer, but not on the Internet?

2. Basketball

Mieko practiced shooting a basketball for $\frac{7}{10}$ of her total practice time. During the other time, she practiced dribbling.

If she practiced dribbling for 18 minutes, how many minutes did she practice shooting?

3. Vacation

Two bike riders, 175 miles apart, begin traveling toward each other at noon. One travels at 20 miles per hour, the other at 15 miles per hour. Also at noon, a fly begins flying between the riders, starting at the front of the slower bike. The fly travels at 20 miles per hour and can change direction without losing any time. How far will the fly travel before the bicycles meet?

Use any strategy!

4. Fruit

Use the table that shows the prices of different amounts of mixed fruit at the grocery store.

How much will 13 pounds of fruit cost?

Pounds	Cost ($)
2	4.50
4	9.00
6	13.50
8	18.00

Vocabulary Check

Vocab

1. Write a few sentences describing the difference between a ratio and a rate.
   TEKS 6.4(C), 6.1(G)

_____

_____

_____

Key Concept Check

2. Complete the graphic organizer by listing the information as ordered pairs and graphing them on the coordinate plane. **TEKS** 6.5(A), 6.1(E)

Rate Table			Graph

Show your work.

Josiah's Savings

Week, x	Savings ($), y	Ordered Pair (x, y)
1	5	
2	10	
3	15	
4	20	
5	25	

_____

3. The ratio of brown tiles to tan tiles is 2 to 3. If an artist needs 16 brown tiles to complete a mosaic, how many tan tiles will the artist need? **TEKS** 6.4(C), 6.1(B)

Multi-Step Problem Solving

4. An artist is using three different colors in a mosaic. The ratio of green to blue to yellow color tiles in the mosaic is 4:6:9. She has 42 blue tiles to use. How many green and yellow tiles does she need? **P** **MP**

Ⓐ 28 green tiles; 63 yellow tiles   Ⓒ 28 green tiles; 19 yellow tiles

Ⓑ 40 green tiles; 45 yellow tiles   Ⓓ 45 green tiles; 40 yellow tiles

 = Proportionality    = Mathematical Processes

Equivalent Ratios and Rates

Andrea spent $26 for two adult tickets to the Dallas Zoo. The next month, she spent $52 for four adult tickets. Did she spend the same amount per ticket each time?

Number of Tickets	Cost ($)
2	26
4	52

1. Express the relationship between the total cost and the number of tickets for each situation as a rate in fraction form.

_____

2. Compare the relationship between the numerators of each rate in Exercise 1. Compare the relationship between the denominators of these rates.

_____

_____

_____

3. Compare the unit costs. What do you notice?

_____

4. Did Andrea spend the same amount per ticket each time? Explain.

_____

_____

Texas Essential Knowledge and Skills

Targeted TEKS
6.5(A) Represent mathematical and real-world problems involving ratios and rates using scale factors, tables, graphs, and proportions. *Also addresses 6.4(B), 6.4(E), 6.4(G).*

Mathematical Processes
6.1(A), 6.1(B), 6.1(C), 6.1(D), 6.1(F)

Vocabulary
proportion

Essential Question
HOW do you use equivalent ratios and rates in the real world?

Which MP Mathematical Processes did you use?
Shade the circle(s) that applies.

(A) Apply Math to the Real World.

(B) Use a Problem-Solving Model.

(C) Select Tools and Techniques.

(D) Use Multiple Representations.

(E) Organize Ideas.

(F) Analyze Relationships.

(G) Justify Arguments.

Use Unit Rates

There are different ways to determine if two rates are equivalent. One way is by examining unit rates. By comparing quantities as rates in simplest form, you can determine if the relationship between the two quantities stays the same.

$$\overset{\div 2}{\frac{\$26}{2\text{ tickets}}} = \frac{\$13}{1\text{ ticket}} \text{ and } \overset{\div 4}{\frac{\$52}{4\text{ tickets}}} = \frac{\$13}{1\text{ ticket}}$$

Since the rates have the same unit rate, they are equivalent.

Tutor

Examples

Use unit rates to determine if each pair of rates is equivalent. Explain your reasoning.

1. **15 pounds in 5 weeks; 12 pounds in 3 weeks**

Express each rate as a fraction. Then determine its unit rate.

$$\overset{\div 5}{\frac{15\text{ pounds}}{5\text{ weeks}}} = \frac{3\text{ pounds}}{1\text{ week}} \qquad \overset{\div 3}{\frac{12\text{ pounds}}{3\text{ weeks}}} = \frac{4\text{ pounds}}{1\text{ week}}$$

Since the rates do not have the same unit rate, they are not equivalent.

. . . .

2. **3 T-shirts for $21; 5 T-shirts for $35**

$$\overset{\div 3}{\frac{\$21}{3\text{ T-shirts}}} = \frac{\$7}{1\text{ T-shirt}} \qquad \overset{\div 5}{\frac{\$35}{5\text{ T-shirts}}} = \frac{\$7}{1\text{ T-shirt}}$$

Since the rates have the same unit rate, they are equivalent.

Got It? Do these problems to find out.

Use unit rates to determine if each pair of rates is equivalent. Explain your reasoning.

　　a. 36 T-shirts in 3 boxes; 60 T-shirts in 6 boxes

　　b. 42 flowers in 7 vases; 54 flowers in 9 vases

Unit Rates

The unit rate in Example 2, $\frac{\$7}{1\text{ T-shirt}}$, is called the unit price or unit cost since it gives the cost per unit.

a. _____

b. _____

Show your work.

Use Equivalent Fractions

You can also use equivalent fractions to decide whether the ratios or rates are equivalent.

Example

Use equivalent fractions to determine if the pair of ratios or rates is equivalent. Explain your reasoning.

3. **3 baskets out of 7 attempts; 9 baskets out of 14 attempts**

Write each rate as a fraction.

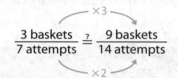

$$\frac{3 \text{ baskets}}{7 \text{ attempts}} \overset{?}{=} \frac{9 \text{ baskets}}{14 \text{ attempts}}$$

The numerator and the denominator are not multiplied by the same number. So, the fractions are not equivalent.

Since the fractions are *not* equivalent, the rates are not equivalent.

> **Got It?** Do this problem to find out.

c. **10 scissors to 6 staplers; 5 scissors to 2 staplers**

c. _____

Use a Proportion

A **proportion** is an equation stating that two ratios or rates are equivalent. By determining that two ratios or rates are equivalent, you are stating that they form a proportion.

Examples

4. **Charlotte's tomato plant produced 16 tomatoes and her pepper plant produced 8 peppers. Ryan's tomato plant produced 4 tomatoes and his pepper plant produced 2 peppers. Do these ratios form a proportion? Explain your reasoning.**

Determine if you can write a proportion.

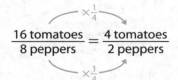

$$\frac{16 \text{ tomatoes}}{8 \text{ peppers}} = \frac{4 \text{ tomatoes}}{2 \text{ peppers}}$$

The numerator and denominator are multiplied by the same scale factor, $\frac{1}{4}$.

The ratios are equivalent. Therefore, the ratios form a proportion.

5. Selena is comparing the cost of two packages of DVDs. A package of 4 DVDs costs $60 and a package of 8 DVDs costs $120. Do these rates form a proportion? Explain your reasoning.

$$\overset{\times 2}{\underbrace{\frac{4 \text{ DVDs}}{\$60}}} = \frac{8 \text{ DVDs}}{\$120}$$
×2

The numerator and the denominator are multiplied by the same scale factor. So, the rates are equivalent.

Since the rates are equivalent, they form a proportion.

Got It? Do this problem to find out.

d. Homeroom A has 25 students and collected 475 cans of food. Homeroom B has 23 students and collected 437 cans of food. Do these collection rates form a proportion? Explain your reasoning.

d. _____

Guided Practice

Use unit rates to determine if each pair of rates is equivalent. Explain.

1. $78 spent in 3 hours; $25 spent in 2 hours
(Examples 1 and 2)

Show your work.

_____

_____

_____

2. 27 grams of fat in 9 servings; 18 grams of fat in 6 servings (Examples 1 and 2)

_____

_____

_____

3. Use equivalent fractions to determine if the ratios 11 purple hats to 14 yellow hats and 45 purple hats to 70 yellow hats are equivalent. (Example 3)

_____

4. A human fingernail grows about 9 millimeters in 3 months. A toenail grows at an average rate of 3 millimeters in 4 months. Do these rates form a proportion? Explain your reasoning.

(Examples 4 and 5) _____

_____

_____

5. **?** **Building on the Essential Question** How can you determine if two ratios or rates are equivalent?

_____

_____

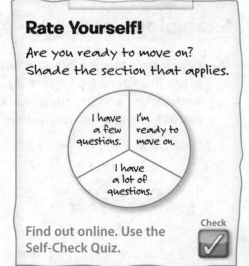

Rate Yourself!

Are you ready to move on? Shade the section that applies.

- I have a few questions.
- I'm ready to move on.
- I have a lot of questions.

Find out online. Use the Self-Check Quiz.

Check ✓

FOLDABLES Time to update your Foldable!

Independent Practice

6.5(A), 6.4(B), 6.4(E), 6.4(G), 6.1(G)   TEKS

Use unit rates to determine if each pair of rates is equivalent. Explain.
(Examples 1 and 2)

1. $4 for 20 donut holes; $7 for 40 donut holes

_____

_____

2. 36 inches of snow in 8 months; 27 inches of snow in 6 months

_____

_____

3. 3 new tires for $210; 4 new tires for $250

_____

_____

4. 14 hours to drive 644 miles; 11 hours to drive 506 miles

_____

_____

5. Jade enlarged the photograph at the right to a poster.
The size of the poster is 105 inches by 175 inches.
Is the ratio of the poster's length and width equivalent
to the ratio of the photograph's length and width?
Explain your reasoning. (Example 3)

3 in.

5 in.

_____

_____

6. Jenny is comparing the cost of two packages of socks. One package has
8 pairs of socks for $12. Another package has 3 pairs of socks for $6.
Do the rates form a proportion? Explain your reasoning. (Examples 4 and 5)

_____

_____

7. **MP Justify Arguments** When creating a necklace, Catie used 68 beads on
17 inches of wire. She used 7 inches of wire for a bracelet. Predict the number
of beads she used for 7 inches of wire. Explain your reasoning.

_____

_____

_____

8. **MP Apply Math to the Real World** Refer to the graphic novel frame below for Exercises a–b.

a. What is the unit price for the cans of lemonade at each of the stores?

_____

_____

b. From which store should Mei, Pilar, and David purchase the cans of lemonade? Explain.

_____

_____

H.O.T. Problems Higher-Order Thinking

9. **Analyze** Identify the rate that does not belong with the other three. Justify your response.

| 4.5 ft/sec | 112.5 feet in 25 seconds | 86.4 feet in 18 seconds | 54 feet in 12 seconds |

_____

_____

10. **Create** Write two ratios that are equivalent to $\frac{5}{7}$.

_____

11. **Analyze** The ratio of girls to boys in the junior high band is 5 to 7. At the beginning of the year, there were 72 students in the band. By the end of the year, the ratio of girls to boys was 3 to 4. If there are now 48 boys in the band, how many girls joined the band during the school year?

_____

Multi-Step Problem Solving

12. Luna wants to burn as many Calories as possible per minute of exercise. Which exercise should Luna choose?

(A) walking

(B) jump rope

(C) biking

(D) aerobics

Exercise	Calories	Minutes
Walking	300	60
Jump rope	110	10
Biking	270	30
Aerobics	160	20

Use a problem-solving model to solve this problem.

1 Analyze

Read the problem. Circle the information you know. Underline what the problem is asking you to find.

2 Plan

What will you need to do to solve the problem? Write your plan in steps.

Step 1 Determine the unit rate for each exercise.

Step 2 Compare the unit rates.

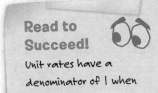

Read to Succeed!

Unit rates have a denominator of 1 when simplified.

3 Solve

Use your plan to solve the problem. Show your steps.

Walking: $\dfrac{300}{60} = \dfrac{\boxed{}}{\boxed{}}$

Jump rope: $\dfrac{110}{10} = \dfrac{\boxed{}}{\boxed{}}$

Biking: $\dfrac{270}{30} = \dfrac{\boxed{}}{\boxed{}}$

Aerobics: $\dfrac{160}{20} = \dfrac{\boxed{}}{\boxed{}}$

The unit rate $\boxed{}$ Calories per minute is the greatest.

So, Luna should _____ . Choice _____ is correct. Fill in that answer choice.

4 Justify and Evaluate

How do you know your solution is accurate?

_____

_____

(P) = Proportionality   (MP) = Mathematical Processes

More **Multi-Step** Problem Solving

Use a problem-solving model to solve each problem.

13. Santiago needs to buy apples to make applesauce. He is looking for a better price than $1.29 per pound. Which store has a better price per pound? P MP

Store	Price ($)	Weight (lb)
Store A	4.08	3
Store B	5.04	4
Store C	12.88	7
Store D	7.35	5

Ⓐ Store A

Ⓑ Store B

Ⓒ Store C

Ⓓ Store D

14. Josh is making a scale model of his grandfather's airplane. Given the information in the diagram, how many inches are the wings of the model? P MP

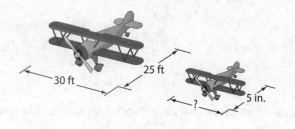

15. Riley and Magdalena bought beads to make a necklace. The beads that Riley bought cost 48¢ for 12. Magdalena bought 20 beads for $1.00. How much less do 15 of Riley's beads cost than 15 of Magdalena's beads? P MP

16. Jacob bought 5 pencils for 80¢. At this same rate, how many pencils can he buy for 40¢? Explain why this answer does not make sense. P MP

P = Proportionality   MP = Mathematical Processes

Model Prediction and Comparison Problems

INQUIRY HOW can I use multiple representations to solve prediction and comparison problems involving ratios and rates?

Jill and Sammy are racing go-karts. Jill completed 6 laps in 12 minutes. If Sammy races at the same rate, how many minutes will it take him to complete 3 laps?

What do you know? _____

_____

What do you need to find? _____

_____

Texas Essential Knowledge and Skills

Targeted TEKS
6.4(B) Apply qualitative and quantitative reasoning to solve prediction and comparison of real-world problems involving ratios and rates.

Mathematical Processes
6.1(C), 6.1(D), 6.1(E), 6.1(F), 6.1(G)

Hands-On Activity 1

Step 1 Use a bar diagram to represent the number of laps Jill completed. The time to travel 6 laps is 12 minutes.

Jill's race

| 12 min |
| 1 lap | 1 lap | 1 lap | 1 lap | 1 lap | 1 lap |

Step 2 Each section represents 1 lap. Determine the number of minutes it took Jill to complete one lap.

Jill completed each lap in 12 ÷ 6, or ☐ minutes.

Step 3 Predict the number of minutes it will take Sammy to complete 3 laps at the same rate.

Jill's race

| 12 min |
| 1 lap | 1 lap | 1 lap | 1 lap | 1 lap | 1 lap |

Sammy's race

| ? min |
| 1 lap | 1 lap | 1 lap |

Each lap was completed in ☐ minutes.

So, Sammy's time is predicted to be 3 × ☐, or ☐ minutes.

Hands-On Activity 2

There are 184 goldfish at a pet store. The goldfish are in 4 tanks, each with the same number of fish. Predict the number of fish in 3 tanks.

Step 1   Use a bar diagram to represent the number of total goldfish.

```
┌───────────────── 184 goldfish ─────────────────┐
├────────┬────────┬────────┬────────┤
│        │        │        │        │
└────────┴────────┴────────┴────────┘
```

[ ] goldfish

Step 2   Label each section "1 tank." There are 184 ÷ 4, or [ ] goldfish in each tank.

So, there are 46 × [ ], or [ ] goldfish in three tanks.

Hands-On Activity 3

Devon drove 171 miles in 3 hours. Logan drove 177 miles in 3 hours. At these rates, how many more miles can Logan drive in 7 hours than Devon?

Step 1   Use bar diagrams to represent the number of miles Devon and Logan drove.

Devon

```
├──────────── [    ] ──────────┤
│                               │
└───────────────────────────────┘
```

Logan

```
├──────────── [    ] ──────────┤
│                               │
└───────────────────────────────┘
```

[ ] miles   [ ] miles

Step 2   Label each section "1 hour." In one hour, Devon drove 171 ÷ 3, or [ ] miles and Logan drove 177 ÷ 3, or [ ] miles.

Devon will drive 7 × [ ], or [ ] miles in 7 hours. Logan will drive 7 × [ ], or [ ] miles in 7 hours. So, Logan will drive [ ] − [ ], or [ ] more miles in 7 hours than Devon.

Investigate

Collaborate

Work with a partner. Use a bar diagram to help solve each problem.

1. Predict the miles traveled in 5 hours at a rate of 189 miles in 3 hours.

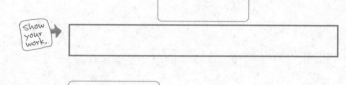

Show your work.

2. Predict the number of ice cubes in 32 glasses at a rate of 20 ice cubes in 5 glasses.

3. Predict the cost of 5 pounds of bananas if 2 pounds cost $1.16.

4. Predict the time needed to deliver 72 papers at a rate of 9 papers in 18 minutes.

5. Predict the number of blue squares in a quilt with 11 green squares if there are 4 green squares in a quilt with 68 blue squares.

6. Predict the number of roses in a garden with 16 sunflowers if there are 3 sunflowers in a garden with 81 roses.

7. How does using a bar diagram help you in predicting the solution to ratio and rate problems?

8. How can you use a bar diagram to check the accuracy of the solution to a ratio or rate problem?

Work with a partner. Refer to Exercise 4 on the previous page.

9. Suppose Marcus delivers papers at a rate of 9 papers in 18 minutes. How much longer would it take him to deliver 100 papers than 72 papers? Justify your response.

10. How can you determine the time it takes to deliver one paper without drawing a bar diagram?

11. Without using a bar diagram, explain how you would solve the following comparison problem. Then solve the problem.

    Ronaldo delivers papers at the rate of 6 papers in 24 minutes. How much longer would it take him to deliver 56 papers than 41 papers?

Create

On Your Own

12. **MP Apply Math to the Real World** Lee can read at the rate of 1,100 words in 5 minutes. Write and solve a prediction problem that uses this information.

13. **MP Apply Math to the Real World** Elyse uses 42 gallons of water for a 10-minute shower. Write and solve a prediction problem that uses this information.

14. **INQUIRY** HOW can I use multiple representations to solve prediction and comparison problems involving ratios and rates?

Solve Prediction and Comparison Problems

An arcade sells game tokens individually or in packages. They are having a sale on token packages, as shown below. Predict the cost of 6 token packages.

Number of Packages	Price ($)
2	9.90
3	14.85

Texas Essential Knowledge and Skills

Targeted TEKS
6.4(B) Apply qualitative and quantitative reasoning to solve prediction and comparison of real-world problems involving ratios and rates. *Also addresses 6.5(A).*

Mathematical Processes
6.1(A), 6.1(B), 6.1(C), 6.1(D), 6.1(F)

Essential Question
HOW do you use equivalent ratios and rates in the real world?

1. How many token packages can you buy with $19.80? ☐
   $24.75? ☐ Explain.

_____

2. What is the unit price?

_____

3. Predict how much it would cost to buy 6 token packages.

_____

4. The arcade sells individual tokens for $0.25 each. If a token package contains 25 tokens, how much would you save by buying a package of 25 tokens instead of 25 individual tokens? Explain.

_____

_____

Which ⓂⓅ **Mathematical Processes** did you use?
Shade the circle(s) that applies.

Ⓐ Apply Math to the Real World.
Ⓑ Use a Problem-Solving Model.
Ⓒ Select Tools and Techniques.
Ⓓ Use Multiple Representations.

Ⓔ Organize Ideas.
Ⓕ Analyze Relationships.
Ⓖ Justify Arguments.

Solve Prediction Problems

You can apply qualitative and quantitative reasoning to solve prediction problems involving ratios and rates.

Examples

Tutor

1. **Two out of three students prefer gel toothpaste. Use this ratio to predict how many students, out of 150, prefer gel toothpaste.**

Write a proportion. Then find the equivalent ratio.

likes gel → total → $\dfrac{2}{3} = \dfrac{\blacksquare}{150}$ ← likes gel ← total

$\overset{\times 50}{\dfrac{2}{3} = \dfrac{100}{150}}$ Since 3 × 50 = 150, multiply 2 by 50.

So, 100 students would prefer gel toothpaste.

---

2. **The Millers drove 105 miles on 4 gallons of gas. At this rate, predict how many miles they can drive on 6 gallons of gas.**

Method 1 **Use a proportion.**

miles → gallons → $\dfrac{105}{4} = \dfrac{\blacksquare}{6}$ ← miles ← gallons

$\overset{\times 1.5}{\dfrac{105}{4} = \dfrac{157.5}{6}}$ Since 4 × 1.5 = 6, multiply 105 by 1.5.

Method 2 **Draw a double number line.**

$105 \div 4 = 26.25$ Find the unit rate.

$26.25 \times 6 = 157.5$ Multiply.

miles   0 [ ]   105   [   ]

gallons 0 1 2 3 4 5 [   ]

So, the Millers can drive 157.5 miles on 6 gallons of gas.

Got It? Do this problem to find out.

a. In a survey, four out of five people preferred creamy over chunky peanut butter. There are 120 people shopping at the grocery store. Use the survey to predict how many people in the store would prefer creamy peanut butter.

Show your work.

a. _____

Solve Comparison Problems

You can apply qualitative and quantitative reasoning to solve comparison problems involving ratios and rates.

  Multi-Step Example 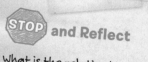 Tutor

3. The ratio of the number of text messages sent by Lucas to the number of text messages sent by his sister is 3 to 4. Lucas sent 18 text messages. How many more text messages did his sister send?

Method 1 Use a bar diagram.

Step 1 Draw a bar diagram. There are 3 sections in the bar for Lucas and 4 sections in the bar for his sister.

Step 2 Determine how many text messages are in each section.

← 18 texts →			← 24 texts →			
6	6	6	6	6	6	6
← Lucas →			← Sister →			

Method 2 Use a proportion.

Write a proportion. Then find the equivalent ratio.

Lucas → $\dfrac{3}{4} = \dfrac{18}{\blacksquare}$ ← Lucas
his sister → $\qquad\qquad$ ← his sister

$$\overset{\times 6}{\dfrac{3}{4} = \dfrac{18}{24}}\underset{\times 6}{}$$

Since 6 × 3 = 18, multiply 4 by 6.

Lucas' sister sent 24 text messages. So, she sent 24 − 18, or 6 more text messages than Lucas did.

Got It? Do this problem to find out.

b. A survey found that 12 out of every 15 people in the United States prefer eating at a restaurant over cooking at home. If 400 people selected eating at a restaurant on the survey, how many more people took the survey?

STOP and Reflect

What is the relationship between ratios and fractions?

 show your work.

b. _____

Multi-Step Example

4. Jeremy rode his motorcycle 138 miles in 3 hours. Graham rode his motorcycle 204 miles in 4 hours. Who rode at a faster average rate?

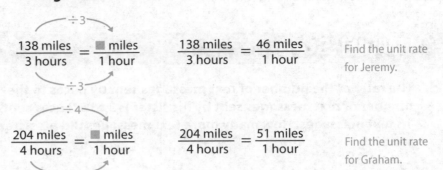

$$\frac{138\ \text{miles}}{3\ \text{hours}} = \frac{\blacksquare\ \text{miles}}{1\ \text{hour}} \qquad \frac{138\ \text{miles}}{3\ \text{hours}} = \frac{46\ \text{miles}}{1\ \text{hour}}$$ Find the unit rate for Jeremy.

$$\frac{204\ \text{miles}}{4\ \text{hours}} = \frac{\blacksquare\ \text{miles}}{1\ \text{hour}} \qquad \frac{204\ \text{miles}}{4\ \text{hours}} = \frac{51\ \text{miles}}{1\ \text{hour}}$$ Find the unit rate for Graham.

So, Graham rode at a faster rate , since 51 > 46.

Got It? Do this problem to find out.

 Show your work.

c. _____

c. **STEM** While resting, a human takes in about 5 liters of air in 30 seconds. At this rate, how many liters of air does he take in during 150 seconds?

Guided Practice

 Show your work.

1. Out of 30 students surveyed, 17 have a dog. Based on these results, predict how many of the 300 students in the school have a dog. (Example 1)

_____

2. Sybrina jogged 2 miles in 30 minutes. At this rate, predict how far she would jog in 75 minutes. (Example 2) _____

3. Five out of 12 students at Perry Middle School share a locker. There are 456 students that attend Perry Middle School. How many more students do not share a locker? (Examples 3 and 4)

_____

4. **?** **Building on the Essential Question** How can you use diagrams and proportions to solve ratio and rate problems?

_____

_____

_____

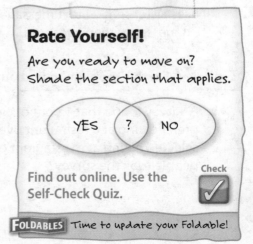

Rate Yourself!

Are you ready to move on? Shade the section that applies.

YES　?　NO

Find out online. Use the Self-Check Quiz.

Check ✓

FOLDABLES Time to update your Foldable!

Independent Practice

6.4(B), 6.5(A), 6.1(A), 6.1(F) **TEKS**

1. Three out of every five cookies on a cookie tray are oatmeal raisin cookies. If there are 45 cookies on the tray, predict how many are oatmeal raisin cookies. (Example 1) _____

2. Four students spent $9.40 on school lunch. At this rate, predict the amount 10 students would spend on the same school lunch. (Example 2) _____

3. Eight out of 21 instruments in the band are woodwinds. If there are 63 instruments in the band, how many more are not woodwinds than are woodwinds? (Example 3) _____

4. In 10 minutes, Caleb's heart can beat 700 times. Steve's heart beats 536 times in 8 minutes. How many more times does Caleb's heart beat in 5 minutes than Steve's heart? (Example 4)

   _____

5. **MP** **Analyze Relationships** The table shows which school subjects are favored by a group of students. Predict the number of students out of 400 that would pick science as their favorite subject. Explain.

   _____

   _____

   _____

Favorite Subject	
Subject	Number of Responses
Math	6
Science	3
English	4
History	7

6. Liliana takes 4 breaths per 10 seconds during yoga. At this rate, about how many breaths would Liliana take in 2 minutes of yoga? Explain.

   _____

   _____

7. **MP** **Justify Arguments** Cara saw an advertisement claiming 5 out of 6 students prefer talking on the phone over texting. She predicts that 500 out of 600 students prefer talking on the phone. Explain why her prediction could be false.

   _____

   _____

   _____

8. **MP** **Select Tools and Techniques** Find a report in a newspaper, magazine, or on the Internet that uses results from a survey. Evaluate how the survey uses ratios to reach conclusions. _____

9. **Find the Error** Elisa's mom teaches at a preschool. There is 1 teacher for every 12 students at the preschool. There are 276 students at the preschool. Elisa is setting up equivalent ratios to find the number of teachers at the preschool. Determine her mistake and correct it.

$$\frac{12}{1} = \frac{\blacksquare}{276}$$

_____

_____

_____

_____

H.O.T. Problems Higher-Order Thinking

10. **Analyze** One rate of an equivalent ratio is $\frac{9}{n}$. Select two other rates, one that can be solved using equivalent fractions and the other that can be solved with unit rates. _____

_____

11. **Analyze** Tell whether the following statement is *always*, *sometimes*, or *never* true for numbers greater than zero. Explain.

In equivalent ratios, if the numerator of the first ratio is greater than the denominator of the first ratio, then the numerator of the second ratio is greater than the denominator of the second ratio.

_____

_____

12. **Analyze** Suppose 25 out of 175 people said they like to play disc golf and 5 out of every 12 of the players have a personalized flying disc. At the same rates, in a group of 252 people, predict how many you would expect to have a personalized flying disc. Explain.

_____

_____

_____

13. **Analyze** A car traveling at a certain speed will travel 76 feet per second. How many miles will the car travel in 3.1 hours if it maintains the same speed? Round to the nearest tenth. (*Hint: There are 5,280 feet in one mile.*)

_____

Multi-Step Problem Solving

14. The table shows the results of a survey of a group of people about their favorite animal. If 600 people were asked about their favorite animal, predict how many more people would prefer dogs than cats.
Ⓟ Ⓜ🅿

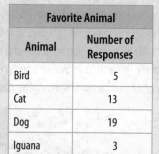

Favorite Animal	
Animal	Number of Responses
Bird	5
Cat	13
Dog	19
Iguana	3

Ⓐ 6   Ⓒ 195

Ⓑ 285   Ⓓ 90

Use a problem-solving model to solve this problem.

1 Analyze

Read the problem. Circle the information you know.
Underline what the problem is asking you to find.

2 Plan

What will you need to do to solve the problem? Write your plan in steps.

Step 1   Determine the total number of people surveyed.

Step 2   Set up equivalent ratios.

Step 3   Subtract to determine how much more.

Read to Succeed!

When setting up equivalent ratios, remember to keep the same attribute in the numerators and the same in the denominators.

3 Solve

Use your plan to solve the problem. Show your steps.

There were 5 + 13 + 19 + 3 or 40 people surveyed.

Dogs: $\frac{19}{40} = \frac{?}{600}$ Cats: $\frac{13}{40} = \frac{?}{600}$

= ☐   = ☐

So, 285 − 195 or ☐ more people chose dogs than cats. Choice _____ is correct.

Fill in that answer choice.

4 Justify and Evaluate

How do you know your solution is accurate?

_____

_____

Ⓟ = Proportionality   Ⓜ🅿 = Mathematical Processes

More Multi-Step Problem Solving

Use a problem-solving model to solve each problem.

15. The table shows the results of a survey of a group of people about their favorite sport. If 100 people were asked about their favorite sport, predict how many more people would prefer hockey than volleyball. Ⓟ ⓂⓅ

Favorite Sport	
Sport	Number of Responses
Baseball	7
Soccer	10
Volleyball	5
Hockey	8

Ⓐ 3

Ⓑ 10

Ⓒ 30

Ⓓ 70

16. Keshia rides her bike 10 miles per hour. At this rate, how many more minutes will it take her to ride 30 miles than 25 miles? Ⓟ ⓂⓅ

_____

17. Marisol pays $12 for 4 notebooks. How many notebooks could she buy with $62? Ⓟ ⓂⓅ

_____

18. Mason is helping a friend with her homework. Look at his friend's work to determine and explain the error she made finding the answer to the problem. Ⓟ ⓂⓅ

If 3 dogs eat 4 pounds of food per day, how many dogs eat 15 pounds of food?

$$\frac{3}{4} = \frac{15}{?}$$

Multiply numerator and denominator by 5. Therefore, 20 dogs eat 15 pounds of food.

_____

_____

_____

_____

Ⓟ = Proportionality   ⓂⓅ = Mathematical Processes

Convert Measurement Units

 ## Launch the Lesson: Real World ▶

The table shows the approximate weights, in tons, of several large land animals. One ton is equivalent to 2,000 pounds. Use a ratio table to convert each weight from tons to pounds. Represent the ratios in a graph.

Animal	Weight (T)
Grizzly bear	1
White rhinoceros	4
Hippopotamus	5
African elephant	8

1. Complete the ratio table. The first two ratios are done for you. To produce equivalent ratios, multiply the quantities in the top row by the scale factor, 2,000.

Tons	1	4	5	8
Pounds	2,000	8,000		

✏) × [ ]

2. Use the coordinate plane shown.
   a. Graph the ordered pairs (tons, pounds) from the table on the coordinate plane.
   b. Label the horizontal axis *Weight in Tons*.
   c. Label the vertical axis *Weight in Pounds*.
   d. Connect the points and describe the graph.

_____

[ ]

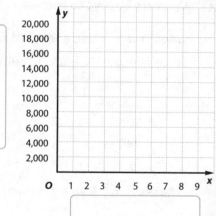

Which ⓂⓅ **Mathematical Processes** did you use?
Shade the circle(s) that applies.

ⒶApply Math to the Real World.   ⒺOrganize Ideas.

ⒷUse a Problem-Solving Model.   ⒻAnalyze Relationships.

ⒸSelect Tools and Techniques.   ⒼJustify Arguments.

ⒹUse Multiple Representations.

Texas Essential Knowledge and Skills

Targeted TEKS
6.4(H) Convert units within a measurement system, including the use of proportions and unit rates.

Mathematical Processes
6.1(A), 6.1(B), 6.1(C), 6.1(D)

Vocab

Vocabulary
dimensional analysis

Essential Question
HOW do you use equivalent ratios and rates in the real world?

Convert Larger Units to Smaller Units

The conversions shown can be written as unit rates. Since 1 yard = 3 feet, you can use the unit rate $\frac{3 \text{ ft}}{1 \text{ yd}}$ to convert from yards to feet. **Dimensional analysis** is the process of including units of measurement as factors when you compute.

Customary Conversions			
Type of Measure	**Larger Unit**	→	**Smaller Unit**
Length	1 foot (ft)	=	12 inches (in.)
	1 yard (yd)	=	3 feet
	1 mile (mi)	=	5,280 feet
Weight	1 pound (lb)	=	16 ounces (oz)
	1 ton (T)	=	2,000 pounds
Capacity	1 cup (c)	=	8 fluid ounces (fl oz)
	1 pint (pt)	=	2 cups
	1 quart (qt)	=	2 pints
	1 gallon (gal)	=	4 quarts

Tutor

Example

Multiplying by 1

The rate $\frac{3 \text{ ft}}{1 \text{ yd}}$ is equivalent to 1 because the numerator and the denominator represent the same amount.

1. Convert 20 feet to inches.

Method 1   Use a unit rate.

Since 1 foot = 12 inches, multiply by the unit rate, $\frac{12 \text{ in.}}{1 \text{ ft}}$.

$20 \text{ ft} = 20 \text{ ft} \times \frac{12 \text{ in.}}{1 \text{ ft}}$ Divide out common units, leaving the desired unit, inches.

$= 20 \times 12 \text{ in.}$ Multiply.

$= 240 \text{ in.}$ Multiply.

Method 2   Use a proportion.

Show your work.

inches → $\frac{12}{1} = \frac{\blacksquare}{20}$ ← inches $\frac{12}{1} = \frac{240}{20}$ Since 1 × 20 = 20,
feet →   ← feet   multiply 12 by 20.

×20   ×20

So, using either method, 20 feet = 240 inches.

Got It? Do these problems to find out.

Complete.

a.   36 yd = $\blacksquare$ ft   b. $\frac{3}{4}$ T = $\blacksquare$ lb   c. $1\frac{1}{2}$ qt = $\blacksquare$ pt

a. _____

b. _____

c. _____

Example

2. Marco mixes 0.45 liter of liquid fertilizer with water before watering his plants. How many milliliters of fertilizer does he use at each watering?

Use a unit rate. Since 1 liter = 1,000 milliliters, the unit rate is $\dfrac{1,000 \text{ mL}}{1 \text{ L}}$.

$0.45 \text{ L} = \dfrac{45}{100} \text{ L} \times \dfrac{1,000 \text{ mL}}{1 \text{ L}}$ Multiply by $\dfrac{1,000 \text{ mL}}{1 \text{ L}}$.

$= \dfrac{45}{100} \cancel{\text{L}} \times \dfrac{1,000 \text{ mL}}{1 \cancel{\text{L}}}$ Divide out common units, leaving millimeters.

$= \dfrac{45}{100} \times \dfrac{1,000 \text{ mL}}{1}$ Multiply.

$= 450 \text{ mL}$ Simplify.

So, 450 milliliters of fertilizer are used at each watering.

> **Got It?** Do this problem to find out.

d. Jen runs 0.75 kilometer before tennis practice. How many meters does she run before practice?

Unit Rates or Proportions?

In Example 2, it is easier to use the unit rate to convert than to use a proportion because one of the measurements, 0.45, can be written as a fraction.

Show your work.

d. _____

Convert Smaller Units to Larger Units

Remember that the unit rates $\dfrac{3 \text{ ft}}{1 \text{ yd}}$ and $\dfrac{1 \text{ yd}}{3 \text{ ft}}$ are equivalent. To convert from smaller units to larger units, choose the unit rate that allows you to divide out the common units.

Example

3. Convert 15 quarts to gallons.

Since 1 gallon = 4 quarts, and quarts are smaller units than gallons, use the unit rate $\dfrac{1 \text{ gal}}{4 \text{ qt}}$.

$15 \text{ qt} = 15 \text{ qt} \times \dfrac{1 \text{ gal}}{4 \text{ qt}}$ Multiply by $\dfrac{1 \text{ gal}}{4 \text{ qt}}$.

$= 15 \cancel{\text{qt}} \times \dfrac{1 \text{ gal}}{4 \cancel{\text{qt}}}$ Divide out common units, leaving the desired unit, gallons.

$= 15 \times \dfrac{1}{4} \text{ gal}$ Multiply.

$= 3\dfrac{3}{4} \text{ gal}$ Simplify.

Unit Rates or Proportions?

In Example 3, it is easier to use the unit rate to convert than to use a proportion because the scale factor from 4 to 15 is not a whole number.

$$\frac{1}{4} = \frac{?}{15}$$
$\times 3\dfrac{3}{4}$

e. _____

f. _____

> **Got It?** Do these problems to find out.

e. 2,640 ft = ■ mi   **f.** 100 oz = ■ lb   **g.** 3 c = ■ pt

g. _____

Example

4. Umeka needs 250 centimeters of fabric to make a costume for a play. How many meters of fabric does she need?

Use a proportion. 100 centimeters is equal to 1 meter.

$$\frac{100 \text{ cm}}{1 \text{ m}} = \frac{250 \text{ cm}}{? \text{ m}}$$

Since $100 \times 2.5 = 250$, multiply 1 by 2.5.

So, Umeka needs 1×2.5 or 2.5 meters of fabric.

Guided Practice

Complete. Use a unit rate or proportion. (Examples 1 and 3)

1. $5\frac{1}{3}$ yd = _____ ft

2. $4\frac{1}{2}$ pt = _____ c

3. 1.2 m = _____ cm

4. 28 g = _____ kg

 Show your work.

5. A large grouper can weigh $\frac{1}{3}$ ton. How much does a large grouper weigh to the nearest pound? Did you choose to use a unit rate or proportion? Explain.

(Example 2) _____

_____

6. One of the world's narrowest electric vehicles is about 1.08 meters wide.

How wide is this vehicle in centimeters? (Example 4) _____

_____

7. 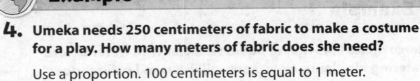 **Building on the Essential Question** Compare and contrast using rates and proportions to convert units of measurement.

_____

_____

_____

_____

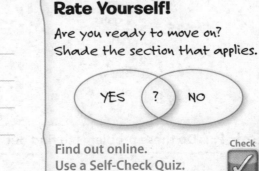

Rate Yourself!

Are you ready to move on?
Shade the section that applies.

YES   ?   NO

Find out online.
Use a Self-Check Quiz.   Check ✓

Independent Practice

6.4(H), 6.5(A), 6.1(D), 6.1(G) **TEKS**

Complete. Use a unit rate or proportion. (Examples 1 and 3)

 Show your work.

1. 18 ft = _____ yd

2. 2 L = _____ mL

3. 6.5 m = _____ km

4. 2 mi = _____ ft

5. 5,000 lb = _____ T

6. $2\frac{3}{4}$ qt = _____ pt

7. One of the largest pumpkins ever grown weighed about $\frac{3}{4}$ ton. How many pounds did the pumpkin weigh? Did you use a unit rate or a proportion? Explain. (Example 2)

_____

_____

_____

 Show your work.

8. Ling is training for a marathon by jogging 6.3 kilometers every other day. How many meters does she jog every other day? (Example 4)

_____

9. A 3-pound pork loin can be cut into 10 pork chops of equal weight. How many ounces is each pork chop? Explain using a proportion.

_____

_____

10. **MP Justify Arguments** Will a 2-quart pitcher hold the entire recipe of citrus punch given at the right? Explain your reasoning.

_____

_____

_____

_____

Citrus Punch Drink

2 cups orange juice
2 cups grapefruit juice
$\frac{1}{4}$ cup apricot nectar
$\frac{1}{3}$ cup pineapple juice
4 cups ginger ale

11. **MP** **Use Multiple Representations** Use the graph at the right.

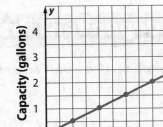

a. **Words** What does an ordered pair from this graph represent? _____

_____

b. **Graph** Use the graph to find the capacity in quarts of a 2.5-gallon container. Explain your reasoning.

_____

_____

c. **Unit Rate** What is the unit rate that converts gallons to quarts?

_____

d. **Proportion** Write a proportion you could use to convert 2.5 gallons to quarts.

_____

_____

H.O.T. Problems Higher-Order Thinking

12. Create Write a real-world problem in which you would need to convert pints to cups. _____

_____

_____

Analyze Fill in each ◯ with <, >, or = to make a true sentence. Justify your answers.

13. 16 in. ◯ $1\frac{1}{2}$ ft

_____

_____

14. 8.75 kg ◯ 875 g

_____

_____

15. Analyze Give two different measurements that are equivalent to $2\frac{1}{2}$ quarts.

_____

16. Create Write a real-world problem that can be represented by the graph.

_____

_____

_____

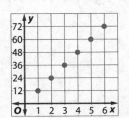

Multi-Step Problem Solving

17. The table shows the amount of water each athlete drinks during soccer practice. How many quarts of water are needed for these five athletes during practice? **P** **MP**

Athlete	Amount (c)
Deon	2
Sierra	1.5
Carmen	3.5
Mia	3
Ella	2

Use a problem-solving model to solve this problem.

1 Analyze

Read the problem. Circle the information you know.
Underline what the problem is asking you to find.

2 Plan

What will you need to do to solve the problem?
Write your plan in steps.

Step 1 Determine the total number of cups drank during practice.

Step 2 Convert cups to quarts.

Read to Succeed!

There are 2 cups in a pint and 2 pints in a quart.

3 Solve

Use your plan to solve the problem. Show your steps.

The total amount drank is 2 + 1.5 + 3.5 + 3 + 2 or _____ cups.

_____ cups = _____ pints = _____ quarts

So, the team drank _____ quarts of water. Grid in _____ on the answer grid.

4 Justify and Evaluate

How do you know your solution is accurate?

_____

_____

_____

P = Proportionality   **MP** = Mathematical Processes

More Multi-Step Problem Solving

Use a problem-solving model to solve each problem.

18. William collects metal to sell to a recycling plant. The table shows the amount of metal he has collected over several days. He needs to collect 4 tons before he can take the load to the recycling plant. How many more pounds does he need to reach 4 tons? **P** **MP**

Day	Metal (lb)
Monday	2,500
Tuesday	1,375
Wednesday	2,550
Thursday	1,075

19. Joaquin drank 6 glasses of water each containing 10 fluid ounces. His goal was to drink 2 quarts. How many more fluid ounces does he have to drink to reach his goal? **P** **MP**

20. A football team needs to travel 80 yards from their current location to their opponent's end zone to score a touchdown. The team is now 6 feet away from their opponent's end zone, ready to score the touchdown. How many feet have they already traveled down the field? **P** **MP**

21. The dimensions of a rectangle are given in the diagram. Jane wanted to know the area in square meters. She used two different methods to determine the area. Which method is correct, and why? **EE** **P** **MP**

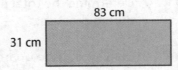

83 cm

31 cm

Method 1   83 cm × 31 cm = 2,573 sq cm

2,573 cm = 25.73 m

The area of the rectangle is 25.73 sq m.

Method 2   83 cm = 0.83 m

31 cm = 0.31 m

0.83 m × 0.31 m = 0.2573 sq m

The area of the rectangle is 0.2573 sq m.

P = Proportionality   **EE** = Expressions, Equations, and Relationships   **MP** = Mathematical Processes

21ST CENTURY CAREER

Cosmetics Chemist

Are you naturally curious and analytical? Do you like discovering new things? If so, a career as a cosmetics chemist might be a good choice for you. Cosmetics chemists spend time researching, mixing, and testing new formulas that will make cosmetic products both effective and safe. A cosmetics chemist explained, "When you're developing a product, you play with chemicals and balance ratios to get it to feel right. Basically, it's trial and error."

Mathematical Process
6.1(A) Apply mathematics to problems arising in everyday life, society, and the workplace.
Targeted TEKS 6.4(B)

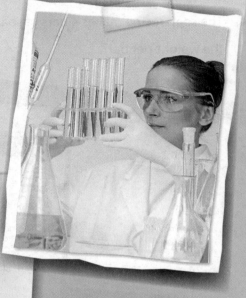

Is This the Career for You?

Are you interested in a career as a cosmetics chemist? Take some of the following courses in high school.

◆ Algebra
◆ Biology
◆ Chemical Science
◆ Chemistry
◆ Statistics

College & Career
READINESS

Explore college and careers at ccr.mcgraw-hill.com

Beauty is Only Science-Deep

Use the information in the recipes below to solve each problem.

1. Using the soap recipe, write a ratio comparing the amount of palm kernel oil to the amount of rose hydrosol as a fraction in simplest form.

_____

2. Write a ratio to compare the amount of jojoba oil to the total amount of the ingredients in the lip balm recipe. _____

3. The lip balm costs about $16 to make. What is the cost per ounce? _____

4. The soap recipe makes 4 bars of soap. What is the weight per bar? _____

5. The lip balm recipe is increased so that 10 ounces of candelilla wax is needed. Complete the ratio table to find the amount of shea butter that is needed. _____

Candelilla wax	2				10
Shea butter	6				

6. The soap recipe is increased so that 75 grams of shea butter are needed. Complete the ratio table to find the amount of sodium hydroxide that is needed. _____

Shea butter	30		75
Sodium hydroxide	42		

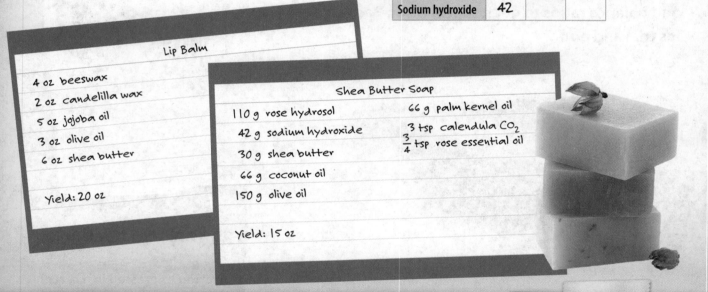

Lip Balm

4 oz beeswax
2 oz candelilla wax
5 oz jojoba oil
3 oz olive oil
6 oz shea butter

Yield: 20 oz

Shea Butter Soap

110 g rose hydrosol
42 g sodium hydroxide
30 g shea butter
66 g coconut oil
150 g olive oil

66 g palm kernel oil
3 tsp calendula CO_2
$\frac{3}{4}$ tsp rose essential oil

Yield: 15 oz

TEKS Career Project

It's time to update you career portfolio! There are many different types of jobs in cosmetics chemistry. Research one of these jobs and write a two- or three-sentence job description.

_____

_____

_____

List other careers that someone with an interest in chemistry could pursue.

• _____
• _____
• _____
• _____

Chapter Review

Vocabulary Check

Work with a partner to complete the crossword puzzle using the vocabulary list at the beginning of the chapter. Seek clarification of each term as needed.

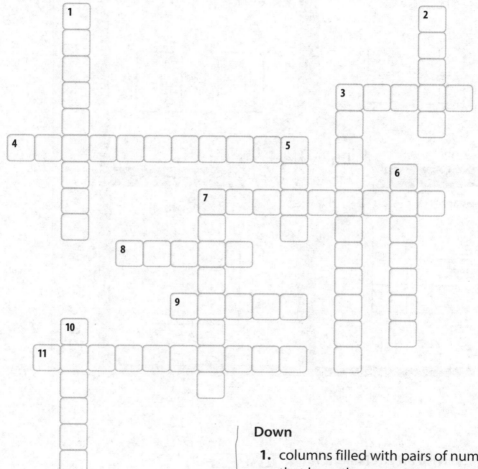

Across

3. the horizontal line on a coordinate plane

4. the number used in multiplying when scaling

7. the cost per unit

8. a multiplicative comparison of two quantities describing the same attribute

9. to place a dot at the point named by an ordered pair

11. equation stating that two ratios or rates are equivalent

Down

1. columns filled with pairs of numbers that have the same rate

2. the vertical line on a coordinate plane

3. the first number of an ordered pair

5. a comparison by division of two quantities having different attributes

6. multiply or divide two quantities by the same number

7. a rate simplified so that it has a denominator of 1

10. (0, 0)

Check ✓

Use Your FOLDABLES®

Collaborate

Use your Foldable to help review the chapter. Share your Foldable with a partner and take turns summarizing what you learned in this chapter, while the other partner listens carefully. Seek clarification of any concepts, as needed. **TEKS** 6.1(E)

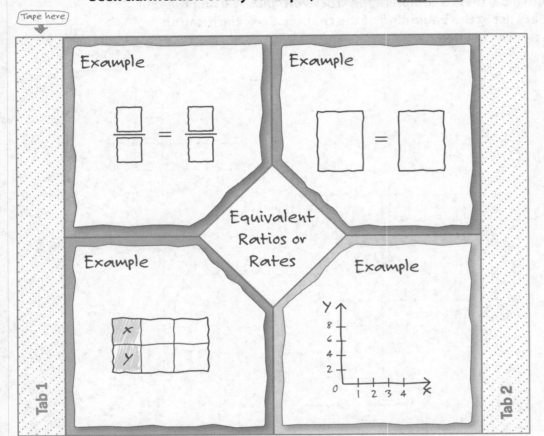

Got it?

Match each ratio with an equivalent ratio. **TEKS** 6.4(C)

1. 65:390

2. $\dfrac{64}{256}$

3. 156:390

4. $\dfrac{204}{306}$

5. 56:84

6. $\dfrac{87}{174}$

a. $\dfrac{2}{5}$

b. $\dfrac{2}{3}$

c. $\dfrac{1}{3}$

d. $\dfrac{1}{6}$

e. $\dfrac{1}{4}$

f. $\dfrac{1}{2}$

Multi-Step Problem Solving

7. Maddie can wash 3 cars in an hour. Her sister can wash 1 car in 30 minutes. At these rates, how many cars can they wash in 5 hours working together? Show the steps you used and justify your solution. (P) (MP)

1 Analyze

2 Plan

3 Solve

4 Justify and Evaluate

_____

_____

_____

Got it?

8. Max's sandbox is shown. What is the length of sandbox in feet? Show the steps you used and justify your solution. (P) (EE) (MP)

_____

_____

_____

_____

_____

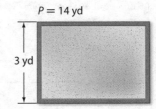

P = 14 yd

3 yd

Reflect

 Answering the Essential Question

Use what you learned about ratios and rates to complete the graphic organizer. **TEKS** 6.1(D), 6.1(E)

 Essential Question

HOW do you use equivalent ratios and rates in the real world?

Ratio
What is it?
Examples
Non-examples

Rate
What is it?
Examples
Non-examples

How are rates and ratios the same?

How are rates and ratios different?

Answer the Essential Question. HOW do you use equivalent ratios and rates in the real world? Verbally share your response with a partner, seeking and providing clarification as needed.

Collaborate

Chapter 5
Apply Proportions to Percent

Texas Essential Knowledge and Skills

Targeted TEKS
6.4 The student applies mathematical process standards to develop an understanding of proportional relationships in problem situations.

Mathematical Processes
6.1, 6.1(A), 6.1(B), 6.1(C), 6.1(D), 6.1(E), 6.1(F), 6.1(G)

Essential Question

WHEN is it better to use a fraction, a decimal, or a percent?

Math in the Real World

Architecture The Water Wall in Houston, Texas, pumps about 72,000 gallons of recycled water every 3 hours. Label the bar diagram to determine about how many gallons of water are pumped per hour.

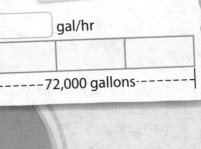

	gal/hr	

‑‑‑‑‑‑‑72,000 gallons‑‑‑‑‑‑‑

What Tools Do You Need?

Vocabulary

benchmark fractions   percent proportion

benchmark percents   proportion

percent

Reading Math

Everyday Meaning The key to understanding word problems is to understand the meaning of the mathematical terms in the problem.

You will use the terms *factor* and *multiple* in this chapter. Here are two sentences that show their everyday meanings.

- Weather was a *factor* in their decision to postpone the picnic.

- The star quarterback won *multiple* post-season awards.

The table shows how the everyday meaning is connected to the mathematical meaning.

Term	Everyday Meaning	Mathematical Meaning	Connection
Factor	something that actively contributes to a decision or result	2 and 3 are factors of 6.	A factor helps to make a decision. In mathematics, factors "make up" a product.
Multiple	consisting of more than one or shared by many	The multiples of 2 are 0, 2, 4, 6, . . .	Multiple means many. In mathematics, a number has infinitely many multiples.

Practice Make a list of other words that have the prefixes *fact-* or *multi-*. Determine what the words in each list have in common. Share your responses with a partner.

Word	Meaning	Connection

Quick Review

Review 6.3(E), 6.4(G)  TEKS

Example 1

Determine $\frac{2}{5} \times 220$.

$\frac{2}{5} \times 220 = \frac{2}{5} \times \frac{220}{1}$ Write 220 as $\frac{220}{1}$.

$= \frac{2}{5} \times \frac{\overset{44}{\cancel{220}}}{\underset{1}{1}}$ Divide by a common factor, 5.

$= \frac{88}{1}$ Multiply.

Example 2

Express 0.38 as a fraction in simplest form.

$0.38 = \frac{38}{100}$ Read 0.38 as *thirty-eight hundredths*.

$= \frac{19}{50}$ Simplify.

Quick Check

Check

Multiply Rational Numbers Multiply.

1. $\frac{8}{9} \times 81$ _____

2. $\frac{6}{11} \times 55$ _____

3. $\frac{53}{100} \times 900$ _____

Show your work.

Fractions and Decimals Express each decimal as a fraction in simplest form.

4. 0.6 _____

5. 0.45 _____

6. 1.7 _____

7. The front gear of a bicycle has 54 teeth. The back gear has $\frac{1}{3}$ the number of teeth as the front gear. How many teeth does the back gear have?

_____

How Did You Do?

**Which problems did you answer correctly in the Quick Check?
Shade those exercise numbers below.**

① ② ③ ④ ⑤ ⑥ ⑦

 Use this Foldable throughout this chapter to help you learn about fractions, decimals, and percents.

 cut on all dashed lines   fold on all solid lines   tape to page 422

Fractions, Decimals, and Percents

percents and fractions

percents and decimals

percent of a whole

FOLDABLES® Use this Foldable throughout this chapter to help you learn about fraction, decimals, and percents.

 cut on all dashed lines   fold on all solid lines   tape to page 422

Write About It

Write About It

Write About It

page 422

Hands-On Lab 1-a
Model Percents

INQUIRY HOW can I use diagrams to communicate mathematical ideas?

Jackie is using 1-inch tiles to make the mosaic shown at the right. She needs a total of 100 tiles. What percent of the tiles are green?

What do you know? _____

_____

What do you need to find? _____

_____

Texas Essential Knowledge and Skills

Targeted TEKS
6.4(E) Represent ratios and percents with concrete models, fractions, and decimals. *Also addresses 6.4(F).*

Mathematical Processes
6.1(C), 6.1(D), 6.1(F), 6.1(G)

Hands-On Activity 1

Tools

A 10 × 10 grid can be used to represent *hundredths*. It can also represent percents. The word *percent* (%) means *out of one hundred*. For example, 50% means 50 out of one hundred.

Step 1 Use a 10 × 10 grid to model the percent of tiles in the mosaic that are green.

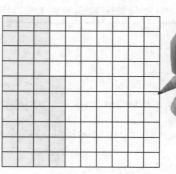

Step 2 In the mosaic, ☐ tiles out of 100 are green.

As a fraction, this is $\dfrac{\boxed{}}{100}$. When the denominator is 100, the numerator gives the numerical value of the percent.

So, ☐ % of the squares are green.

Common percents are 1%, 10%, 25%, and $33\frac{1}{3}$%. Using these percents and their multiples makes mental math easier.

Hands-On Activity 2

Model 25% with a 10 × 10 grid.

Step 1   25% means [ ] out of 100.

Step 2   Shade the squares, filling one column at a time.

Shade [ ] squares out of 100.

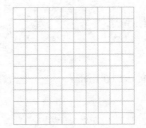

1. What fraction of the 10 × 10 grid is shaded? _____

2. What decimal represents the shaded

part of the grid? _____

Hands-On Activity 3

Percents can also be modeled with bar diagrams or strip diagrams. The entire bar represents 100%. The bar diagram below is divided into 10 equal sections, each representing 10%. The shaded region represents 40%.

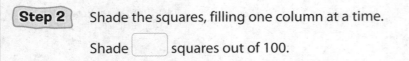

0%   40%   100%

10%	10%	10%	10%	10%	10%	10%	10%	10%	10%

Model 60% with a bar diagram.

Step 1   The bar diagram below is divided into [ ] equal sections.

To find the value of each section, divide. 100% ÷ 5 = 20%.

So, each section represents [ ] %.

Step 2   [ ] % + [ ] % + [ ] % = 60%

Shade [ ] sections of the diagram.

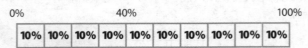

0%   100%

You can represent percents with the concrete models found on page MM9.

Investigate

Collaborate

Work with a partner. Identify each percent modeled.

3. _____

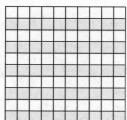

4. _____

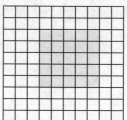

5. _____

6. _____

0%   50%   100%

Work with a partner. Model each percent.

7. 37%

Show your work.

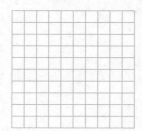

8. 8%

9. 45%

0%   50%   100%

10. 5%

0%   50%   100%

Analyze and Reflect

Collaborate

Work with a partner to determine the number of shaded sections for each model. The first one is done for you.

Percent	Number of Shaded Sections using each Model		
	10 × 10 Grid	Bar Diagram with 10 Equal Sections	Bar Diagram with 20 Equal Sections
45	45	4.5	9
11. 15			
12. 30			
13. 55			
14. 70			

15. Write the percent shown by each model. Explain your reasoning.

a.

_____
_____
_____

b.

_____
_____
_____

c.

_____
_____

16. **MP Analyze Relationships** How can you use a model to write a percent as

a fraction with a denominator of 100? _____

_____

Create

On Your Own

17. **MP Apply Math to the Real World** Write a real-world problem that involves

a percent. Then model the percent used in the problem. _____

_____

18. **INQUIRY** HOW can I use diagrams to communicate mathematical ideas?

_____

Percents and Fractions

Texas Essential Knowledge and Skills

Targeted TEKS
6.4(G) Generate equivalent forms of fractions, decimals, and percents using real-world problems, including problems that involve money. *Also addresses 6.4(E), 6.5(C).*

Mathematical Processes
6.1(A), 6.1(B), 6.1(D)

Students were asked to choose their favorite sport to play. How can we display these results?

1. For each sport, shade a 10 × 10 grid that represents the number of students that chose the sport.

Basketball: 3 out of 20   **Football:** 3 out of 25

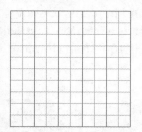 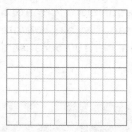

Vocabulary
percent

Essential Question
WHEN is it better to use a fraction, a decimal, or a percent?

Gymnastics: 1 out of 20   **Swimming:** 9 out of 100

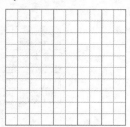 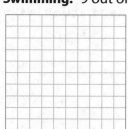

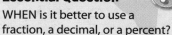

2. What fraction with a denominator of 100 represents each sport?

Basketball: ☐☐   Football: ☐☐

Gymnastics: ☐☐   Swimming: ☐☐

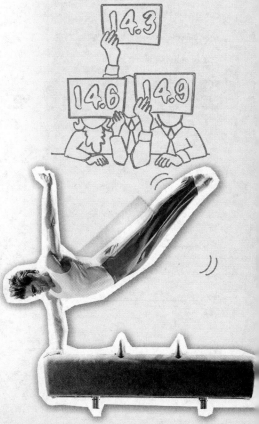

**Which (MP) Mathematical Processes did you use?
Shade the circle(s) that applies.**

Ⓐ Apply Math to the Real World.   Ⓔ Organize Ideas.

Ⓑ Use a Problem-Solving Model.   Ⓕ Analyze Relationships.

Ⓒ Select Tools and Techniques.   Ⓖ Justify Arguments.

Ⓓ Use Multiple Representations.

Percents as Fractions

Words   A **percent** is a ratio that compares a number to 100.

Example   45% ⇒ 45 out of 100 or $\frac{45}{100}$

Models

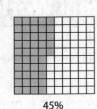

45%

0%   45%   100%

You can generate equivalent forms of fractions and percents to show equal parts of the same whole. To write a percent as a fraction, first write the percent as a rate per 100 because the whole is 100. Then simplify.

Watch   Tutor

Examples

1.   Express 50% as a fraction in simplest form.

50% means *50 out of 100*.

$50\% = \dfrac{50}{100}$ Definition of percent

$= \dfrac{\overset{1}{\cancel{50}}}{\underset{2}{\cancel{100}}}$ or $\dfrac{1}{2}$ Simplify. Divide the numerator and the denominator by the GCF, 50.

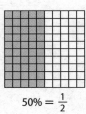

$50\% = \dfrac{1}{2}$

2.   In a recent survey, 55% of cell phone owners said they send text messages. What fraction of cell phone owners is this?

$55\% = \dfrac{55}{100}$ Definition of percent

$= \dfrac{11}{20}$ Simplify.

So, $\dfrac{11}{20}$ of cell phone owners send text messages.

Got It? Do these problems to find out.

Express each percent as a fraction in simplest form.

  a. 75%   **b.** 90%   **c.** 38%

Work Zone

Check for Reasonableness

In Example 2, you can conclude that $\frac{11}{20}$ is a reasonable answer because 55% is a little more than 50%, and $\frac{11}{20}$ is a little more than $\frac{10}{20}$ or $\frac{1}{2}$.

Show your work.

a. _____

b. _____

c. _____

Example

Tutor

3. The table shows the percent of each movie type rented during a month. What fraction of the rentals were action movies?

$35\% = \dfrac{35}{100}$ Definition of percent

$= \dfrac{\overset{7}{\cancel{35}}}{\underset{20}{\cancel{100}}}$ Divide the numerator and denominator by the GCF, 5.

Action movies were rented $\dfrac{7}{20}$ of the time.

Types of Movies	
action	35%
children's	5%
comedy	45%
drama	5%
horror	5%
romance	5%

 Got It? Do this problem to find out.

d. Write the fraction of rentals that were horror movies.

 Show your work.

 d. _____

Fractions as Percents

To write a fraction as a percent, find an equivalent fraction with 100 as a denominator or whole. The numerator indicates the percent.

Example

Tutor

4. Express the fraction $\dfrac{6}{8}$ as a percent.

$\dfrac{6}{8} = \dfrac{3}{4}$ Simplify by dividing by the GCF, 2.

$\dfrac{3}{4} = \dfrac{\blacksquare}{100}$ Write equivalent fractions. One fraction is the simplified fraction. The other fraction is the unknown value compared to 100.

$\dfrac{3}{4} = \dfrac{75}{100}$ $\times 25$ Since $4 \times 25 = 100$, multiply 3 by 25 to find the unknown value.

So, $\dfrac{75}{100}$ or 75% of the rectangle is shaded.

 Got It? Do this problem to find out.

e. Express the fraction $\dfrac{9}{12}$ as a percent.

 e. _____

 Example

5. Mitch made 12 out of 40 shots during the championship game. What percent of his shots did Mitch make?

$$\frac{12}{40} = \frac{3}{10}$$ Simplify $\frac{12}{40}$ by dividing the numerator and denominator by the GCF, 4.

$$\frac{3}{10} = \frac{\blacksquare}{100}$$ Write equivalent fractions.

$$\frac{3}{10} = \frac{30}{100}$$ Since $10 \times 10 = 100$, multiply 3 by 10 to find the unknown value.

So, $\frac{12}{40} = \frac{30}{100}$ or 30%.

Show your work.

Got It? Do this problem to find out.

f. Alana spelled 19 out of 25 words correctly. What percent of the words did Alana spell correctly?

f. _____

Guided Practice

Express each percent as a fraction in simplest form. (Examples 1–3)

1. 15% = _____

2. 80% = _____

3. 33% = _____

Show your work.

Express each fraction as a percent. Use a model if needed. (Example 4)

4. $\frac{3}{10}$ = _____

5. $\frac{3}{20}$ = _____

6. $\frac{2}{5}$ = _____

7. Elsa ran 7 out of 10 days. What percent of the days did she run? (Example 5)

_____

8. **Building on the Essential Question** How can you generate equivalent forms of fractions and percents to show equal parts of the same whole?

_____

_____

_____

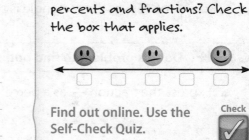

Rate Yourself!

How confident are you about percents and fractions? Check the box that applies.

Find out online. Use the Self-Check Quiz.

Check

FOLDABLES Time to update your Foldable!

Independent Practice

6.4(E), 6.4(G), 6.5(C), 6.1(D)

Express each percent as a fraction in simplest form. (Examples 1–3)

1. 2% = _____

2. 20% = _____

3. 85% = _____

4. 4% = _____

Show your work.

Express each fraction as a percent. Use a model if needed. (Example 4)

5. $\frac{2}{10}$ = _____

6. $\frac{3}{4}$ = _____

7. $\frac{7}{20}$ = _____

8. $\frac{11}{25}$ = _____

9. During his workout, Elan spent 28% of the time on the treadmill. What fraction of his workout was on the treadmill? (Examples 1–3)

_____

10. A cat spends about 7 out of 10 hours sleeping. About what percent of a cat's day is spent sleeping? (Example 5)

_____

11. A survey showed that 82% of youth most often use the Internet at home. What fraction of youth surveyed use the Internet most often somewhere else?

_____

12. Cedro collects state quarters. He has 42 out of 50 available quarters. What is 42 out of 50 as a percent?

_____

13. Use the table to determine what percent of students prefer school uniforms and what percent do not prefer school uniforms. What is the relationship between these two percents?

_____

Prefer School Uniforms	
No	Yes
𝍩𝍩𝍩 𝍩𝍩𝍩 𝍩𝍩𝍩 𝍩	||||

14. **Use Multiple Representations** The table shows the percent of Earth's atmosphere that is each element.

Element	Percent
Nitrogen	78
Oxygen	21
Other	1

a. Bar Diagram Model 21% using a bar diagram.

0%   100%

b. Fraction Express the percent of Earth's atmosphere that is nitrogen as a fraction in simplest form. _____

H.O.T. Problems Higher-Order Thinking

15. Analyze Write three fractions that can be expressed as percents between 50% and 75%. Justify your solution.

_____

16. Analyze For each model below, write the shaded region as a percent and as a fraction.

a.

b.

c.

_____   _____   _____

17. Evaluate Identify the number that does *not* belong with the other three. Explain your reasoning.

| $\frac{9}{20}$ | $\frac{45}{100}$ | 45% | $\frac{8}{45}$ |

_____

18. Analyze Complete each blank to find an expression that is equal to 16%.

a. _____ for every 100   **b.** _____ for every 50

c. 1 for every _____   **d.** 0.5 for every _____

19. Analyze Explain the difference between $33\frac{1}{3}$% and 33%. _____

_____

Multi-Step Problem Solving

20. The table shows the percent of time Allison spent studying each of her school subjects last week. What fraction of the subjects studied were math or history? (P) (MP)

Ⓐ $\frac{1}{10}$

Ⓒ $\frac{3}{10}$

Ⓑ $\frac{2}{5}$

Ⓓ $\frac{4}{5}$

Subject	Time Spent Studying (% of week)
Math	30
Science	10
Language Arts	15
History	10
Reading	20
Music	15

Use a problem-solving model to solve this problem.

1 Analyze

**Read the problem. Circle the information you know.
Underline what the problem is asking you to find.**

2 Plan

What will you need to do to solve the problem? Write your plan in steps.

Step 1 Determine the total percent for both math and history.

Step 2 Express the percent as a fraction in simplest form.

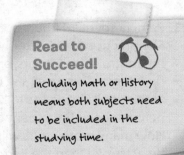

Read to Succeed!

Including Math or History means both subjects need to be included in the studying time.

3 Solve

Use your plan to solve the problem. Show your steps.

Math: ☐ %

History: ☐ %

Total percentage spent on Math and History: ☐ %

So, the simplified fraction is ☐ % or ☐/☐. So, choice ☐ is correct.
Fill in that answer choice.

4 Justify and Evaluate

How do you know your solution is accurate?

_____

_____

(P) = Proportionality   (MP) = Mathematical Processes

More Multi-Step Problem Solving

Use a problem-solving model to solve each problem.

21. The table shows the percent of each type of car rented last month. What fraction of the rentals were for a sedan or a truck? **P** **MP**

Type of Car	Percent Rented
Minivan	13
Sport utility	37
Sedan	9
Convertible	4
Sports car	6
Truck	31

Ⓐ $\frac{9}{100}$ Ⓒ $\frac{3}{20}$

Ⓑ $\frac{1}{10}$ Ⓓ $\frac{2}{5}$

22. Benito had 10 days of vacation. He spent $\frac{1}{5}$ of his vacation fishing. He spent 30% of his vacation at soccer camp. He spent the rest of the time at the beach. What percent of his vacation did Benito spend at the beach? **P** **MP**

_____

23. Patricia spent 10 hours at the pool last week. She practiced the butterfly for 2 hours, the breaststroke for 5 hours, and the backstroke for 3 hours. This week she only has 5 hours at the pool. She wants to keep the same percentage of time spent on each stroke. How many more hours will she practice the breaststroke than the backstroke? **P** **MP**

_____

24. Ramiro's garden is shown below. What percent of the total area of the garden do the cucumbers cover? Explain. **P** **MP**

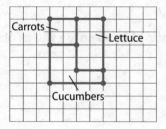

_____

_____

_____

_____

_____

Percents and Decimals

 Watch **Launch the Lesson: Real World**

Texas Essential Knowledge and Skills

Targeted TEKS
6.4(G) Generate equivalent forms of fractions, decimals, and percents using real-world problems, including problems that involve money. *Also addresses 6.4(E), 6.5(C).*

Mathematical Processes
6.1(A), 6.1(B), 6.1(D)

A recent survey shows the favorite subjects of students at Martin Middle School. What part of the students chose each subject?

Math: 24%
Art: 18%

Science: 23%
English: 11%

Social Studies: 17%
Other: 7%

Essential Question
WHEN is it better to use a fraction, a decimal, or a percent?

1. Write a fraction to represent the percent for each subject.

Math: $\dfrac{\boxed{}}{100}$ Science: $\dfrac{\boxed{}}{100}$

Art: $\dfrac{\boxed{}}{100}$ Social Studies: $\dfrac{\boxed{}}{100}$

English: $\dfrac{\boxed{}}{100}$ Other: $\dfrac{\boxed{}}{100}$

2. Write each fraction from Exercise 1 as a decimal.

Math: ☐   Science: ☐

Art: ☐   Social Studies: ☐

English: ☐   Other: ☐

3. **MP Analyze Relationships** Look back at Exercise 2. Compare the decimals to the percents. Explain how to write a percent as a decimal. _____

_____

_____

Which MP Mathematical Processes did you use?
Shade the circle(s) that applies.

Ⓐ Apply Math to the Real World.
Ⓑ Use a Problem-Solving Model.
Ⓒ Select Tools and Techniques.
Ⓓ Use Multiple Representations.
Ⓔ Organize Ideas.
Ⓕ Analyze Relationships.
Ⓖ Justify Arguments.

Express Percents as Decimals

You can generate equivalent forms of percents and decimals to show equal parts of the same whole.

Words   To express a percent as a decimal, write the percent as a fraction with a denominator of 100, because the whole is 100. Then write the fraction as a decimal, because the part is represented by the *hundredths* place.

Model

Example $48\% = \dfrac{48}{100}$ or 48 hundredths

$= 0.48$

Percents as Decimals

Another way to express a percent as a decimal is to divide by 100 and remove the % sign. This is the same as moving the decimal point two places to the left.

Examples

Tutor

Express each percent as a decimal.

1. **38%**

$38\% = \dfrac{38}{100}$ Rewrite the percent as a fraction with a denominator of 100.

$= 0.38$ Express *38 hundredths* as a decimal.

2. **9%**

$9\% = \dfrac{9}{100}$ Rewrite the percent as a fraction with a denominator of 100.

$= 0.09$ Express *9 hundredths* as a decimal.

3. **2%**

$2\% = \dfrac{2}{100}$ Rewrite the percent as a fraction with a denominator of 100.

$= 0.02$ Express *2 hundredths* as a decimal.

Show your work.

Got It? Do these problems to find out.

a. 22%   **b.** 7%   **c.** 93%

a. _____

b. _____

c. _____

Express Decimals as Percents

You can also express decimals as percents to show equal parts of the same whole.

Words To express a decimal as a percent, write the decimal as a fraction with a denominator of 100, because the part is represented by the *hundredths* place. Then write the fraction as a percent, because the whole is 100.

Model

Example $0.36 = 36$ *hundredths* or $\frac{36}{100}$
$= 36\%$

Examples

Tutor

Why does it help to write a decimal as a fraction with a denominator of 100 when writing decimals as percents?

4. **Express 0.29 as a percent.**

$0.29 = \frac{29}{100}$ Express *29 hundredths* as a fraction.

$= 29\%$ Express the fraction as a percent.

5. **Express 0.6 as a percent.**

$0.6 = \frac{6}{10}$ Express *6 tenths* as a fraction.

$\times 10$

$\frac{6}{10} = \frac{60}{100}$ Write the equivalent fraction with a denominator of 100.

$\times 10$

$= 60\%$ Express the fraction as a percent.

Got It? Do these problems to find out.

Express each decimal as a percent.

d. 0.81   **e.** 0.73   **f.** 0.55

Show your work.

d. _____

e. _____

f. _____

Example

6. Texas produces more beef than any other state, producing almost 0.2 of the total beef production. Express 0.2 as a percent.

0.2 = 0.20	Annex a zero.
= 20 *hundredths*	0.20 is read as *20 hundredths*.
= $\frac{20}{100}$ or 20%	Write as a fraction with a denominator of 100.

Show your work.

Got It? Do this problem to find out.

g. _____

g. Express 0.38 as a percent.

Guided Practice

Express each percent as a decimal. (Examples 1–3)

 Show your work.

1. 37% = _____

2. 12% = _____

3. 6% = _____

Write each decimal as a percent. (Examples 4 and 5)

4. 0.3 = _____

5. 0.82 = _____

6. 0.51 = _____

7. **STEM** About 0.15 of the human body is bone. What percent is equivalent to 0.15? (Example 6) _____

8. **?** **Building on the Essential Question** How can you generate equivalent forms of fractions, decimals, and percents that show equal parts of the same whole?

_____

_____

_____

_____

Rate Yourself!

How well do you understand percents and decimals? Circle the image that applies.

Clear   Somewhat Clear   Not So Clear

Find out online. Use the Self-Check Quiz.

Check

FOLDABLES Time to update your Foldable!

Independent Practice

6.4(E), 6.4(G), 6.5(C), 6.1(B)

Express each percent as a decimal. (Examples 1–3)

1. 57% = _____

2. 1% = _____

3. 31% = _____

4. 92% = _____

Express each decimal as a percent. (Examples 4 and 5)

5. 0.18 = _____

6. 0.79 = _____

7. 0.1 = _____

8. 0.76 = _____

9. Financial Literacy A bank offers an interest rate of 4% on a savings account. Express 4% as a decimal. (Examples 1–3)

_____

10. When making a peanut butter and jelly sandwich, 96% of people put the peanut butter on first. Express 96% as a decimal. (Examples 1–3)

_____

11. In a recent year, 0.12 of Americans downloaded a podcast from the Internet. What percent is equivalent to 0.12? (Example 6)

_____

12. In a recent year, the number of people with smartphones grew 0.03 from the previous year. Express 0.03 as a percent. (Example 6)

_____

13. Financial Literacy The formula $I = prt$ gives the simple interest I earned on an account where an amount p is deposited at an interest rate r for a certain number of years t. Use the table to order the accounts from least to greatest interest earned after 5 years.

_____

_____

Accounts at First Savings Bank		
Account	p ($)	r (%)
A	350	4
B	500	3.5
C	280	4.25

14. Write the shaded portion of the model as fraction, decimal, and percent.

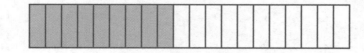

_____

15. **Use a Problem-Solving Model** Daphne wants to buy a coat that costs $100. The store that sells the coat has multiple locations. The sales tax in each city is shown in the table. How much more would the coat cost in Austin than Suffolk?

City	Tax Rate
Austin	8.25%
Martinsville	$7\frac{1}{4}$
Suffolk	0.0675

16. Dante took three tests on Friday. He got a 92% on his English test, an 88% on his math test and a 90% on his science test. Express each percent as a decimal in order from least to greatest.

H.O.T. Problems Higher-Order Thinking

17. Analyze Write a percent between 25% and 50%. Then express it as a decimal and as a fraction in simplest form.

18. Analyze How would you express $43\frac{3}{4}\%$ as a decimal?

19. Create Write a problem about a real-world situation in which you would either express a percent as a decimal or express a decimal as a percent.

20. Analyze Express $66\frac{2}{3}\%$ as a fraction in simplest form. Draw a bar diagram to explain.

21. Evaluate Which of the following numbers is greatest given the same whole? Explain your reasoning.

$$\frac{2}{5}, 0.45, 35\%, 3 \text{ out of } 8$$

22. Analyze Explain why percents are rational numbers.

Multi-Step Problem Solving

23. A yogurt company decreased the amount of yogurt in each container it sells. The new containers contain 15% less yogurt than the original containers. The number line shows the original amount in each container. Which point represents the new amount? **P** **MP**

Ⓐ Point *A*

Ⓑ Point *B*

Ⓒ Point *C*

Ⓓ Point *D*

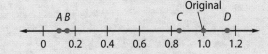

Use a problem-solving model to solve this problem.

1 Analyze

Read the problem. Circle the information you know.
Underline what the problem is asking you to find.

2 Plan

What will you need to do to solve the problem? Write your plan in steps.

Step 1 Determine the new percentage of the amount of yogurt.

Step 2 Locate the percent as a decimal on the number line.

Read to Succeed!

To express a percent as a decimal, move the decimal point two places to the left and remove the percent symbol.

3 Solve

Use your plan to solve the problem. Show your steps.

The new percentage of yogurt is 100% — 15% or [   ]%.

As a decimal, 85% is [   ].

Point [   ] is located at 0.85. So, choice [   ] is correct. Fill in that answer choice.

4 Justify and Evaluate

How do you know your solution is accurate?

_____

_____

_____

P = Proportionality   **MP** = Mathematical Processes

More **Multi-Step** Problem Solving

Use a problem-solving model to solve each problem.

24. Dexter is tracking his progress in completing math assignments. He has completed 30% of his assignments. What decimal represents the part he has *not* completed? **P** **MP**

(A) 0.03

(B) 0.07

(C) 0.3

(D) 0.7

25. Trista deposited money into a savings account and left it there for several years. She earned a total of 12% interest on her deposit. How much did she earn per dollar? **P** **MP**

_____

26. The table shows the number of students who earned various grades in English. What percent of the students earned an A or a B? **P** **MP**

Grade	Tally	Frequency
A	||||| ||||	9
B	||||| ||	7
C	|||	3
D			1

27. Autumn used 0.675 of the battery life on her MP3 player. Her brother borrowed it to play a game and used 0.2 of the total battery life. If her MP3 player shows the battery life that remains as a percentage, what does it show after her brother is finished? **P** **N** **MP**

_____

Percents Greater than 100% and Percents Less than 1%

  Watch

Launch the Lesson: Real World

Texas Essential Knowledge and Skills

Targeted TEKS
6.4(G) Generate equivalent forms of fractions, decimals, and percents using real-world problems, including problems that involve money. *Also addresses 6.4(E), 6.5(C).*

Mathematical Processes
6.1(A), 6.1(B), 6.1(D)

There are over 220,000 species of plants on Earth. Of those, 590 are carnivorous. Plants such as a Venus Fly Trap catch their prey as food. What percent of the plant species are carnivorous?

1. Express the fraction of species of carnivorous plants in simplest form.

$$\frac{\boxed{}}{220,000} \div \frac{\boxed{}}{\boxed{}} = \frac{\boxed{}}{22,000}$$

2. Express your answer to Exercise 1 as a decimal rounded to the nearest thousandth. Use division to determine your answer.

 $\boxed{} \approx \boxed{}$

Essential Question

WHEN is it better to use a fraction, a decimal, or a percent?

3. Express your answer to Exercise 2 as a fraction. _____

4. **MP** **Analyze Relationships** Since 0.3 = 30% and 0.03 = 3%, what percent is equal to 0.003? Explain.

_____

_____

5. What percent of the plant species are carnivorous? _____

 Which MP Mathematical Processes did you use?
Shade the circle(s) that applies.

Ⓐ Apply Math to the Real World. Ⓔ Organize Ideas.
Ⓑ Use a Problem-Solving Model. Ⓕ Analyze Relationships.
Ⓒ Select Tools and Techniques. Ⓖ Justify Arguments.
Ⓓ Use Multiple Representations.

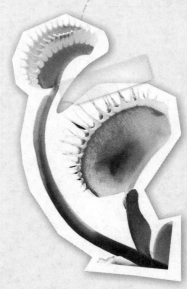

Percents as Decimals and Fractions

Percents greater than 100% or less than 1% can also be expressed as decimals or as fractions to show equal parts of the same whole.

 Tutor

Examples

Percent

A percent less than 1% equals a number less than 0.01 or $\frac{1}{100}$. A percent greater than 100% equals a number greater than 1.

1. **Express 0.2% as a decimal and as a fraction in simplest form.**

$$0.2\% = 00.2 \qquad \text{Divide by 100 and remove \% symbol.}$$
$$= 0.002 \qquad \text{Decimal form}$$
$$= \frac{2}{1,000} \text{ or } \frac{1}{500} \qquad \text{Fraction form}$$

2. **Express 170% as a mixed number in simplest form and as a decimal.**

$$170\% = \frac{170}{100} \qquad \text{Definition of percent}$$
$$= 1\frac{70}{100} \text{ or } 1\frac{7}{10} \qquad \text{Mixed number form}$$
$$= 1.7 \qquad \text{Decimal form}$$

 Show your work.

Got It? Do these problems to find out.

Write each percent as a decimal and as a mixed number or fraction in simplest form.

a. 0.25%   **b.** 300%   **c.** 530%

a. _____

b. _____

c. _____

 Real World

Example

Tutor

3. **Jimmy's savings increased by 250%. Express 250% as a mixed number in simplest form and as a decimal.**

$$250\% = \frac{250}{100} \qquad \text{Definition of percent}$$
$$= 2\frac{50}{100} \text{ or } 2\frac{1}{2} \qquad \text{Mixed number form}$$
$$= 2.5 \qquad \text{Decimal form}$$

So, Jimmy's savings is 2.5 times more than it was originally.

Got It? Do this problem to find out.

d. _____

d. The stock price for a corporation increased by 0.11%. Write 0.11% as a decimal and as a fraction in simplest form.

Mixed Numbers and Decimals as Percents

To express a decimal as a percent, multiply by 100 and add a percent sign. To express a mixed number as a percent, first express the mixed number as an improper fraction.

Example

4. **Express $1\frac{1}{4}$ as a percent.**

$1\frac{1}{4} = \frac{5}{4}$ Express $1\frac{1}{4}$ as an improper fraction.

$\frac{5}{4} = \frac{\blacksquare}{100}$ Find an equivalent fraction with a denominator of 100.

$$\overset{\times 25}{\frac{5}{4}} = \underset{\times 25}{\frac{125}{100}}$$ Since $4 \times 25 = 100$, multiply 5 by 25 to find an equivalent fraction.

So, $1\frac{1}{4}$ is $\frac{125}{100}$ or 125%.

Got It? Do these problems to find out.

Express each mixed number as a percent.

e. $2\frac{9}{10}$ **f.** $3\frac{2}{5}$

Examples

5. **Express 1.68 as a percent.**

$1.68 = 1.68$ Multiply by 100.

$= 168\%$ Add % symbol.

- -

6. **Express 0.0075 as a percent.**

$0.0075 = 0.0075$ Multiply by 100.

$= 0.75\%$ Add % symbol.

Got It? Do these problems to find out.

g. 2.5   **h.** 0.004   **i.** 0.0016

Alternative Method

$1 = 100\%$

$\frac{1}{4} = 25\%$

So, $1\frac{1}{4} = 125\%$.

Show your work.

e. _____

f. _____

STOP and Reflect

Is the decimal 6.7 equal to 67%? Explain below.

g. _____

h. _____

i. _____

Example

 Real World

7. **STEM** The cheetah is the fastest land mammal in the world. The peregrine falcon is the fastest bird in the world. Its speed is 2.1 times as fast as the cheetah. Express this number as a percent.

$2.1 = 2.10$ Multiply by 100.

    $= 210\%$ Add % symbol.

The peregrine falcon's speed is 210% of the cheetah's speed.

Got It? Do this problem to find out.

Show your work.

j. **STEM** The slowest land mammal is the sloth. Its speed is about 0.0016 that of a cheetah. Express this number as a percent.

j. _____

Guided Practice

Express each percent as a decimal and as a mixed number or fraction in simplest form. (Examples 1–3)

 Show your work.

1. $325\% = $ _____

2. $480\% = $ _____

3. $0.6\% = $ _____

Express each mixed number or decimal as a percent. (Examples 4–6)

4. $1\frac{4}{5} = $ _____

5. $0.0015 = $ _____

6. $2.75 = $ _____

7. A manufacturing company finds that 0.0019 of the light bulbs it makes are defective. Express this as a percent. (Example 7) _____

_____

8. **?** **Building on the Essential Question** For a percent greater than 100%, are the equivalent fraction and decimal forms less than, equal to, or greater than 1? Justify your response.

_____

_____

_____

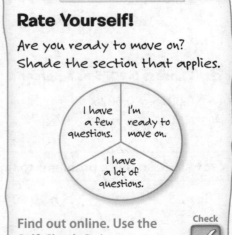

Rate Yourself!

Are you ready to move on? Shade the section that applies.

I have a few questions. | I'm ready to move on.

I have a lot of questions.

Find out online. Use the Self-Check Quiz.

Check

Independent Practice

6.4(E), 6.4(G), 6.5(C), 6.1(C) TEKS

Express each percent as a decimal and as a mixed number or fraction in simplest form. (Examples 1–3)

Show your work.

1. 350% = _____

2. 600% = _____

3. 0.15% = _____

4. 0.55% = _____

Express each mixed number as a percent. (Example 4)

5. $2\frac{1}{2}$ = _____

6. $9\frac{3}{4}$ = _____

7. $4\frac{1}{5}$ = _____

8. $7\frac{3}{10}$ = _____

Express each decimal as a percent. (Examples 5 and 6)

9. 8.5 = _____

10. 2.64 = _____

11. 0.009 = _____

12. 0.0034 = _____

13. The cost of a large milkshake is 1.4 times the cost of a medium milkshake. Express 1.4 as a percent. (Example 7)

_____

14. **STEM** Fresh water from lakes accounts for only 0.001 of the world's water supply. Express this decimal as a percent. (Example 7)

_____

15. In a recent year, the United States Census Bureau reported that 0.3% of the population in the United States was Japanese. Express this percent as a decimal and as a fraction. Then interpret its meaning as a ratio of the United States population.

_____

16. Adrienne answered all 21 multiple-choice questions correctly on her science test. If her teacher decided to let one of the questions count as a bonus, worth the same number of points as the other problems on the test, what was Adrienne's test score? Express your answer as a decimal and as a percent.

_____

17. (MP) **Select Tools and Techniques** Refer to the table at the right.

a. Express the percent of magnesium found in the human body as a decimal.

_____

_____

b. Which element makes up $\frac{1}{400}$ of the human body?

_____

_____

Elements in the Human Body	
Element	**Percent**
Magnesium	0.05
Potassium	0.35
Sodium	0.15
Sulfur	0.25

18. Find the Error Raj is writing $\frac{3}{2,000}$ as a percent. Find his mistake and correct it.

_____

_____

_____

_____

$$\frac{3}{2,000} = 0.0015$$
$$= 15\%$$

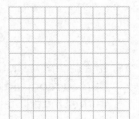 **Problems** Higher-Order Thinking

19. Analyze The speed of a giraffe is 250% the speed of a squirrel. If a squirrel's speed is 12 miles per hour, determine the speed of a giraffe.

_____

20. Create Write a real-world problem involving a percent greater than 100%.

Then solve the problem. _____

_____

_____

21. Analyze Explain how you would show 135% on a 10-by-10 grid. Use the grids given.

_____

_____

_____

22. Create Write a real-world problem involving a percent less than 1%.
Then solve the problem.

_____

_____

Multi-Step Problem Solving

23. The table shows a salesperson's commissions during several consecutive years. If the 2010 commission is considered 100% of expected commissions, what percent of expected commissions is the 2011 value?

Use a problem-solving model to solve this problem.

1 Analyze

Read the problem. Circle the information you know.
Underline what the problem is asking you to find.

2 Plan

What will you need to do to solve the problem? Write your plan in steps.

Step 1 Locate the amounts for 2010 and 2011.

Step 2 Express the amount of 2011 in relation to 2010 as a fraction and convert to a percent.

Read to Succeed!
The amount for 2010 is 100%. So, $10,000 is 100%.

3 Solve

Use your plan to solve the problem. Show your steps.

$$2011 \longrightarrow \frac{\$12,150}{\$10,000} = \boxed{} = \boxed{}\%$$
$$2010 \longrightarrow$$

So, the amount for 2011 is 121.5% of 2010. Complete the grid.

4 Justify and Evaluate

How do you know your solution is accurate?

_____

_____

_____

N = Number and Operations   P = Proportionality   MP = Mathematical Processes

More **Multi-Step** Problem Solving

Use a problem-solving model to solve each problem.

24. It is recommended that 13-year-old girls get 45 mg of Vitamin C each day. The table shows the Vitamin C content of various foods. What percentage of the recommended daily amount will Adelina receive if she eats all of these foods in one day?

Food	Approx. Vitamin C Content (mg)
1 orange	70
1 green pepper	100
1 cup cooked broccoli	100

25. Adam has read $\frac{3}{20}$ of a novel in one week. The table shows the fraction of his reading that he completed each day. What percent of the novel did he read on Wednesday?

Day	Fraction of Reading Completed
Monday	$\frac{1}{6}$
Tuesday	$\frac{2}{9}$
Wednesday	$\frac{1}{30}$
Thursday	$\frac{4}{9}$
Friday	$\frac{2}{15}$

26. If the volume of Rectangular Prism *A* is 0.01% of the volume of Rectangular Prism *B*, what is the ratio of the number of unit cubes it takes to fill Prism *B* to the number it takes to fill Prism *A*?

27. Shina wants to plot the values below as decimals on a histogram. Arrange the parts of the same whole shown in increasing order.

0.01%   0.05   0.5%   0.500   50   500%   1%

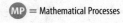

N = Number and Operations   **P** = Proportionality   **EE** = Expressions, Equations, and Relationships   **MP** = Mathematical Processes

380   **Chapter 5** Apply Proportions to Percent

Mathematical Process
6.1(B) Use a problem-solving model that incorporates analyzing given information, formulating a plan or strategy, determining a solution, justifying the solution, and evaluating the problem-solving process and the reasonableness of the solution.
Targeted TEKS 6.4(G)

First Place Pizza

The daily lunch report indicated that 80% of the 340 students at Midtown Middle School chose pizza for lunch.

How many students did not buy pizza for lunch?

1 Analyze *What are the facts?*

- The lunch report says 80% chose pizza.
- There are 340 students at the school.

2 Plan *What is your strategy to solve this problem?*

Solve a simpler problem by finding 10% of the total students. Then use the result to find 80% of the total students. Subtract to find the number of students that did not buy pizza.

3 Solve *How can you apply the strategy?*

Complete the bar diagram. Fill in the value of each section.

```
|------------------ 340 students ------------------|
|    |    |    |    |    |    |    |    |    |    |
0%  10%  20%  30%  40%  50%  60%  70%  80%  90%  100%
```

There are 340 ÷ 10, or 10 groups with ☐ students in each group.

Multiply. ☐ × 8 = ☐

So, ☐ students chose pizza for lunch.

Therefore 340 − ☐ , or ☐ students did not buy pizza.

4 Justify and Evaluate *Does the answer make sense?*

You know that 80% chose pizza, so 20% did not. Since 10% of 340 is 34, then 20% is 2 × 34 or 68. So, the answer is accurate.

Top Tip

Heidi's dad wants to leave an 18% tip for a restaurant bill. The appetizer cost $4.80, the dinner cost $14.90, and the dessert was $4.90.

```
            <------ total bill ------>
    |-----|-----|-----|-----|-----|-----|-----|-----|-----|-----|
   0%   10%  20%  30%  40%  50%  60%  70%  80%  90%  100%
```

About how much money should he leave?

1 Analyze

Read the problem. What are you being asked to find?

I need to estimate _____.

What information do you know?

Heidi's dad wants to leave an _____ on a _____ bill.

2 Plan

Choose a problem-solving strategy.

I will use the _____ strategy.

3 Solve

Use your problem-solving strategy to solve the problem.

4 Justify and Evaluate

Use information from the problem to check your answer.

$0.18 \times 24.60 =$ _____. So, $5 is a reasonable estimate.

Work with a small group to solve the following problems.
Show your work on a separate piece of paper.

1. Time
Three 24-hour clocks show the time to be 12 noon. One of the clocks is always correct, one loses a minute every 24 hours, and one gains a minute every 24 hours.

How many days will pass before all three clocks show the correct time again?

2. Palindromes
The number 272 is a palindrome because it reads the same forward or backward.

How many numbers from 10 to 1,000 are palindromes?

3. Candy
In one minute, a candy factory makes the individually-wrapped pieces of chocolate candy shown in the table.

How many pieces are caramel?

Type	Number	Percent
Cream	60	5
Cherry	204	17
Peanut Butter	348	29
Caramel	■	35
Mint	168	14

Use any strategy!

4. Border
Part of a strip of border for a bulletin board is shown. All of the sections of the border are the same width.

1 in.

If the first shape on the strip is a triangle and the strip is 74 inches long, what is the last shape on the strip?

Vocabulary Check

1. Define *percent*. Express $\frac{25}{100}$ as a percent. Then express $\frac{25}{100}$ as a decimal.
   TEKS 6.4(E), 6.1(G)

Key Concept Check

2. Complete the graphic organizer by explaining how to convert from one form of a number to another. **TEKS** 6.4(E), 6.1(E)

Fraction	Decimal	Percent
To a decimal:	To a fraction:	To a fraction:
To a percent:	To a percent:	To a decimal:

3. The number of chorus students increased by a factor of 1.2 from the previous year. Express 1.2 as a percent. **TEKS** 6.4(E), 6.1(B)

Multi-Step Problem Solving

4. According to a survey, 64% of sixth graders prefer to text than instant message. Which ratio could represent the students that prefer to instant message to the total number of students? **P** **MP**

   Ⓐ 64 to 100   Ⓒ 9 to 25

   Ⓑ 36 to 64   Ⓓ 9 to 16

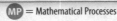 **P** = Proportionality   **MP** = Mathematical Processes

Benchmark Percents

Texas Essential Knowledge and Skills TEKS

Targeted TEKS
6.4(F) Represent benchmark fractions and percents such as 1%, 10%, 25%, $33\frac{1}{3}$%, and multiples of these values using 10 by 10 grids, strip diagrams, number lines, and numbers. *Also addresses 6.5(B).*

Mathematical Processes
6.1(C), 6.1(D), 6.1(E), 6.1(F), 6.1(G)

INQUIRY HOW can I use multiple representations to represent benchmark fractions and percents?

About 27% of the population of Texas is younger than 18 years old. There are 200 people that live in a neighborhood. About how many of those people are younger than 18 years old?

Vocab

Vocabulary
benchmark fractions
benchmark percents

Hands-On Activity 1

Benchmark fractions and their corresponding **benchmark percents** can be used when estimating part of a whole. Some common benchmark percents are 1%, 10%, 25%, $33\frac{1}{3}$%, and their multiples.

You can use models to generate equivalent fractions and decimals of these percents.

Label the bar diagram with the multiples of the benchmark percent 25% and the multiples of its corresponding benchmark fraction $\frac{1}{4}$. Label the number line with the multiples of the decimal equivalent 0.25.

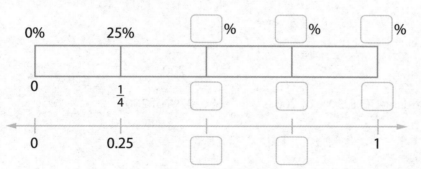

1. How can you check the accuracy of your model?

_____

_____

2. How can you extend the model for multiples of 25% greater than 100%?

_____

_____

_____

You can create models for other benchmark percents and their corresponding benchmark fractions and equivalent decimals.

Hands-On Activity 2

Part of a whole can also be estimated by representing benchmark fractions percents on a bar diagram, double number line, and 10 by 10 grid. You can solve the percent problem on the previous page using models.

Model 1: Bar Diagram
27% is close to 25%. So, the benchmark percent is [ ]%. Label the bar diagram.

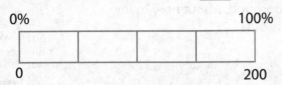

0%   100%

0   200

The part that corresponds to 25% is [ ]. So, about [ ] people in the neighborhood are younger than 18 years old.

Model 2: Number Line

27% of 200 is close to [ ]% of 200. 30% is a multiple of [ ]%, so the

benchmark percent is [ ]%. The benchmark fraction is _____.

Draw a double number line. Label the benchmark percent and its multiples.

0   10%

0   200

Locate the part that corresponds to 30%. 30% of 200 is [ ]. So, 27% of 200 is about [ ].

Model 3: 10 by 10 Grid

You can use a 10 by 10 grid to estimate part of a whole. Each column represents the benchmark fraction $\frac{1}{10}$ and the benchmark percent of 10%.

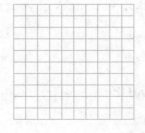

Since 27% is about 30%, shade 30% or 3 columns.

Each column represents one-tenth of 200, which is [ ].

So, 27% of 200 is about 3 × 20 or [ ].

3. **MP** **Analyze Relationships** Explain why using different benchmark percents resulted in different estimations for 27% of 200.

_____

_____

Investigate

Work with a partner. Complete the models to show benchmark fractions and percents and their equivalent decimals.

4.

5.

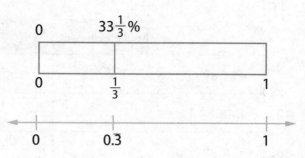

6.

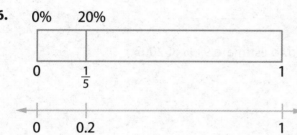

7.

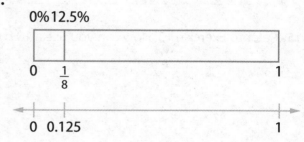

Work with a partner. Use a bar diagram to estimate each part of a whole.

8. 11% of 130 ≈ _____

9. 34% of 90 ≈ _____

Work with a partner. Use a double number line to estimate each part of a whole.

10. 52% of 180 ≈ _____

11. 67% of 9 ≈ _____

Analyze and Reflect

Work with a partner to determine the benchmark percent and the estimate for each part of a whole. The first one is done for you. Use a model if needed.

	Benchmark Percent	Multiple of Benchmark Percent	Estimate
49% of 600	25%	50%	300
12. 34% of 18			
13. 91% of 200			
14. 76% of 140			

15. Refer to Exercise 13. How can you use a 10 by 10 grid to estimate 91% of 200?

_____

_____

_____

16. When using a 10 by 10 grid to represent a whole, what percent does each square represent? What benchmark fraction? How can you use this to find the part of a whole?

_____

_____

_____

17. Use the 10 by 10 grid at the right to find 4% of 600. Explain.

_____

_____

Create

On Your Own

18. **INQUIRY** HOW can I use multiple representations to represent benchmark fractions and percents?

_____

_____

_____

_____

Estimate using Benchmark Percents

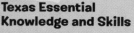

Texas Essential Knowledge and Skills

Targeted TEKS

6.4(F) Represent benchmark fractions and percents such as 1%, 10%, 25%, $33\frac{1}{3}$%, and multiples of these values using 10 by 10 grids, strip diagrams, number lines, and numbers.

Mathematical Processes
6.1(A), 6.1(B)

Josefina surveyed 298 students and found that 52% like scary movies. About how many students like scary movies?

1. 52% of 298 is close to 50% of 300. Of what benchmark percent is 50% a multiple? _____

2. Draw and label a bar diagram that represents how the benchmark percent 25% and its multiples can be used to find 50% of 300.

Essential Question

WHEN is it better to use a fraction, a decimal, or a percent?

3. About how many students like scary movies? _____

4. **Create** Draw and label a bar diagram that represents how a benchmark percent and its multiples can be used to estimate 73% of 400. What is an estimate for 73% of 400? _____

Help!

Which MP **Mathematical Processes** did you use?
Shade the circle(s) that applies.

(A) Apply Math to the Real World.
(B) Use a Problem-Solving Model.
(C) Select Tools and Techniques.
(D) Use Multiple Representations.

(E) Organize Ideas.
(F) Analyze Relationships.
(G) Justify Arguments.

Estimate Part of a Whole

Estimating with percents will provide a reasonable solution to many real-world problems. You can estimate part of a whole by representing benchmark percents and their multiples on a bar diagram.

Tutor

Examples

1. **Estimate 47% of 692.**

47% is close to 50%. Round 692 to 700.

$50\% = 25\% \times 2$ 50% is a multiple of the benchmark percent 25%.

Draw and label a bar diagram to represent the benchmark percent 25% and its multiples.

The model shows that 50% of 700 is 350.

So, 47% of 692 is about 350.

2. **Estimate 60% of 27.**

Round 27 to 25.

$60\% = 10\% \times 6$ 60% is a multiple of the benchmark percent 10%.

Draw and label a bar diagram to represent the benchmark percent 10% and its multiples.

The model shows that 60% of 25 is 15.

So, 60% of 27 is about 15.

Compatible Numbers

You can also use compatible numbers to estimate part of a whole. In example 2, 60% is $\frac{3}{5}$. $\frac{3}{5}$ of 27 ≈ $\frac{3}{5}$ of 25 which is about 15.

← Show your work.

Got It? Do these problems to find out.

Estimate each part of a number.

a. _____

b. _____

c. _____

a. 48% of 76   b. 18% of 42   c. 73% of 41

Estimate Part of a Whole to Solve Problems

You can estimate part of a whole to solve multi-step real-world problems.

Multi-Step Example

Tutor

3. **STEM** Polar bears can eat as much as 10% of their body weight in one feeding. The table gives the weight of the polar bears at a local zoo. If the zoo has 500 pounds of food on hand, about how many feedings can they provide to the polar bears?

Polar Bear	Weight (lb)
Jack	715
Emma	622
Samantha	345

Step 1 Determine the total weight of the polar bears.

$$715 + 622 + 345 = 1,682$$

Step 2 Determine the approximate amount of food needed for each feeding.

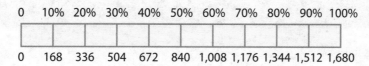

0	10%	20%	30%	40%	50%	60%	70%	80%	90%	100%
0	168	336	504	672	840	1,008	1,176	1,344	1,512	1,680

The bar diagram shows that 10% of 1,680 = 168.

Step 3 Determine the approximate number of feedings the zoo can provide with 500 pounds of food.

$$500 \div 168 \approx 3$$

So, the zoo can provide about 3 feedings to the polar bears.

Got It? Do this problem to find out.

d. Kayleigh decided to donate 30% of her savings over a three-week period of time. The table shows how much money she saved. Her parents decide to match the amount she donated. About how much will be donated altogether?

Week	Saved ($)
1	94
2	31
3	113

Show your work.

d. _____

Estimate Using the Rate per 100

You can also estimate with percents using a rate per 100.

Tutor

Example

4. Estimate 17% of 198.

17% = 17 out of 100   Write the percent as a rate per 100.

198 ≈ 200   Round to the nearest hundred.

Since 200 is 100 + 100, add 17 + 17 to estimate 17% of 198.

34 is about 17% of 198.

Got It? Do these problems to find out.

Estimate using a rate per 100.

e. 27% of 307

f. 76% of 192

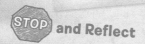

STOP and Reflect

When would you use mental math to estimate the percent of a number? Explain below.

e. _____

f. _____

Guided Practice

Estimate each part of a whole. (Examples 1 and 2)

1. 19% of $53 ≈ _____

2. 21% of 96 ≈ _____

3. 59% of 16 ≈ _____

4. Mr. Marcucci received a bonus of 15% of his monthly salary from his employer. He has to pay 33% of his bonus to taxes. If he makes $3,084 a month, about how much will Mr. Marcucci pay in taxes for his bonus? (Example 3)

_____

5. A purse that originally cost $29.99 is on sale for 50% off. About how much is the sale price of the purse? (Example 4)

_____

6. ❓ **Building on the Essential Question** When is an estimate more useful than an exact answer?

_____

_____

Rate Yourself!

How confident are you about estimating with percents? Shade the ring on the target.

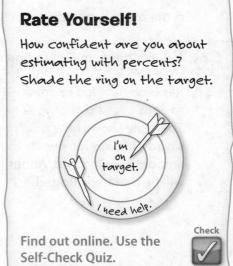

I'm on target.

I need help.

Find out online. Use the Self-Check Quiz.

Check

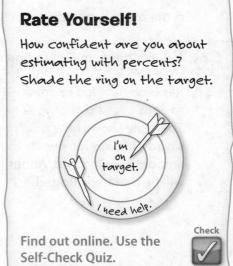

Independent Practice

6.4(F), 6.1(A), 6.1(C) TEKS

Estimate each part of a whole. Use a bar diagram. (Examples 1 and 2)

Show your work.

1. 47% of $118 ≈

_____

2. 42% of 16 ≈

_____

3. 67% of 296 ≈

_____

4. **STEM** Penguins spend almost 75% of their lives in the sea. An Emperor penguin in the wild has a life span of about 18 years. About how many more years does this penguin spend in the sea than on land? (Example 3)

_____

_____

5. In Nathan's baseball card collection, 58% of the cards are players from the National League. He has 702 baseball cards. About how many more baseball cards are players from the National League than from the American League? (Example 3)

_____

_____

Estimate using a rate per 100. (Example 4)

6. 24% of 289 ≈ _____

7. 67% of 208 ≈ _____

8. **MP** **Apply Math to the Real World** Refer to the graphic novel frame below for Exercises a–b.

a. Suppose Angel is shooting baskets and makes 40% of the 15 shots. Does he win a prize? Explain your reasoning.

_____

b. About what percent of the baskets need to be made in order to win a prize?

_____

9. About 42% of Alaska's population lives in the city of Anchorage. If Alaska has a total population of 648,818, about how many people live in Anchorage?

_____

_____

10. During the basketball season, Tyrone made 37 baskets out of 71 attempts. About what percent of his shots did he miss?

_____

_____

11. The table shows Carli's daily caloric intake. Protein accounted for 18% of her day. About how many Calories did Carli take in through carbohydrates? Explain.

Type	Calories
Protein	194
Fat	522
Carbohydrate	?

_____

_____

H.O.T. Problems Higher-Order Thinking

12. Evaluate Rachel wants to buy a shirt regularly priced at $32. It is on sale for 40% off. Rachel estimates that she will save $\frac{2}{5}$ of $30 or $12. Will the actual amount be more or less than $12? Explain.

_____

_____

_____

13. Analyze Order 10% of 20, 20% of 20, and $\frac{1}{5}$% of 20 from least to greatest.

_____

_____

_____

14. Analyze A classmate is trying to estimate 42% of $122. Explain how your classmate should solve the problem.

_____

_____

_____

_____

15. Create Melissa's homeroom has raised 63% of its goal for the school fundraiser. Matt's homeroom has raised 48%. Create a situation in which Matt's homeroom raised more money than Melissa's homeroom.

_____

_____

_____

Multi-Step Problem Solving

16. Sabrina takes her car to the car wash and gets the Gold Star service that includes a wash, wax, and interior cleaning. This service costs $51.99, but she must also pay a 6% sales tax. Estimate the total amount Sabrina paid at the car wash.

 Ⓐ $3.00

 Ⓑ $47.50

 Ⓒ $53.00

 Ⓓ $75.00

Use a problem-solving model to solve this problem.

1 Analyze

Read the problem. Circle the information you know. Underline what the problem is asking you to find.

2 Plan

What will you need to do to solve the problem? Write your plan in steps.

Step 1   Determine the benchmark percent and use it to determine the tax.

Step 2   Add to determine the total spent.

3 Solve

Use your plan to solve the problem. Show your steps.

6% is a multiple of ☐ %. $51.99 is about $☐ .

Using the benchmark percent, 1% of $50 is $☐ .

The total tax is 6 × $0.50 or $☐ .

The total spent is about $☐ + $☐ or $☐ .

So, Sabrina will spend about $☐ . Choice ☐ is correct. Fill in that answer choice.

Read to Succeed!

By using a benchmark percent, you can mentally estimate the total.

4 Justify and Evaluate

How do you know your solution is accurate?

_____

_____

 **P** = Proportionality   **MP** = Mathematical Processes

Use a problem-solving model to solve each problem.

17. A sporting goods store purchases a skateboard for $100 and marks the price up by 40%. The store is having a sale where everything is 15% off the sticker price. Estimate the final price of a skateboard.

Ⓐ $119

Ⓑ $125

Ⓒ $140

Ⓓ $155

18. Emilio buys 3 pizzas, 4 subs, and 8 sodas for a party. The sales tax is 7.5%. What is the minimum number of $20 bills Emilio should pay with? Ⓟ Ⓝ ⓂⓅ

Item	Cost ($)
Pizza	10
Sub	5
Soda	1

19. There were 485 people who went to an amusement park on Monday. Sixty percent of the people wanted to ride the new roller coaster. Twenty-three percent of those people decided not to ride the coaster because the line was too long. About how many people waited in line? Ⓟ Ⓝ ⓂⓅ

20. Suppose the area of the rectangle below was increased by 20%. What would be the perimeter of the larger rectangle if the length of 15 feet stayed the same? Explain the steps you used to solve this problem. Ⓟ Ⓝ ⒠⒠ ⓂⓅ

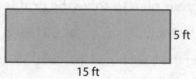

15 ft

5 ft

Ⓝ = Number and Operations   Ⓟ = Proportionality   ⒠⒠ = Expressions, Equations, and Relationships   ⓂⓅ = Mathematical Processes

396   **Chapter 5** Apply Proportions to Percent

Hands-On Lab 5-a
Part of a Whole

Texas Essential Knowledge and Skills TEKS

Targeted TEKS
6.5(B) Solve real-world problems to find the whole given a part and the percent, to find the part given the whole and the percent, and to find the percent given the part and the whole including the use of concrete and pictorial models.

Mathematical Processes
6.1(C), 6.1(D), 6.1(F), 6.1(G)

INQUIRY HOW can I select tools to model the part of a number?

There were 180 people in a movie theater. Twenty percent of them received the student discount and 10% received the senior citizen discount. The rest did not receive a discount. How many people did not receive a discount?

What do you know? _____

_____

What do you need to find? _____

_____

Hands-On Activity

Model the situation using two bar diagrams found on page MM9.

Step 1   Use a bar diagram to represent 100%. Then use another bar diagram of equal length to represent 180 people.

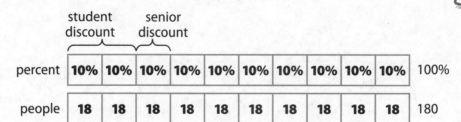

Step 2   Divide each bar into 10 equal parts. Think: 180 ÷ 10 = ☐

So, each part of 180 represents ☐ people.

Step 3   Determine how many people did not receive a discount. Shade 2 sections of each bar diagram to represent the student discount. Shade 1 section of each bar diagram to represent the senior discount.

There are ☐ unshaded sections in each bar diagram.

☐ × ☐ = ☐

So, ☐ people at the movie did not receive a discount.

Investigate

MP Select Tools and Techniques Work with a partner. Find the part of each whole using two bar diagrams.

1. 50% of 80 children = _____

		100%

		children

2. 25% of $32 = _____

Analyze and Reflect

3. MP Analyze Relationships Explain how to use two bar diagrams to find 45% of $60.

_____

_____

_____

_____

Create

4. Create Write and solve a real-world problem that uses a multiple of the benchmark percent 10%.

_____

_____

_____

5. INQUIRY How can I select tools to model the part of a whole?

_____

_____

Find the Part of a Whole

 Launch the Lesson: Real World

In a survey, 200 students chose their favorite snacks. Complete the table to find the number of students who chose each snack.

Snack	Percent	Fraction	Equivalent Fraction	Number of Responses
Fruit	23%	$\frac{23}{100}$	$\frac{46}{200}$	46 out of 200
Cheese	15%	$\frac{}{100}$	$\frac{}{200}$	☐ out of 200
Veggies	17%			
Cookies	15%			
Chips	18%			
No Snack	12%			

Check   Add the number of responses in the last column.

$46 + \boxed{} + \boxed{} + \boxed{} + \boxed{} + \boxed{} = 200$ ✓

1. How does finding the percent as a rate per 100 help you find the number of responses out of 200?

_____

_____

Texas Essential Knowledge and Skills

Targeted TEKS
6.5(B) Solve real-world problems to find the whole given a part and the percent, to find the part given the whole and the percent, and to find the percent given the part and the whole including the use of concrete and pictorial models. *Also addresses 6.5(C).*

Mathematical Processes
6.1(A), 6.1(B)

Essential Question

WHEN is it better to use a fraction, a decimal, or a percent?

Which ⓂⓅ Mathematical Processes did you use?
Shade the circle(s) that applies.

Ⓐ Apply Math to the Real World.

Ⓔ Organize Ideas.

Ⓑ Use a Problem-Solving Model.

Ⓕ Analyze Relationships.

Ⓒ Select Tools and Techniques.

Ⓖ Justify Arguments.

Ⓓ Use Multiple Representations.

Work Zone

Find the Part of a Whole

You can solve real-world problems to find the part given the whole and the percent. To do this, you can use models. You can also express the percent as a fraction or decimal to show an equivalent part of the same whole.

Example

1. Refer to the circle graph. Suppose there are 300 students at York Middle School. Determine the number of students that have cheese as a snack.

Snacks
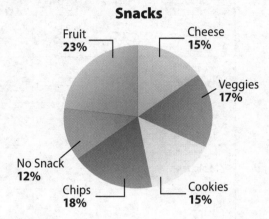

Fruit 23% | Cheese 15% | Veggies 17% | Cookies 15% | Chips 18% | No Snack 12%

Percents as Decimals

In Example 1, you can also generate equivalent forms of 15% by writing 15% as a decimal.

15% of 300 = 0.15 × 300
= 45

Method 1 Use a bar diagram.

The benchmark percent is 10%.

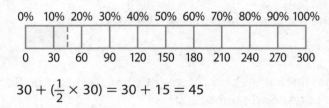

$30 + (\frac{1}{2} \times 30) = 30 + 15 = 45$

Method 2 Write the percent as a fraction.

$15\% = \frac{15}{100}$ or $\frac{3}{20}$ — Write the percent as a rate per 100.

$\frac{3}{20}$ of $300 = \frac{3}{20} \times 300$ — Multiply.

$= 45$

So, 45 students have cheese as a snack.

Got It? Do this problem to find out.

a. Find the number of students at York Middle School that have chips as a snack.

a. _____

Percents Greater Than 100% and Less Than 1%

You may choose whether to write a percent as a fraction or as a decimal based on the problem.

Examples

Tutor

2. **Determine 145% of 320.**

$145\% = \frac{145}{100}$ or $\frac{29}{20}$ Write 145% as a rate per 100. Then simplify.

145% of $320 = \frac{29}{20} \times 320$ Write the multiplication problem.

$\quad = \frac{29}{\cancel{20}_{1}} \times \frac{\cancel{320}^{16}}{1}$ Divide the numerator and denominator by 20.

$\quad = 29 \times 16$ Simplify.

$\quad = 464$ Multiply.

So, 145% of 320 is 464.

3. **Determine 220% of 65.**

Draw bar diagrams to show 220%.

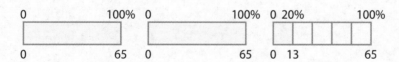

$65 + 65 + 13 = 143$

So, 220% of 65 is _____.

4. **Determine 0.25% of 58.**

$0.25\% = 0.0025$ Write 0.25% as a decimal.

0.25% of $58 = 0.0025 \times 58$ Write the multiplication problem.

$\quad = 0.145$ Multiply.

So, 0.25% of 58 is 0.145.

Got It? Do these problems to find out.

Determine the part of each whole.

b. 128% of 550   **c.** 0.3% of 200   **d.** 0.85% of 600

Show your work.

b. _____

c. _____

d. _____

Multi-Step Example

Tutor

5. Financial Literacy Monique takes a taxi from her school to the airport. The taxi charges a base fee of $5.50 and then $0.75 for each mile. She wants to tip the driver 15%. How much would the total be for a 15-mile trip to the airport? Round to the nearest cent.

Step 1 Determine the total before the tip.

$$5.50 + 0.75(15) = 5.50 + 11.25$$
$$= 16.75$$

Step 2 Determine the amount of the tip.

$$15\% \text{ of } 16.75 = 0.15 \times 16.75$$
$$\approx 2.51$$

Step 3 Add to determine the total.

$$16.75 + 2.51 = 19.26$$

So, it would cost $19.26 for a taxi ride from her school to the airport.

Guided Practice

Determine the part of each whole. Draw a model if necessary. (Examples 1–4)

1. 32% of 60 = _____

2. 0.55% of 220 = _____

3. 275% of 4 = _____

Show your work.

4. Troy wants to buy a jersey of his favorite MLS team. The jersey is 30% off the original price. The original price of the jersey is $35. He has a $10 giftcard. What is the amount Troy will spend? (Example 5)

_____

5. Building on the Essential Question Describe two strategies you can use to find part of a whole.

_____

_____

_____

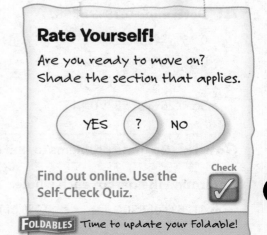

Rate Yourself!

Are you ready to move on? Shade the section that applies.

YES ? NO

Find out online. Use the Self-Check Quiz.

Check ✓

FOLDABLES Time to update your Foldable!

Independent Practice

6.5(B), 6.5(C), 6.1(C) **TEKS**

The cafeteria at Midtown Middle School surveyed 575 students about their favorite food. Determine the number of students that responded for each of the following. Draw a model if necessary. (Example 1)

1. chicken: 8% =

_____

2. salad: 20% =

_____

3. burgers: 16% =

_____

4. fruit: 24% =

_____

Show your work.

Find the part of each whole. Draw a model if necessary. (Examples 2–4)

5. 0.9% of 1,000 =

_____

6. 0.46% of 80 =

_____

7. 350% of 96 =

_____

8. 222% of 55 =

_____

9. Financial Literacy The original price of a pair of shoes is $42. The sale price is 20% off the original price. Sales tax of 7% is added to the sale price. What is the final cost of the pair of shoes? Round to the nearest cent. (Example 5)

_____

10. Torri had $20 to buy a birthday present for her dad. She decided to buy a DVD for $18. The sales tax is 7%. Does she have enough money? Explain your reasoning.

_____

11. Twenty-four students in Jamal's class are wearing tennis shoes. There are thirty students in his class. Jamal says that 70% of his class is wearing tennis shoes. Draw a model to determine if Jamal is correct. Explain.

12. MP Select Tools and Techniques Marisol keeps track of her weekly quiz grades as shown in the table.

a. Complete the table.

b. In which class did Marisol have the higher score? _____

Test	Number Correct	Score	Total
Math	68		85
Science		90%	70

c. Suppose Marisol scored a 96% on an English test. There were 50 questions on the test. How many did Marisol answer correctly?

_____

13. (MP) **Organize Ideas** Use the graphic organizer to compare and contrast percents and fractions. Use the phrases *less than*, *equal to*, and *greater than* to complete each statement. Write an example in the space provided.

Percent	Shared Concept	Fraction
A whole is represented by a percent that is _____ 100%. Example: _____	Whole	A whole is represented by a fraction with a numerator that is _____ the denominator. Example: _____
Part of a whole represented by a percent that is _____ 100%. Example: _____	part of a whole	Part of a whole is represented by a fraction with a numerator that is _____ the denominator. Example: _____
An amount that is greater than one is represented by a percent that is _____ 100%. Example: _____	more than one	An amount that is greater than one is represented by a fraction with a numerator that is _____ the denominator. Example: _____

H.O.T. Problems Higher-Order Thinking

14. Create Write and solve a real-world problem in which the part of a whole results in a number greater than the whole itself.

_____

_____

_____

15. Evaluate Is 16% of 40 the same as 40% of 16? Explain your reasoning.

_____

_____

16. Analyze Find 15% of 15% of 15% of 500. How does this compare to finding 45% of 500?

_____

_____

17. Analyze A number n is 25% of some number a and 35% of a number b. Is $a > b$, $a < b$, or is it impossible to determine the relationship? Explain.

_____

_____

Multi-Step Problem Solving

18. Students were asked which night they planned on attending the book fair. The results of a survey are shown in the table. If 25% of the people who responded with Thursday did not go to the book fair that night, how many people did go on Thursday? (P) (MP)

Day	Number of People
Monday	55
Tuesday	80
Wednesday	70
Thursday	112
Friday	65

Ⓐ 112

Ⓑ 100

Ⓒ 84

Ⓓ 28

Use a problem-solving model to solve this problem.

1 Analyze

Read the problem. Circle the information you know. Underline what the problem is asking you to find.

2 Plan

What will you need to do to solve the problem? Write your plan in steps.

Step 1 Determine the number of people that did not go to the book fair on Thursday.

Step 2 Subtract to determine the number of people that did go on Thursday.

3 Solve

Use your plan to solve the problem. Show your steps.

The number of people that did not go to the book fair on

Thursday is 25% of 112 or ⬚ .

The number of people that did go on Thursday is 112 − ⬚

or ⬚ .

So, choice ⬚ is correct. Fill in that answer choice.

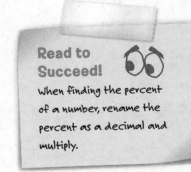

Read to Succeed!

When finding the percent of a number, rename the percent as a decimal and multiply.

4 Justify and Evaluate

How do you know your solution is accurate?

_____

_____

_____

 P = Proportionality   **MP** = Mathematical Processes

More Multi-Step Problem Solving

Use a problem-solving model to solve each problem.

19. Students were surveyed about their summer plans. Of the people that stated they were traveling abroad, 30% did not actually travel abroad. Of the people that stated they were going to summer camp, 25% did not actually go. How many more students went to summer camp than traveled abroad? N P MP

Summer Plans	Number of People
Summer camp	252
Traveling abroad	180
Visiting grandparent	327

Ⓐ 315

Ⓑ 189

Ⓒ 126

Ⓓ 63

20. Five hundred students were asked what color they prefer for the new school colors. The results are shown in the circle graph. How many students prefer red or black? N P MP

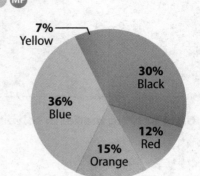

7%— Yellow

30% Black

36% Blue

12% Red

15% Orange

21. Carmen is going to buy a pair of sneakers that cost $63. The sales tax rate is 7.5%. What is the total cost of the sneakers to the nearest cent? N P MP

22. Aaron is estimating the growth of his puppy over time. If the puppy continues to grow at the same rate, how old will the puppy be when it is 250% of its 2-month weight? P MP

Age (months)	Weight (lb)
2	4
3	5.5

N = Number and Operations   P = Proportionality   MP = Mathematical Processes

Find the Percent and the Whole

INQUIRY HOW can you model finding the percent and finding the whole?

Ten of the wrestlers on Edison Middle School's wrestling team are in sixth grade. This is $33\frac{1}{3}$ % of the total number of wrestlers on the team. How many students are on the wrestling team?

What do you know? _____

_____

What do you need to find? _____

_____

Texas Essential Knowledge and Skills TEKS

Targeted TEKS
6.5(B) Solve real-world problems to find the whole given a part and the percent, to find the part given the whole and the percent, and to find the percent given the part and the whole including the use of concrete and pictorial models. *Also addresses 6.4(F).*

Mathematical Processes
6.1(C), 6.1(D), 6.1(E), 6.1(F), 6.1(G)

Hands-On Activity 1

10 is $33\frac{1}{3}$ % of what number?

The part is 10. The percent is $33\frac{1}{3}$ %. We need to find the whole. You can use the models found on page MM5.

Step 1 Model $33\frac{1}{3}$ % by dividing a number line into ⬚ parts, since $100 \div 3 = 33\frac{1}{3}$. Label the benchmark percent of $33\frac{1}{3}$% and its multiple.

Step 2 Write 10 at the $33\frac{1}{3}$ % mark. Add ⬚ at each mark to find the whole.

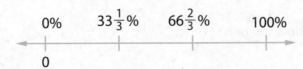

The number ⬚ is at the 100% mark.

So, 10 is $33\frac{1}{3}$ % of _____. There are _____ students on the wrestling team.

Hands-On Activity 2

Mr. Kelly's homeroom collected 30 pounds of canned goods for a food drive. They collected 9 pounds of canned fruit. What percent of the canned goods are canned fruit?

The part is 9. The whole is 30. We need to find the percent.

Step 1 Use the GCF to find each interval for a bar diagram that can be found on page MM9. The GCF of 9 and 30 is ☐.

Step 2 Since 30 ÷ 3 = 10, draw a bar diagram with ☐ sections. Label each section a multiple of ☐.

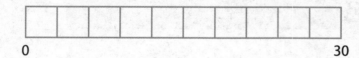

0   30

Step 3 Since 100 ÷ 10 = ☐, the benchmark percent is ☐ %. Label the bar diagram with the multiples of ☐ %.

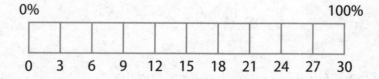

0%   100%

0   3   6   9   12 15 18 21 24 27 30

Step 4 Shade the bar diagram to show the part, ☐.

0% 10% 20% 30% 40% 50% 60% 70% 80% 90%100%

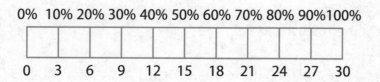

0   3   6   9   12 15 18 21 24 27 30

The corresponding percent is ＿＿ %. So, 9 is ＿＿ % of 30.

Investigate

Collaborate

Work with a partner. Use a number line to determine each whole.

1. 14 is 10% of what number? _____

2. 22 is $33\frac{1}{3}$ % of what number? _____

<--------------------------------->

<--------------------------------->

3. 60 is 75% of what number? _____

4. 19 is 20% of what number? _____

<--------------------------------->

<--------------------------------->

Work with a partner. Use a bar diagram to determine each percent.

5. 180 is what percent of 200? _____

6. 126 is what percent of 189? _____

7. 85 is what percent of 340? _____

8. 21 is what percent of 30? _____

Work with a partner to determine the benchmark percent and whole. The first one is done for you.

	Benchmark Percent	Multiple of Benchmark	Whole
63 is 30% of what number?	10%	10% × 3 = 30%	210
9. 90 is 75% of what number?			
10. 36 is 60% of what number?			
11. 148 is $66\frac{2}{3}$% of what number?			

12. Explain how to determine the interval to use on a number line or bar diagram when finding the whole. _____

_____

_____

13. Explain how to determine the number of sections to use in a bar diagram when finding the percent. _____

_____

Create
On Your Own

14. Write a real-world problem that involves finding the whole when given the part and percent. Then model the problem with a bar diagram. _____

_____

_____

_____

15. **INQUIRY** HOW can you model finding the percent and finding the whole?

_____

_____

_____

_____

Find the Percent and the Whole

 ## Launch the Lesson: Vocabulary

A **proportion** is an equation that shows that two ratios are equivalent. In a **percent proportion**, one ratio compares a part to the whole. The other ratio is the equivalent percent written as a fraction with a denominator of 100.

How do you compare part and whole?

fraction	ratio	percent
$\dfrac{2}{5}$ $\dfrac{\text{part}}{\text{whole}}$ What do you call the numerator? The denominator?	Using the information in the first ratio, fill in the others. $\dfrac{2}{5}$ ☐ to ☐ ☐ : ☐	$\dfrac{2}{5} = \dfrac{\Box}{100}$ ☐ % of 5 = 2

Texas Essential Knowledge and Skills

Targeted TEKS
6.5(B) Solve real-world problems to find the whole given a part and the percent, to find the part given the whole and the percent, and to find the percent given the part and the whole including the use of concrete and pictorial models. *Also addresses 6.4(F).*

Mathematical Processes
6.1(A), 6.1(B), 6.1(D), 6.1(F)

Vocabulary
proportion
percent proportion

Essential Question
WHEN is it better to use a fraction, a decimal, or a percent?

Real-World Investigation

Kara is on her school basketball team. She has completed 9 out of 12 free throw shots successfully. Express the ratio as a percent and as a fraction in simplest form.

Which MP **Mathematical Processes** did you use?
Shade the circle(s) that applies.

(A) Apply Math to the Real World.

(B) Use a Problem-Solving Model.

(C) Select Tools and Techniques.

(D) Use Multiple Representations.

(E) Organize Ideas.

(F) Analyze Relationships.

(G) Justify Arguments.

Use Models to Solve Percent Problems

If you know the part and the percent, you can find the whole. Also, if you know the part and the whole, you can find the percent. You have used bar diagrams and double number lines to solve percent problems.

Tutor

Examples

1. **10 is what percent of 40?**

The part is 10. The whole is 40. Use the GCF to find the intervals for a bar diagram.

Since the GCF of 10 and 40 is 10, use intervals of 10.

0	25%	50%	75%	100%

| 0 | 10 | 20 | 30 | 40 |

Write 100% at the 40 mark. Since there are 4 sections, the benchmark percent is 100 ÷ 4 or 25%. Label the bar diagram with the multiples of 25%.

The number 10 is at the 25% mark. So, 10 is 25% of 40.

2. **Country music makes up 75% of Landon's music library. If he has downloaded 90 country music songs, how many songs does Landon have in his music library?**

Use a double number line to model 75% and 90.

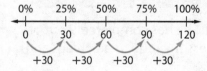

To model 75%, divide the number line into four parts.

90 ÷ 3 = 30. Add 30 at each mark to find the whole.

The number 120 is at the 100% mark.

So, Landon has 120 songs in his music library.

Check Look back at the number lines. The number 90 should line up with 75%. ✓

Show your work.

Got It? Do these problems to find out.

a. 30 is what percent of 60?   **b.** 60 is 20% of what number?

c. Peyton spent 60% of her money to buy a new television. If the television cost $300, how much money did she have?

a. _____

b. _____

c. _____

Use the Percent Proportion

The diagram uses a percent proportion to show that 75% of 32 is 24.

$$\text{part} \longrightarrow \frac{24}{32} = \frac{75}{100} \Big\}\ \text{percent}$$
$$\text{whole} \longrightarrow$$

Examples

 Tutor

3. **15 is 30% of what number?**

> **Words** 15 is 30% of what number?
>
> **Proportion** $\dfrac{\text{part}}{\text{whole}} \longrightarrow \dfrac{15}{\blacksquare} = \dfrac{30}{100} \Big\}\ \text{percent}$

$\dfrac{15}{\blacksquare} = \dfrac{30}{100}$ Write the proportion.

$\overset{\div 2}{\dfrac{15}{50} = \dfrac{30}{100}}$ Since 15 is one half of 30, divide 100 by 2.
$\underset{\div 2}{}$

So, 15 is 30% of 50.

4. **225 is what percent of 300?**

$\dfrac{225}{300} = \dfrac{\blacksquare}{100}$ Write the proportion.

$\dfrac{225}{300} = \dfrac{75}{100}$ Since 300 ÷ 3 = 100, divide 225 by 3.

So, 225 is 75% of 300.

Check Use a bar diagram to check.

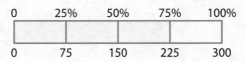

0	25%	50%	75%	100%
0	75	150	225	300

Got It? Do these problems to find out.

d. 75 is 15% of what number?

e. 9 is 36% of what number?

f. 7 is what percent of 10?

g. 7 is what percent of 20?

STOP and Reflect

Write a percent proportion below to show that 50 is 25% of 200.

 Show your work.

d. _____

e. _____

f. _____

g. _____

Example

5. Before 1982, pennies were 95% zinc and 5% copper. If 100 pennies minted in 1980 have an approximate mass of 15 grams of copper, what is the total mass of 100 pennies?

The percent is 5 and the part is 15. You need to find the whole.

$$\frac{15}{\blacksquare} = \frac{5}{100}$$ Write the proportion.

$$\frac{15}{300} = \frac{5}{100}$$ Since 5 × 3 = 15, multiply 100 by 3.

×3

The total mass of 100 pennies is 300 grams.

Guided Practice

Use a double number line to determine the whole or percent. (Example 1)

1. 40 is 20% of what number? _____

2. 90 is what percent of 360? _____

Show your work.

Write a percent proportion and solve each problem. (Examples 3 and 4)

3. 120 is 30% of what number?

_____

4. 60 is what percent of 400?

_____

5. In the first year of ownership, a new car can lose 20% of its value. If a car lost $4,200 of value in the first year, how much did the car originally cost? (Examples 2 and 5)

_____

_____

6. ❓ **Building on the Essential Question** Describe two strategies you can use to find the whole or percent in a percent problem.

_____

_____

_____

_____

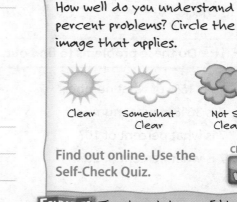
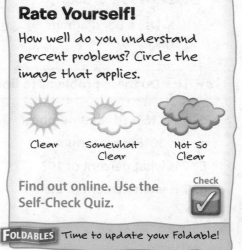

Rate Yourself!

How well do you understand percent problems? Circle the image that applies.

Clear   Somewhat Clear   Not So Clear

Find out online. Use the Self-Check Quiz.

Check ✓

FOLDABLES Time to update your Foldable!

Independent Practice

6.5(B), 6.4(F), 6.1(D), 6.1(F) **TEKS**

Use a double number line to determine the missing number. (Example 1)

1. 63 is 90% of what number? _____

2. 80 is what percent of 320? _____

Write a percent proportion and solve each problem. (Examples 3 and 4)

3. 22 is 44% of what number?

_____

4. 450 is what percent of 600?

_____

5. A store is having a sale where winter clothes are 60% of the original price. A sweater is on sale for $30. What was the original price of the sweater? (Examples 2 and 5)

_____

_____

6. Kai calculates that he spends 75 minutes of a school day in science class. If he spends 500 minutes in school, what percent of his school day does Kai spend in science class? (Examples 2 and 5)

_____

_____

For Exercises 7–9, use the table.

7. If you have 3 cups of pineapple juice, how many total cups of punch can you make? _____

_____

Punch Recipe	
Ginger Ale	40%
Orange Juice	25%
Pineapple Juice	20%
Sorbet	15%

8. How many cups of sorbet are used in 8 cups of punch?

_____

_____

9. Elise does not like sorbet, so she omits that ingredient and adds 5 percent of each of the other ingredients. How many cups of punch will she have if she uses 6 cups of orange juice?

_____

_____

10. **MP** **Analyze Relationships** Complete the following graphic organizers. Identify the missing information.

a.

$\frac{3}{4}$	part	3
	whole	

b.

47%	part	
	whole	100

c.

12% of 225	part	
	whole	

d.

120 out of 400	part	
	whole	

e. How does identifying the part and the whole help you to write the percent proportion? _____

_____

_____

H.O.T. Problems   Higher-Order Thinking

11. Create Write a percent proportion where the part and the whole are known. Solve the problem to find the percent.

_____

12. Evaluate Using what you know about percents, explain why a commercial that says "80% of dentists use this toothpaste" might be misleading.

_____

_____

_____

_____

13. Analyze The purity of gold is listed in karats. Refer to the table. If a necklace is 75% gold, what karat is it? Explain your reasoning.

Karats	Pure Gold (%)
24	100
12	50

_____

14. Evaluate Omar scored an 82% on his first test of the quarter. Will a score of 38 out of 50 on the second test help or hurt his grade? Explain your

reasoning. _____

_____

15. Analyze At a zoo, an Asian elephant weighs about 3 tons and eats about 300 pounds of food a day. What percentage of its body weight does the elephant eat each day?

_____

Multi-Step Problem Solving

16. The table shows the percentage of each type of popcorn flavor at a specialty food store. A store clerk put all of the bags of cinnamon popcorn and cheese popcorn in a display in the front of the store. If the clerk put 60 bags up front, how many bags of popcorn does the store have in all? **P** **MP**

Popcorn Flavor	
Kettle corn	60%
Cinnamon	15%
Caramel	10%
Cheese	15%

    Ⓐ 18

    Ⓑ 100

    Ⓒ 200

    Ⓓ 400

Use a problem-solving model to solve this problem.

1 Analyze

**Read the problem. Circle the information you know.
Underline what the problem is asking you to find.**

2 Plan

What will you need to do to solve the problem? Write your plan in steps.

Step 1   Determine the total percentage of bags displayed.

Step 2   Use the percent proportion to determine the whole.

3 Solve

Use your plan to solve the problem. Show your steps.

The percentage of bags displayed is 15% + 15% or ⬚ %.

The situation can be represented by the proportion: $\frac{60}{\blacksquare} = \frac{30}{100}$.

Since 30 × ⬚ is 60, multiply 100 × ⬚ .

So, the total number of bags the store has is 100 × 2 or ⬚ .

Choice ⬚ is correct. Fill in that answer choice.

Read to Succeed!
The percent proportion is $\frac{part}{whole} = \frac{percent}{100}$.

4 Justify and Evaluate

How do you know your solution is accurate?

_____

_____

P = Proportionality   **MP** = Mathematical Processes

More **Multi-Step** Problem Solving

Use a problem-solving model to solve each problem.

17. The table shows the percentage of each type of puzzle in a toy store. During a sale, the store sold all of the 300-piece and 500-piece puzzles. If they sold 120 puzzles, how many puzzles did the store have before the sale? Ⓟ Ⓜ

Jigsaw Puzzles	
300-piece	50%
500-piece	30%
750-piece	15%
1,000-piece	5%

- Ⓐ 150
- Ⓑ 240
- Ⓒ 400
- Ⓓ 600

18. Rachel surveyed 150 students about their favorite sport. The results are shown in the circle graph. How many more students chose basketball than tennis? Ⓟ Ⓜ

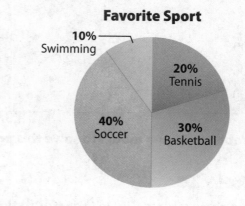

Favorite Sport

10% Swimming
20% Tennis
40% Soccer
30% Basketball

_____

19. A tile wall is shown below. Each square tile has a side length of 4 inches. What percent of the wall is red? Ⓟ Ⓜ

_____

20. The perimeter of a square is 30% of the perimeter of a larger square. If the perimeter of the smaller square is 4.8 inches, what is the side length of the larger square? Explain how you found your answer. Ⓟ Ⓜ

_____

_____

_____

_____

Ⓟ = Proportionality   Ⓜ = Mathematical Processes

Special Effects Animator

Are you fascinated by how realistic the special effects in movies are today? If you have creative talent and are good with computers, a career in special effects animation might be a great fit for you. Special effects animators use their artistic ability and expertise in computer-generated imagery (CGI) to simulate real-life objects like water and fire. They are also able to create fantastic images like flying superheroes, exploding asteroids, and monsters taking over cities.

Mathematical Process
6.1(A) Apply mathematics to problem arising in everyday life, society, and the workplace.
Targeted TEKS 6.4(E)

Is This the Career for You?

Are you interested in a career as a special effects animator? Take some of the following courses in high school.

◆ **Digital Animation**
◆ **Calculus**
◆ **Geometry**
◆ **Physics**
◆ **Art/Sculpture**

College & Career
READINESS

Explore college and careers at ccr.mcgraw-hill.com

The Effects are Amazing!

Special effects animators must specify when objects fade or change color. Table 1 shows when an object starts fading out. Table 2 shows the percent of an object's total lifetime that it has the initial color, cross-fading of colors, and the final color. Use the tables to solve each problem.

1. Express the part of total lifetime for each object in Table 1 as a fraction in simplest form. _____

2. At what percent of the light beam's total lifetime does it begin to fade out? _____

3. In Table 2, express the percents for the cross-fading of both objects as decimals. _____

4. Which best describes the part of the robot's lifetime in which it has the initial color: $\frac{3}{100}$, $\frac{3}{10}$, or $1\frac{3}{10}$? _____

5. What fraction of the tornado's lifetime does it have the initial color? _____

6. What fraction of the robot's lifetime does it have the final color? _____

Table 1 Fading Out an Object	
Object	**Part of Total Lifetime**
Explosion	0.72
Fog	0.24
Light beam	0.65

Table 2 Changing Color of an Object			
Object	**Percent of Total Lifetime**		
	Initial Color	**Cross-Fading**	**Final Color**
Robot	30%	15%	55%
Tornado	12%	77%	11%

TEKS Career Project

It's time to update your career profile! Choose one of your favorite movies. Use the Internet to research how the movie's special effects were created. Write a brief description of the processes used by the special effects animators. Prepare a brief oral presentation and present it to your classmates. As others are presenting, listen carefully to their presentations. At the end, ask any clarifying questions.

_____

_____

_____

List several jobs that are created by the movie industry.

• _____
• _____
• _____
• _____

Chapter Review

Vocabulary Check

 Work with a partner to unscramble each of the clue words. After unscrambling all of the terms, use the numbered letters to find the phrase. Seek clarification of each vocabulary term as needed.

INROALAT NUEMBR

☐ ☐ ☐ ☐ ☐ ☐ ☐   ☐ ☐ ☐ ☐ ☐ ☐
10   6   9   12   1

TEEPNCR

☐ ☐ ☐ ☐ ☐ ☐ ☐
         4

HEANBMKCR ERTENPCS

☐ ☐ ☐ ☐ ☐ ☐ ☐ ☐ ☐   ☐ ☐ ☐ ☐ ☐ ☐ ☐ ☐
       2   8

PIONORTOPR

☐ ☐ ☐ ☐ ☐ ☐ ☐ ☐ ☐ ☐
         5   7

CTREENP ROIPPTORNO

☐ ☐ ☐ ☐ ☐ ☐ ☐   ☐ ☐ ☐ ☐ ☐ ☐ ☐ ☐ ☐
  11   3   13

F ☐ ☐ ☐ ☐ ☐ ☐ ☐   ☐ ☐ ☐   **F** ☐ ☐
 1 2 3 4 5 6 7 8   9 10 11   12 13

Complete each sentence using one of the unscrambled words above.

1. A _____ is a ratio that compares a number to 100.

2. A _____ is an equation that shows that two ratios are equivalent.

3. In a _____, one ratio compares a part to a whole.

4. A number that can be written as a fraction is a _____.

5. Percents that are easy to use are _____.

Use Your FOLDABLES

Collaborate

Use your Foldable to help review the chapter. Share your Foldable with a partner and take turns summarizing what you learned in this chapter, while the other partner listens carefully. Seek clarification of any concepts, as needed. **TEKS** 6.1(E)

Tape here

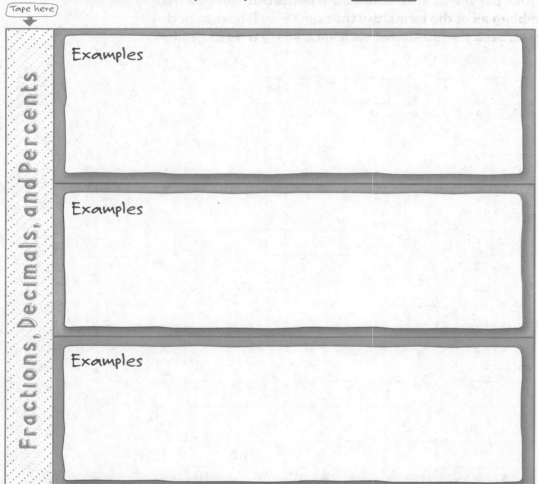

Fractions, Decimals, and Percents

Examples

Examples

Examples

Got it?

The problems below may or may not contain an error. If the problem is correct, write a "✓" by the answer. If the problem is not correct, write an "X" over the answer and correct the problem. **TEKS** 6.4(E)

1. $\frac{4}{5} = 0.4$ ✗

2. $0.55 = \frac{11}{20}$

3. $120\% = \frac{3}{25}$

The first one is done for you. ➤

$$\frac{4}{5} \rightarrow 5\overline{)4.0} \\ \begin{array}{r}0.8\\ -40 \\ \hline 0 \end{array}$$

Multi-Step Problem Solving

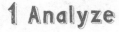

4. Of the 840 students at a middle school, 65% own at least one pet. Of the students that own a pet, 364 students own a dog. What percent of the students who own a pet own a dog? Round to the nearest tenth. Show the steps you used and justify your solution. Ⓝ Ⓟ ⓂⓅ

1 Analyze

2 Plan

3 Solve

4 Justify and Evaluate

_____

_____

_____

Got it?

5. The width of a placemat is 85% of its length. What is the area of the placemat? Show the steps you used and justify your solution. Ⓟ ⓂⓅ

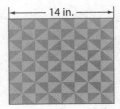

14 in.

_____

_____

_____

 Ⓝ = Number and Operations   Ⓟ = Proportionality   ⓂⓅ = Mathematical Processes

Reflect

? Answering the Essential Question

Use what you learned about fractions, decimals, and percents to complete the
graphic organizer. **TEKS** 6.1(D), 6.1(F), 6.1(G)

? Essential Question

**WHEN is it better to use a fraction,
a decimal, or a percent?**

Equivalent Parts of the Same Whole	
Fraction $\frac{1}{8}$ ⟹	Decimal:
	Percent:
Decimal 0.8 ⟹	Percent:
	Fraction:
Percent 55% ⟹	Fraction:
	Decimal:

? Answer the Essential Question. WHEN is it better to use a
fraction, a decimal, or a percent? Verbally share your response with
a partner, seeking and providing clarification as needed.

The eGlossary contains words and definitions in the following 13 languages:

Arabic	Cantonese	Hmong	Spanish	Urdu
Bengali	English	Korean	Tagalog	Vietnamese
Brazilian Portuguese	Haitian Creole	Russian		

English Español

Aa

absolute value The distance between a number and zero on a number line.

valor absoluto Distancia entre un número y cero en la recta numérica.

acute angle An angle with a measure greater than 0° and less than 90°.

ángulo agudo Ángulo que mide más de 0° y menos de 90°.

acute triangle A triangle having three acute angles.

triángulo acutángulo Triángulo con tres ángulos agudos.

Addition Property of Equality If you add the same number to each side of an equation, the two sides remain equal.

propiedad de adición de la igualdad Si sumas el mismo número a ambos lados de una ecuación, los dos lados permanecen iguales.

additive inverse Two integers that are opposites. The sum of an integer and its additive inverse is zero.

inverso aditivo Dos enteros opuestos.

additive relationship An algebraic relationship that compares the independent and dependent quantities of a relationship using addition. Written in the form $y = x + a$, where a is any rational number.

relación aditiva Una relación algebraica que compara las cantidades independientes y dependientes en una relación usando la adición. Está escrito en la forma $y = x + a$, cuando a es cualquier número racional.

adjacent angles Angles that have the same vertex, share a common side, and do not overlap.

ángulos adyacentes Ángulos que comparten el mismo vértice y un común lado, pero no se sobreponen.

algebra A mathematical language of symbols, including variables.

álgebra Lenguaje matemático que usa símbolos, incluyendo variables.

algebraic expression A combination of variables, numbers, and at least one operation.

expresión algebraica Combinación de variables, números y, por lo menos, una operación.

analyze To use observations to describe and compare data.

analizar Usar observaciones para describir y comparar datos.

angle   Two rays with a common endpoint form an angle. The rays and vertex are used to name the angle.

∠ABC, ∠CBA, or ∠B

ángulo   Dos rayos con un extremo común forman un ángulo. Los rayos y el vértice se usan para nombrar el ángulo.

∠ABC, ∠CBA o ∠B

area   The number of square units needed to cover the surface of a closed figure.

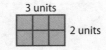

area = 6 square units

área   Número de unidades cuadradas necesarias para cubrir la superficie de una figura cerrada.

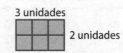

área = 6 unidades cuadradas

arithmetic sequence   A sequence in which the difference between any two consecutive terms is the same.

sucesión aritmética   Sucesión en la cual la diferencia entre dos términos consecutivos es constante.

Associative Property   The way in which numbers are grouped does not change the sum or product.

propiedad asociativa   La forma en que se agrupan tres números al sumarlos o multiplicarlos no altera su suma o producto.

average   The sum of two or more quantities divided by the number of quantities; the mean.

promedio   La suma de dos o más cantidades dividida entre el número de cantidades; la media.

balance a check register   To keep an account of all transactions and the final balance in the account.

hacer el balance del registro de cheques   Llevar la cuenta de todas las transacciones y el saldo final en la cuenta.

bar notation   A bar placed over digits that repeat to indicate a number pattern that repeats indefinitely.

notación de barra   Barra que se coloca sobre los dígitos que se repiten para indicar el número de patrones que se repiten indefinidamente.

base   Any side of a parallelogram.

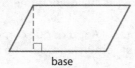

base

base   Cualquier lado de un paralelogramo.

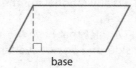

base

base   In a power, the number used as a factor. In 10^3, the base is 10. That is, $10^3 = 10 \times 10 \times 10$.

base   En una potencia, el número usado como factor. En 10^3, la base es 10. Es decir, $10^3 = 10 \times 10 \times 10$.

benchmark fractions   Fractions that are used when estimating part of a whole. For example, $\frac{1}{100}, \frac{1}{10}, \frac{1}{4}, \frac{1}{3}$ and their multiples.

fracciónes de referencia   Los fracciónes se utilizan para calcular una parte de un todo. Por ejemplo, $\frac{1}{100}, \frac{1}{10}, \frac{1}{4}, \frac{1}{3}$ y sus múltiplos.

benchmark percents   Percents that are used when estimating part of a whole. For example, 1%, 10%, 25%, $33\frac{1}{3}$% and their multiples.

porcentajes de referencia   Los porcentajes se utilizan para calcular una parte de un todo. Por ejemplo, 1%, 10%, 25%, $33\frac{1}{3}$% y sus múltiplos.

borrower   Someone who borrowers money from a lender.

prestatario   Alguien que toma dinero a préstamo de un prestamista.

box plot   A diagram that is constructed using five values.

diagrama de caja   Diagrama que se construye usando cinco valores.

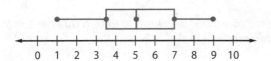

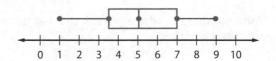

categorical data   Data that can be divided into categories based on attributes of the data.

datos categóricos   Datos que se pueden dividir en categorías basado en atributos de los datos.

checking account   A type of bank account in which users deposit money and from which they can withdraw money to make purchases or pay bills.

cuenta de cheques   Tipo de cuenta bancaria en la cual los usuarios depositan dinero y de la cual pueden retirar dinero para hacer compras o pagar cuentas.

check register   A written record of all transactions.

registro de cheques   Registro escrito de todas las transacciones.

circle graph   A graph that shows data as parts of a whole. In a circle graph, the percents add up to 100.

gráfica circular   Gráfica que muestra los datos como partes de un todo. En una gráfica circular los porcentajes suman 100.

Area of Oceans

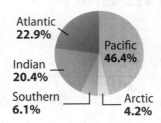

Área de superficie de los océanos

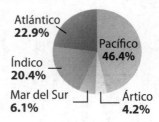

cluster   Data that are grouped closely together.

agrupamiento   Conjunto de datos que se agrupan.

coefficient   The numerical factor of a term that contains a variable.

coeficiente   El factor numérico de un término que contiene una variable.

Commutative Property   The order in which numbers are added or multiplied does not change the sum or product.

propiedad commutativa   La forma en que se suman o multiplican dos números no altera su suma o producto.

compatible numbers   Numbers that are easy to use to perform computations mentally.

números compatibles   Números que son fáciles de usar para realizar computations mentales.

complementary angles   Two angles are complementary if the sum of their measures is 90°.

∠1 and ∠2 are complementary angles.

composite number   A whole number that has more than two factors.

congruent   Having the same measure.

congruent angles   Angles that have the same measure.

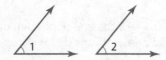

1 and ∠ 2 are congruent angles.

congruent figures   Figures that have the same size and same shape; corresponding sides and angles have equal measures.

constant   A term without a variable.

coordinate plane   A plane in which a horizontal number line and a vertical number line intersect at their zero points.

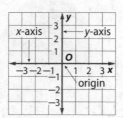

credit card   A card that allows a buyer to put off paying for a purchase until a time in the future.

credit history   A record of financial performance.

credit report   A summary of an individual's financial history.

ángulos complementarios   Dos ángulos son complementarios si la suma de sus medidas es 90°.

∠1 y ∠2 son complementarios.

número compuesto   Número entero que tiene más de dos factores.

congruente   Ques tienen la misma medida.

ángulos congruentes   Ángulos que tienen la misma medida.

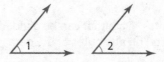

∠ 1 y ∠ 2 son congruentes.

figuras congruentes   Figuras que tienen el mismo tamaño y la misma forma; los lados y los ángulos correspondientes con igual medida.

constante   Un término sin una variable.

plano de coordenadas   Plano en que una recta numérica horizontal y una recta numérica vertical se intersecan en sus puntos cero.

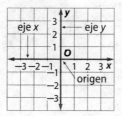

tarjeta de crédito   Tarjeta que permite a un comprador postergar el pago de una compra hasta algún momento en el futuro.

historial de crédito   Registro del desempeño financiero.

informe crediticio   Resumen del historial financiero de una persona.

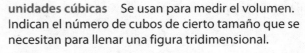

cubic units Used to measure volume. Tells the number of cubes of a given size it will take to fill a three-dimensional figure.

3 cubic units

unidades cúbicas Se usan para medir el volumen. Indican el número de cubos de cierto tamaño que se necesitan para llenar una figura tridimensional.

3 unidades cúbicas

Dd

data Information, often numerical, which is gathered for statistical purposes.

debit card A card that allows a buyer to make purchases while immediately removing money from a linked account.

decimal A number that has a digit in the tenths place, hundredths place, and beyond.

defining the variable Choosing a variable and deciding what the variable represents.

dependent quantity The variable in a relation with a value that depends on the value of the independent quantity.

deposit Add money to an account.

dimensional analysis The process of including units of measurement when you compute.

distribution The arrangement of data values.

Distributive Property To multiply a sum by a number, multiply each addend by the number outside the parentheses.

Division Property of Equality If you divide each side of an equation by the same nonzero number, the two sides remain equal.

dot plot A diagram that shows the frequency of data on a number line. Also known as a line plot.

datos Información, con frecuencia numérica, que se recoge con fines estadísticos.

tarjeta de débito Tarjeta que permite a un comprador hacer compras extrayendo de inmediato dinero de una cuenta asociada.

decimal Número que tiene un dígito en el lugar de las décimas, centésimas y más allá.

definir la variable Elegir una variable y decidir lo que representa.

la cantidad dependiente La variable en una relación cuyo valor depende del valor de la cantidad independiente.

depositar Agregar dinero a una cuenta.

análisis dimensional Proceso que incluye las unidades de medida al hacer cálculos.

distributión El arreglo de valores de datos.

propiedad distributiva Para multiplicar una suma por un número, multiplica cada sumando por el número fuera de los paréntesis.

propiedad de igualdad de la división Si divides ambos lados de una ecuación entre el mismo número no nulo, los lados permanecen iguales.

diagrama de puntos Diagrama que muestra la frecuencia de los datos sobre una recta numérica.

Ee

equals sign A symbol of equality, =.

equation A mathematical sentence showing two expressions are equal. An equation contains an equals sign, =.

signo de igualdad Símbolo que indica igualdad, =.

ecuación Enunciado matemático que muestra que dos expresiones son iguales. Una ecuación contiene el signo de igualdad, =.

Glossary   GL5

equiangular triangle   A triangle having three congruent angles.

equilateral triangle   A triangle having three congruent sides.

equivalent expressions   Expressions that have the same value.

equivalent ratios   Ratios that express the same relationship between two quantities.

evaluate   To find the value of an algebraic expression by replacing variables with numbers.

exponent   In a power, the number that tells how many times the base is used as a factor. In 5^3, the exponent is 3. That is, $5^3 = 5 \times 5 \times 5$.

triángulo equiangular   Triángulo con tres ángulos congruentes.

triángulo equilátero   Triángulo con tres lados congruentes.

expresiones equivalentes   Expresiones que poseen el mismo valor, sin importer los valores de la(s) variable(s).

razones equivalentes   Razones que expresan la misma relación entre dos cantidades.

evaluar   Calcular el valor de una expresión sustituyendo las variables por número.

exponente   En una potencia, el número que indica las veces que la base se usa como factor. En 5^3, el exponente es 3. Es decir, $5^3 = 5 \times 5 \times 5$.

Ff

factor the expression   The process of writing numeric or algebraic expressions as a product of their factors.

factor tree   Diagram that can be used to find the prime factorization of a number.

first quartile   For a data set with median M, the first quartile is the median of the data values less than M.

formula   An equation that shows the relationship among certain quantities.

fraction   A number that represents part of a whole or part of a set.

$$\frac{1}{2}, \frac{1}{3}, \frac{1}{4}, \frac{3}{4}$$

frequency distribution   How many pieces of data are in each interval.

frequency table   A table that shows the number of pieces of data that fall within the given intervals.

factorizar la expresión   El proceso de escribir expresiones numéricas o algebraicas como el producto de sus factores.

árbol de factores   Una diagrama que se puede utiliza hallar la factorización prima de un número.

primer cuartil   Para un conjunto de datos con la mediana M, el primer cuartil es la mediana de los valores menores que M.

fórmula   Ecuación que muestra la relación entre ciertas cantidades.

fracción   Número que representa parte de un todo o parte de un conjunto.

$$\frac{1}{2}, \frac{1}{3}, \frac{1}{4}, \frac{3}{4}$$

distribución de frecuencias   Cantidad de datos asociada con cada intervalo.

tabla de frecuencias   Tabla que muestra el número de datos en cada intervalo.

Gg

gap   An empty space or interval in a set of data.

laguna   Espacio o intervalo vacío en un conjunto de datos.

geometric sequence   A sequence in which each term is found by multiplying the previous term by the same number.

sucesión geométrica   Sucesión en la cual cada término después del primero se determina multiplicando el término anterior por el mismo número.

grants   Awards from non-profit organizations.

subvenciones   Concesiones de organizaciones sin fines de lucro.

graph   To place a dot at a point named by an ordered pair.

gráfica   Colocar una marca puntual en el punto que corresponde a un par ordenado.

Greatest Common Factor (GCF)   The greatest of the common factors of two or more numbers.

The greatest common factor of 12, 18, and 30 is 6.

máximo común divisor (MCD)   El mayor de los factores comunes de dos o más números.

El máximo común divisor de 12, 18 y 30 es 6.

Hh

height   The shortest distance from the base of a parallelogram to its opposite side.

altura   La distancia más corta desde la base de un paralelogramo hasta su lado opuesto.

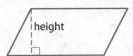

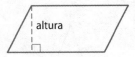

histogram   A type of bar graph used to display numerical data that have been organized into equal intervals.

histograma   Tipo de gráfica de barras que se usa para exhibir datos que se han organizado en intervalos iguales.

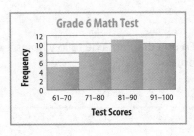

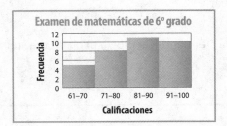

Ii

Identity Properties   Properties that state that the sum of any number and 0 equals the number and that the product of any number and 1 equals the number.

propiedades de identidad   Propiedades que establecen que la suma de cualquier número y 0 es igual al número y que el producto de cualquier número y 1 es igual al número.

independent quantity   The quantity in a relationship with a value that is subject to choice.

la cantidad independiente   Cantidad en una relación cuyo valor está sujeto a elección.

inequality A mathematical sentence indicating that two quantities are not equal.

desigualdad Enunciado matemático que indica que dos cantidades no son iguales.

integer Any number from the set {… −4, −3, −2, −1, 0, 1, 2, 3, 4 …} where … means *continues without end*.

entero Cualquier número del conjunto {… −4, −3, −2, −1, 0, 1, 2, 3, 4 …} donde … significa que *continúa sin fin*.

interest A charge for the use of credit or borrowed money if the balance is not paid off in a set amount of time.

interés Cantidad que se cobra o se paga por el uso del dinero

interquartile range A measure of variation in a set of numerical data, the interquartile range is the distance between the first and third quartiles of the data set.

rango intercuartil El rango intercuartil, una medida de la variación en un conjunto de datos numéricos, es la distancia entre el primer y el tercer cuartil del conjunto de datos.

intersecting lines *Lines* that meet or cross at a common *point*.

rectas secantes *Rectas* que se intersectan o se cruzan en un *punto* común.

interval The difference between successive values on a scale.

intervalo La diferencia entre valores sucesivos de una escala.

inverse operations Operations which *undo* each other. For example, addition and subtraction are inverse operations.

operaciones inversas Operaciones que se *anulan* mutuamente. La adición y la sustracción son operaciones inversas.

isosceles triangle A triangle having at least two congruent sides.

triángulo isósceles Triángulo que tiene por lo menos dos lados congruentes.

---

key In a stem-and-leaf plot, it explains the stems and leaves.

leyenda En una diagrama de tallo y hojas, explica los tallos y las hojas.

---

least common denominator (LCD) The least common multiple of the denominators of two or more fractions.

mínimo común denominador (mcd) El menor múltiplo común de los denominadores de dos o más fracciones.

least common multiple (LCM) The smallest whole number greater than 0 that is a common multiple of each of two or more numbers.

The LCM of 2 and 3 is 6.

mínimo común múltiplo (mcm) El menor número entero, mayor que 0, múltiplo común de dos o más números.

El mcm de 2 y 3 es 6.

leaves The digits of the least place value of data in a stem-and-leaf plot.

hoja En un diagrama de tallo y hojas, los dígitos del menor valor de posición.

lender   Someone who loans money to a borrower.

prestamista   Alguien que presta dinero a un prestatario.

lifetime income   The total amount a worker is paid during their working career.

ingresos de toda la vida   Cantidad total que cobra un trabajador durante su vida laboral.

like terms   Terms that contain the same variable(s) to the same power.

términos semejantes   Términos que contienen la misma variable o variables elevadas a la misma potencia.

linear relationship   A relationship that forms a line when graphed.

relación lineal   Relación cuya gráfica es una recta.

line graph   A graph used to show how a set of data changes over a period of time.

gráfica lineal   Gráfica que se use para mostrar cómo cambian los valores durange un período de tiempo.

line plot   A diagram that shows the frequency of data on a number line. Also known as a dot plot.

esquema lineal   Diagrama que muestra la frecuencia de los datos sobre una recta numérica.

Mm

mean   The sum of the numbers in a set of data divided by the number of pieces of data.

media   La suma de los números en un conjunto de datos dividida entre el número total de datos.

measures of center   Numbers that are used to describe the center of a set of data. These measures include the mean, median, and mode.

medidas del centro   Numéros que se usan para describir el centro de un conjunto de datos. Estas medidas incluyen la media, la mediana y la moda.

measures of spread   A measure used to describe the distribution of data.

medidas de dispersión   Medida usada para describir la distribución de los datos.

median   A measure of center in a set of numerical data. The median of a list of values is the value appearing at the center of a sorted version of the list— or the mean of the two central values, if the list contains an even number of values.

mediana   Una medida del centro en un conjunto de datos numéricos. La mediana de una lista de valores es el valor que aparece en el centro de una versión ordenada de la lista, o la media de los dos valores centrales si la lista contiene un número par de valores.

mode   The number(s) or item(s) that appear most often in a set of data.

moda   Número(s) de un conjunto de datos que aparece(n) más frecuentemente.

Multiplication Property of Equality   If you multiply each side of an equation by the same nonzero number, the two sides remain equal.

propiedad de multiplicación de la igualdad   Si multiplicas ambos lados de una ecuación por el mismo número no nulo, lo lados permanecen iguales.

multiplicative relationship   An algebraic relationship that compares the independent and dependent quantities of a relationship using multiplication. Written in the form $y = ax$, where a is any rational number.

relación multiplicativa   Una relación algebraica que compara las cantidades independientes y dependientes en una relación usando la multiplicación. Está escrito en la forma $y = ax$, cuando a es cualquier número racional.

Nn

negative integer   A number that is less than zero. It is written with a − sign.

entero negativo   Número que es menor que cero y se escribe con el signo −.

numerical expression   A combination of numbers and operations.

expresión numérica   Una combinación de números y operaciones.

obtuse angle   Any angle that measures greater than 90° but less than 180°.

ángulo obtuso   Cualquier ángulo que mide más de 90° pero menos de 180°.

obtuse triangle   A triangle having one obtuse angle.

triángulo obtusángulo   Triángulo que tiene un ángulo obtuso.

opposites   Two integers are opposites if they are represented on the number line by points that are the same distance from zero, but on opposite sides of zero. The sum of two opposites is zero.

opuestos   Dos enteros son opuestos si, en la recta numérica, están representados por puntos que equidistan de cero, pero en direcciones opuestas. La suma de dos opuestos es cero.

ordered pair   A pair of numbers used to locate a point on the coordinate plane. The ordered pair is written in the form (x-coordinate, y-coordinate).

par ordenado   Par de números que se utiliza para ubicar un punto en un plano de coordenadas. Se escribe de la forma (coordenada x, coordenada y).

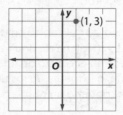

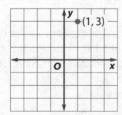

order of operations   The rules that tell which operation to perform first when more than one operation is used.

1. Simplify the expressions inside grouping symbols, like parentheses.

2. Find the value of all powers.

3. Multiply and divide in order from left to right.

4. Add and subtract in order from left to right.

orden de las operaciones   Reglas que establecen cuál operación debes realizar primero, cuando hay más de una operación involucrada.

1. Primero ejecuta todas las operaciones dentro de los símbolos de agrupamiento.

2. Evalúa todas las potencias.

3. Multiplica y divide en orden de izquierda a derecha.

4. Suma y resta en orden de izquierda a derecha.

origin The point of intersection of the *x*-axis and *y*-axis on a coordinate plane.

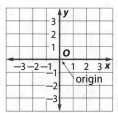

origen Punto de intersección de los ejes axiales en un plano de coordenadas.

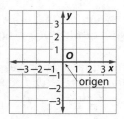

outlier A value that is much higher or much lower than the other values in a set of data.

valor atípico Dato que se encuentra muy separado de los otros valores en un conjunto de datos.

parallelogram A quadrilateral with opposite sides parallel and opposite sides congruent.

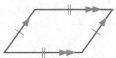

paralelogramo Cuadrilátero cuyos lados opuestos son paralelos y congruentes.

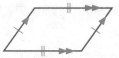

peak The most frequently occurring value in a line plot.

pico El valor que ocurre con más frecuencia en un diagrama de puntos.

percent A ratio that compares a number to 100.

por ciento Razón en que se compara un número a 100.

percent bar graph A graph that shows the relative frequency of each category in a single bar.

gráfica de barras de porcentaje Una gráfica que muestra la frecuencia relativa de cada categoría en una sola barra.

percent proportion One ratio or fraction that compares part of a quantity to the whole quantity. The other ratio is the equivalent percent written as a fraction with a denominator of 100.

$$\frac{part}{whole} = \frac{percent}{100}$$

proporción porcentual Razón o fracción que compara parte de una cantidad a toda la cantidad. La otra razón es el porcentaje equivalente escrito como fracción con 100 de denominador.

$$\frac{parte}{todo} = \frac{porcentaje}{100}$$

perfect square Numbers with square roots that are whole numbers. 25 is a perfect square because the square root of 25 is 5.

cuadrados perfectos Números cuya raíz cuadrada es un número entero. 25 es un cuadrado perfecto porque la raíz cuadrada de 25 es 5.

perimeter The distance around a figure.

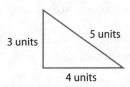

$$P = 3 + 4 + 5 = 12 \text{ units}$$

perímetro La distancia alrededor de una figura.

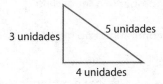

$$P = 3 + 4 + 5 = 12 \text{ unidades}$$

population The entire group of items or individuals from which the samples under consideration are taken.

positive integer A number that is greater than zero. It can be written with or without a + sign.

powers Numbers expressed using exponents. The power 3^2 is read *three to the second power*, or *three squared*.

prime factorization A way of expressing a composite number as a product of its prime factors.

prime number A whole number with exactly two factors, 1 and itself.

prism A three-dimensional figure with at least three rectangular lateral faces and top and bottom faces parallel.

properties Statements that are true for any number.

proportion An equation stating that two ratios or rates are equivalent.

población El grupo total de individuos o de artículos del cual se toman las muestras bajo estudio.

entero positivo Número que es mayor que cero y se puede escribir con o sin el signo +.

potencias Números que se expresan usando exponentes. La potencia 3^2 se lee *tres a la segunda potencia* o *tres al cuadrado*.

factorización prima Una manera de escribir un número compuesto como el producto de sus factores primos.

número primo Número entero que tiene exactamente dos factores, 1 y sí mismo.

prisma Figura tridimensional que tiene por lo menos tres caras laterales rectangulares y caras paralelas superior e inferior.

propiedades Enunciados que son verdaderos para cualquier número.

proporción Ecuación que indica que dos razones o tasas son equivalentes.

quadrants The four regions in a coordinate plane separated by the x-axis and y-axis.

quadrilateral A closed figure having four sides and four angles.

quartiles Values that divide a data set into four equal parts.

cuadrantes Las cuatro regiones de un plano de coordenadas separadas por el eje *x* y el eje *y*.

cuadrilátero Figura cerrada que tiene cuatro lados y cuatro ángulos.

cuartiles Valores que dividen un conjunto de datos en cuatro partes iguales.

radical sign The symbol used to indicate a nonnegative square root, $\sqrt{}$.

range The difference between the greatest number and the least number in a set of data.

rate A ratio comparing two quantities with different kinds of units.

rate of change A rate that describes how one quantity changes in relation to another. A rate of change is usually expressed as a unit rate.

signo radical Símbolo que se usa para indicar una raíz cuadrada no negativa, $\sqrt{}$.

rango La diferencia entre el número mayor y el número menor en un conjunto de datos.

tasa Razón que compara dos cantidades que tienen diferentes tipos de unidades.

tasa de cambio Tasa que describe cómo cambia una cantidad con respecto a otra. Por lo general, se expresa como tasa unitaria.

ratio A comparison of two quantities by division. The ratio of 2 to 3 can be stated as 2 out of 3, 2 to 3, 2 : 3, or $\frac{2}{3}$.

rational number A number that can be written as a fraction.

ratio table A table with columns filled with pairs of numbers that have the same ratio.

reciprocals Any two numbers that have a product of 1. Since $\frac{5}{6} \times \frac{6}{5} = 1$, $\frac{5}{6}$ and $\frac{6}{5}$ are reciprocals.

rectangle A parallelogram having four right angles.

rectangular prism A prism that has rectangular bases.

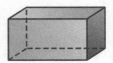

relative frequency A ratio that compares the frequency of each category to the total.

repeating decimal The decimal form of a rational number.

rhombus A parallelogram having four congruent sides.

right angle An angle that measures exactly 90°.

right triangle A triangle having one right angle.

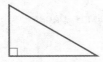

razón Comparación de dos cantidades mediante división. La razón de 2 a 3 puede escribirse como 2 de cada 3, 2 a 3, 2 : 3 ó $\frac{2}{3}$.

número racional Número que se puede expresar como fracción.

tabla de razones Tabla cuyas columnas contienen pares de números que tienen una misma razón.

recíproco Cualquier par de números cuyo producto es 1. Como $\frac{5}{6} \times \frac{6}{5} = 1$, $\frac{5}{6}$ y $\frac{6}{5}$ son recíprocos.

rectángulo Paralelogramo con cuatro ángulos rectos.

prisma rectangular Una prisma que tiene bases rectangulares.

frecuencia relativa Razón que compara la frecuencia de cada categoría al total.

decimal periódico La forma decimal de un número racional.

rombo Paralelogramo que tiene cuatro lados.

ángulo recto Ángulo que mide exactamente 90°.

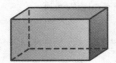

triángulo rectángulo Triángulo que tiene un ángulo recto.

Ss

salary Payment for work.

salario Pago por el trabajo.

sample   A randomly selected group chosen for the purpose of collecting data.

savings   Money that is set aside for the future.

scale   The set of all possible values of a given measurement, including the least and greatest numbers in the set, separated by the intervals used.

scale   The scale gives the ratio that compares the measurements of a drawing or model to the measurements of the real object.

scale drawing   A drawing that is used to represent objects that are too large or too small to be drawn at actual size.

scale factor   A scale written as a ratio without units in simplest form.

scalene triangle   A triangle having no congruent sides.

scaling   To multiply or divide two related quantities by the same number.

scholarships   Awards for good performance.

sequence   A list of numbers in a specific order, such as 0, 1, 2, 3, or 2, 4, 6, 8.

solution   The value of a variable that makes an equation true. The solution of $12 = x + 7$ is 5.

solve   To replace a variable with a value that results in a true sentence.

square   A rectangle having four right angles and four congruent sides.

square root   The factors multiplied to form perfect squares.

statistical question   A question that anticipates and accounts for a variety of answers.

statistics   Collecting, organizing, and interpreting data.

muestra   Grupo escogido al azar o aleatoriamente que se usa con el propósito de recoger datos.

ahorros   Dinero que se guarda para el futuro.

escala   Conjunto de todos los valores posibles de una medida dada, incluyendo el número menor y el mayor del conjunto, separados por los intervalos usados.

escala   Razón que compara las medidas de un dibujo o modelo a las medidas del objeto real.

dibujo a escala   Dibujo que se usa para representar objetos que son demasiado grandes o demasiado pequeños como para dibujarlos de tamaño natural.

factor de escala   Escala escrita como una razón sin unidades en forma simplificada.

triángulo escaleno   Triángulo sin lados congruentes.

homotecia   Multiplicar o dividir dos cantidades relacionadas entre un mismo número.

becas   Concesiones por el buen desempeño.

sucesión   Lista de números en un orden específico como, por ejemplo, 0, 1, 2, 3 ó 2, 4, 6, 8.

solución   Valor de la variable de una ecuación que hace verdadera la ecuación. La solución de $12 = x + 7$ es 5.

resolver   Reemplazar una variable con un valor que resulte en un enunciado verdadero.

cuadrado   Rectángulo con cuatro ángulos rectos y cuatro lados congruentes.

raíz cuadrada   Factores multiplicados para formar cuadrados perfectos.

cuestión estadística   Una pregunta que se anticipa y da cuenta de una variedad de respuestas.

estadística   Recopilar, ordenar e interpretar datos.

stem-and-leaf plot A system where data are organized from least to greatest. The digits of the least place value usually form the leaves, and the next place-value digits form the stems.

Stem	Leaf
1	2 4 5
2	
3	1 2 3 3 9
4	0 4 6 7

4 | 7 = 47

stems The digits of the greatest place value of data in a stem-and-leaf plot.

straight angle An angle that measures exactly 180°.

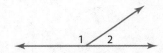

student loans Borrowed amounts of money to pay for education.

Subtraction Property of Equality If you subtract the same number from each side of an equation, the two sides remain equal.

supplementary angles Two angles are supplementary if the sum of their measures is 180°.

∠1 and ∠2 are supplementary angles.

survey A question or set of questions designed to collect data about a specific group of people, or population.

symmetric distribution Data that are evenly distributed.

term Each number in a sequence.

term Each part of an algebraic expression separated by a plus or minus sign.

terminating decimal A decimal is called terminating if its repeating digit is 0.

third quartile For a data set with median M, the third quartile is the median of the data values greater than M.

diagrama de tallo y hojas Sistema donde los datos se organizan de menor a mayor. Por lo general, los dígitos de los valores de posición menores forman las hojas y los valores de posición más altos forman los tallos.

Tallo	Hojas
1	2 4 5
2	
3	1 2 3 3 9
4	0 4 6 7

4 | 7 = 47

tallo Los dígitos del mayor valor de posición de los datos en un diagrama de tallo y hojas.

ángulo llano Ángulo que mide exactamente 180°.

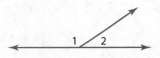

préstamos estudiantiles Cantidades de dinero que se toman prestadas para el pago de la educación.

propiedad de sustracción de la igualdad Si sustraes el mismo número de ambos lados de una ecuación, los dos lados permanecen iguales.

ángulos suplementarios Dos ángulos son suplementarios si la suma de sus medidas es 180°.

∠1 y ∠2 son suplementarios.

encuesta Pregunta o conjunto de preguntas diseñadas para recoger datos sobre un grupo específico de personas o población.

distribución simétrica Datos que están distribuidos.

término Cada uno de los números de una sucesión.

término Cada parte de un expresión algebraica separada por un signo más o un signo menos.

decimal finito Un decimal se llama finito si el dígito que se repite es 0.

tercer cuartil Para un conjunto de datos con la mediana M, el tercer cuartil es la mediana de los valores mayores que M.

three-dimensional figure   A figure with length, width, and height.

figura tridimensional   Una figura que tiene largo, ancho y alto.

transaction   The movement or exchange of money.

transacción   Movimiento o intercambio de dinero.

transfer   A type of transaction that occurs when money is moved between accounts.

transferencia   Tipo de transacción que ocurre cuando se mueve dinero entre cuentas.

trapezoid   A quadrilateral with one pair of parallel sides.

trapecio   Cuadrilátero con un único par de lados paralelos.

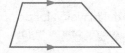

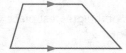

triangle   A figure with three sides and three angles.

triángulo   Figura con tres lados y tres ángulos.

Uu

unit price   The cost per unit.

precio unitario   El costo por cada unidad.

unit rate   A rate that is simplified so that it has a denominator of 1.

tasa unitaria   Tasa simplificada para que tenga un denominador igual a 1.

unit ratio   A unit rate where the denominator is one unit.

razón unitaria   Tasa unitaria en que el denominador es la unidad.

Vv

variable   A symbol, usually a letter, used to represent a number.

variable   Un símbolo, por lo general, una letra, que se usa para representar un número.

vertical angles   Opposite angles formed by the intersection of two lines. Vertical angles are congruent.

ángulos opuestos por el vértice   Ángulos opuestos formados por la intersección de dos rectas. Los ángulos opuestos por el vértice son congruentes.

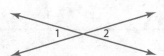

∠ 1 and ∠ 2 are vertical angles.

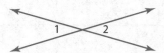

∠ 1 y ∠ 2 son ángulos opuestos por el vértice.

volume   The amount of space inside a three-dimensional figure. Volume is measured in cubic units.

volumen   Cantidad de espacio dentro de una figura tridimensional. El volumen se mide en unidades cúbicas.

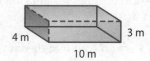

$V = 10 \times 4 \times 3 = 120$ cubic meters

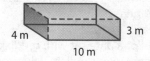

$V = 10 \times 4 \times 3 = 120$ metros cúbicos

withdrawal Take out money from an account.	**retiro** Extracción de dinero de una cuenta.
work-study A program providing financial aid in return for student labor.	**empleo y estudio** Programa que proporciona asistencia financiera a cambio del trabajo del estudiante.

x-axis The horizontal line of the two perpendicular number lines in a coordinate plane.

eje x La recta horizontal de las dos rectas numéricas perpendiculares en un plano de coordenadas.

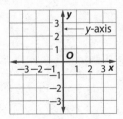

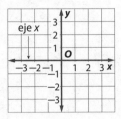

x-coordinate The first number of an ordered pair. The x-coordinate corresponds to a number on the x-axis.

coordenada x El primer número de un par ordenado, el cual corresponde a un número en el eje x.

y-axis The vertical line of the two perpendicular number lines in a coordinate plane.

eje y La recta vertical de las dos rectas numéricas perpendiculares en un plano de coordenadas.

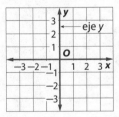

y-coordinate The second number of an ordered pair. The y-coordinate corresponds to a number on the y-axis.

coordenada y El segundo número de un par ordenado, el cual corresponde a un número en el eje y.

zero pair The result when one positive counter is paired with one negative counter. The value of a zero pair is 0.

par nulo Resultado de hacer coordinar una ficha positiva con una negativa. El valor de un par nulo es 0.

Chapter 1 Rational Numbers and the Coordinate Plane

Page 22   Chapter 1   Are You Ready?

1. =   **3.** <   **5.** >   **7.** peanuts

Pages 31–32   Lesson 1-1   Independent Practice

1. −3; The integer 0 represents at sea level.   **3** −5; The integer 0 represents neither moving backward nor moving forward.

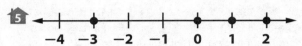

7.

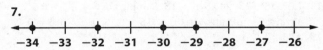

9. Sample answers are given.

Positive Integer	Negative Integer
• gain	• lose
• above	• below
• earn	• spend
• +	• −

11. −1   **13.** Negative; Sample answer: A drop of 15° would result in a temperature of 0°F. Since the drop of 20° is greater than 15°, the temperature is below zero and will be represented by a negative integer.   **15.** Sample answer: The temperature at midnight was 0°F. At 2 A.M., the temperature was −6°F. How many degrees did the temperature fall in those two hours?

Pages 33–34   Lesson 1-1   Multi-Step Problem Solving

17. C   **19.** 2   **21.** D and E

Pages 41–42   Lesson 1-2   Independent Practice

1. −6   **3.** 0   **5.** −9   **7.** 14   **9** 21   **11.** 4 feet
13 70°F   **15.** 14   **17.** Absolute value cannot be a negative number. So, the absolute value of −14 is 14, not −14.
19. Never; distance cannot be negative.   **21.** Absolute value is distance and distance cannot be negative.   **23.** sometimes; If n is positive, then $−n$ is negative. If n is negative, then $−n$ is positive.

Page 44   Lesson 1-2   Multi-Step Problem Solving

25. C   **27.** 16

Pages 49–50   Lesson 1-3   Independent Practice

1. >;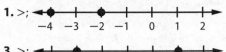

3. >;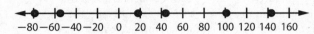

5 −9 < 26; The temperature in Flagstaff, Arizona, was warmer.
7 −79, −55, 18, 44, 101, 143;

9a. Sun   **9b.** Sun, 100-Watt Bulb, Full Moon, Venus, Andromeda Galaxy, Alpha Centauri   **9c.** −27   **11.** Sample answer: Elise owes her brother $15. Jacob has $7. Elise has less money than Jacob.   **13.** $−\frac{12}{4}, −\frac{1}{2}, \frac{1}{6}, \frac{7}{8},$ and $\frac{5}{2}$

Pages 51–52   Lesson 1-3   Multi-Step Problem Solving

15. D   **17.** Day 4   **19.** $|−2|, \frac{1}{2}, −0.5, −1, −|−3|$; Sample answer: $|−2| = 2$ which is greater than $\frac{1}{2}$. The other numbers are less than zero, which are also less than 2.

Page 55   Focus on Mathematical Processes

1. 2.86 mi   **3.** $70

Pages 61–62   Lesson 1-4   Independent Practice

1. $\frac{1}{2}$ **3.** $\frac{33}{100}$ **5** 0.385   **7.** 0.16   **9** Mercury: 87.96; Venus: 224.7; Mars: 686.98   **11a.** meat: $\frac{7}{20}$; vegetables: $\frac{3}{20}$; sauce: $\frac{1}{20}$; bread: $\frac{1}{20}$ **11b.** $\frac{1}{5}$ lb   **11c.** $\frac{3}{5}$ lb   **13** Sample answer: $\frac{1}{5}$ in. and $\frac{7}{20}$ in.   **15.** always; A decimal that ends in the thousandths place can have a denominator of 1,000. Since 1,000 is divisible by 2 and 5, the denominator of every such terminating decimal is divisible by 2 and 5.   **17.** $3\frac{4}{5}$ yd

Page 64   Lesson 1-4   Multi-Step Problem Solving

19. 0.45   **21.** Thursday, 0.75

Pages 73–74   Lesson 1-5   Independent Practice

1 $0.4\overline{6}$ **3.** $−0.\overline{6}$ **5.** whole, integer, rational   **7.** $0.\overline{34}$
9. false; 0.5 is a rational number but not an integer.
11. false; 5 is a rational number but is also a whole number.   **13.** $\frac{4}{13}$ **15** $0.\overline{7}$ **17a.** 43   **17b.** $\frac{24}{43}$; 0.558
19. $\frac{17}{36}$ is not a terminating decimal since decimals are based on powers of 10 and 36 is not a factor of any power of 10.   **21.** $\frac{1}{11} = 0.\overline{09}; \frac{2}{11} = 0.\overline{18}; \frac{3}{11} = 0.\overline{27}$; The digits that are repeated are the numerator times 9. So, $\frac{7}{11} = 0.\overline{63}$ and $\frac{8}{11} = 0.\overline{72}$.

Page 76　Lesson 1-5　Multi-Step Problem Solving

23. C　**25.** 2

Pages 81–82　Lesson 1-6　Independent Practice

1. >　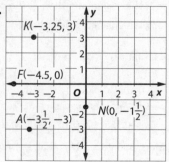**3** =　**5** $-2\frac{3}{4}$, $-2.\overline{2}$, 2.8, $3\frac{1}{8}$　**7.** $-4\frac{1}{2}$ m, $-2\frac{3}{8}$ m, 1.35 m, 5.6 m　**9.** -4.56, -3.11, -1.98, -0.23

11. always; The greater a number is, the farther away from zero. Therefore, its opposite will also be farther from zero.　**13.** The first decimal is a terminating decimal, so its thousandths place is zero. The second decimal has a repeating digit of 3, so its thousandths place is 3. $-0.330 > -0.\overline{333}$
15. Sample answer: The temperature of a freezer changed throughout a day as the door was opened and shut. The temperatures were $-11°$F, $13°$F, $-12°$F, and $15°$F. Order the set of temperatures from least to greatest. $-12°$F, $-11°$F, $13°$F, $15°$F

Page 84　Lesson 1-6　Multi-Step Problem Solving

17. A　**19.** 0.2

Pages 89–90　Lesson 1-7　Independent Practice

1. (2, 2); I　**3.** (−4, 2); II　**5** (5, 0); none　**7** Z; II　**9.** A; IV
11. N; none

13, 14, 15, 16.

17. Sample answer: The first coordinate tells how far to go left or right on the *x*-axis. The second coordinate tells how far up or down. If the coordinates are reversed, then the point would be located in a different direction.　**19a.** no　**19b.** yes
19c. no　**19d.** no　**21.** Quadrants I and III; Sample answer: In Quadrant I, both coordinates are positive and in Quadrant III, both coordinates are negative.　**23.** Sample answer: The first coordinate corresponds to a number on the *x*-axis. The second coordinate corresponds to a number on the *y*-axis. A point is defined by only one ordered pair.
25 Sample answer: (2, 4), (4, 4), (−2, −6), (−4, −6)

Page 92　Lesson 1-7　Multi-Step Problem Solving

27. A　**29.** 65

Page 95　Chapter Review

1. rational number　**3.** positive integer　**5.** terminating decimal

Page 96　Chapter Review

1. 4　**3.** *x*-coordinate　**5.** 6.543

Page 97　Chapter Review

7. yes; Sample answer: Convert each fraction to a decimal: $2\frac{2}{3} \approx 2.67$, $1\frac{1}{4} = 1.25$, and $1\frac{3}{4} = 1.75$. Then add all the decimals: $1.5 + 2.67 + 1.25 + 2.4 + 1.75 = 9.57$. Since 9.57 is close to 10, the estimate is reasonable.

Chapter 2　Multiply and Divide Rational Numbers

Pages 102　Chapter 2　Are You Ready?

1. $7 + 5 = 12$　**3.** $12 - 6 = 6$　**5.** $4\frac{11}{21}$　**7.** $6\frac{7}{8}$ in.

Pages 109–110　Lesson 2-1　Independent Practice

1. 2.8　**3** 1.092　**5.** 167.0067　**7** 84.474 ft; $46.93 \times 1.8 \approx 45 \times 2 = 90$; $84.474 \approx 90$　**9** $5.76; Each price is about $1. He bought about 6 pounds of fruit. $6 \times 1 = 6 \approx 5.76
11. 1.03515　**13.** 209.6 mi　**15.** Sample answer: 0.1×0.6
17. always; Sample answer: $0.3 \times 0.5 = 0.15$; $0.75 \times 0.6 = 0.45$
19. 0.75

Pages 111–112　Lesson 2-1　Multi-Step Problem Solving

21. A　**23.** 6.4　**25.** Name brand cereal: $0.25 per ounce; Grocery store cereal: $0.31 per ounce; The name brand cereal is a better buy.

Pages 119–120　Lesson 2-2　Independent Practice

1. 3.6　**3** 250　**5.** 450　**7.** 20 steps　**9a.** 5 days
9b. $14.99　**11 a.** 2.2 times　**b.** 3.8 times　**13.** $49 \div 7$; The quotient is 7 and all of the other problems have a quotient of 0.7.

Pages 121–122　Lesson 2-2　Multi-Step Problem Solving

15. C　**17.** $3.25　**19.** The quotient of $8.54 \div 5.23$ is greater. If you divide by a lesser number, the quotient will be greater.

Pages 127–128　Lesson 2-3　Independent Practice

1. 15　**3.** 2　**5.** $\frac{22}{5}$ or $4\frac{2}{5}$　**7** $2\frac{2}{5}$ in.　**9** neither; $\frac{4}{5} \times 30 = 24$ and $\frac{2}{3} \times 36 = 24$. So, $24 = 24$.　**11.** seventh grade

13. Sample answer: Melinda baked a dozen cookies. Three-fourths of the cookies were oatmeal raisin. How many cookies were oatmeal raisin cookies? $\frac{3}{4} \times 12 = 9$

15. $1\frac{7}{8}$c

Page 130　Lesson 2-3　Multi-Step Problem Solving

17. C　**19.** 12

Pages 139–140 Lesson 2-4 Independent Practice

1. $\frac{2}{15}$; decrease; $\frac{2}{5} < 1$ **3** $2\frac{2}{3}$; increase; $4 > 1$ **5.** less than since $\frac{1}{4} < 1$; $\frac{1}{6}$ **7** $\frac{3}{8}$ **9** $\frac{3}{10}$ **11a.** Sample answer: Olivia withdrew $\frac{3}{4}$ of her savings. She used $\frac{1}{5}$ of what was left to buy a book. If she had $100 in savings, how much did she spend on the book?

11b.

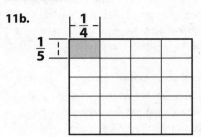

11c. Sample answer: Multiply $\frac{1}{5} \times \frac{1}{4}$. Multiply the product, $\frac{1}{20}$ by $100. She spent $5 on a book.

13. Sample answer: $a = \frac{3}{8}$ and $b = \frac{5}{7}$; $a = \frac{5}{8}$ and $b = \frac{3}{7}$; $a = \frac{5}{14}$ and $b = \frac{3}{4}$ **15.** Sample answer: Makayla gives her cat $\frac{3}{4}$ cup of cat food each day. How much cat food will she have given her cat after 14 days? Since $\frac{3}{4}$ is close to 1, Makayla will have given her cat about 1×14 or 14 cups of cat food. $\frac{3}{4} \times 14 = 10\frac{1}{2}$ which is close to 14.

Page 142 Lesson 2-4 Multi-Step Problem Solving

17. A **19.** $\frac{18}{25}$ m^2

Page 145 Focus on Mathematical Processes

1. $95.40 **3.** 383.5; 1,153; 3,461.5; Multiply by 3, then add 2.5.

Pages 155–156 Lesson 2-5 Independent Practice

1. $\frac{5}{3}$ **3.** 1 **5.** $5 \times \frac{4}{3}$; $6\frac{2}{3}$ **7.** $6 \times \frac{5}{3}$; 10 **9** $4 \times \frac{9}{8}$; $4\frac{1}{2}$ **11** 110 horses **13.** 6 activities; $4 \div \frac{2}{3} = 4 \times \frac{3}{2} = \frac{12}{2} = 6$ **15.** $7 \times \frac{2}{3}$; Sample answer: Dividing by $\frac{2}{3}$ is equivalent to multiplying by $\frac{3}{2}$. **17.** 2 pounds; Sample answer: To find the total amount of trail mix, multiply. $9\frac{1}{3} \times 3 = 28$; To find the amount in each package, divide. $28 \div 14 = 2$

Pages 157–158 Lesson 2-5 Multi-Step Problem Solving

19. B **21.** $78 **23.** $\frac{7}{16}$ pound

Pages 167–168 Lesson 2-6 Independent Practice

1. $\frac{1}{8} \times \frac{2}{1}$; $\frac{1}{4}$ **3** $\frac{3}{4} \times \frac{1}{9}$; $\frac{1}{12}$ **5.** $\frac{1}{3} \times \frac{1}{8}$; $\frac{1}{24}$

7. Sample answer: David has $\frac{5}{6}$ foot of tape. He uses $\frac{1}{12}$ foot of tape to hang each photo on the bulletin board. How many photos can he hang on the bulletin board? 10 photos;

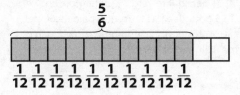

9 $\frac{3}{4} \div \frac{3}{8} = 2$; 2 T-shirts

11.

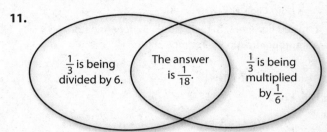

13. greater than 1; the dividend is greater than the divisor; less than 1; the dividend is less than the divisor **15.** $\frac{2}{3} \div \frac{1}{6}$

Page 170 Lesson 2-6 Multi-Step Problem Solving

17. B **19.** 3

Pages 175–176 Lesson 2-7 Independent Practice

1. $1\frac{1}{6}$ **3.** 22 **5** $8\frac{2}{3}$ **7** $9\frac{1}{4}$ mi **9.** 15 strips **11a.** about $69\frac{27}{40}$ million mi **11b.** about $139\frac{7}{20}$ million mi **11c.** about $487\frac{29}{40}$ million mi **11d.** about $882\frac{11}{20}$ million mi **13.** Sample answers provided. **13a.** The first product is less than $\frac{3}{4}$ because the first factor is less than one. You only want a part of a whole, so the product is less than the second factor. **13b.** The second product is equal to the second factor because of the Identity Property. The product of any number and one is that number. **13c.** The third product is greater than the second factor because the first factor is greater than one. So, the product is greater than $\frac{3}{4}$.

Pages 177–178 Lesson 2-7 Multi-Step Problem Solving

15. A **17.** 77 **19.** less than; The first number, $1\frac{1}{2}$, is smaller than the last number, $2\frac{5}{6}$, and therefore is divided into a greater number of parts.

Pages 183–184 Lesson 2-8 Independent Practice

1. $1\frac{1}{2}$ **3** $\frac{6}{7}$ **5.** $11\frac{1}{4}$ in. **7** 30 gal **9.** 12.5 tbsp

11. Sample answer: Mark divided the area, $888\frac{8}{9}$ square yards, of the lawn he mowed by the amount he earned, $9. He should have divided the amount he earned by the area. He actually earned $0.01 per square yard.   **13.** Sample answer: Franklin bought 1.75 pounds of walnuts and paid $9.60 per pound. He had a $0.50 coupon. Excluding tax, how much did Franklin pay for the walnuts? $16.30

Pages 185–186   Lesson 2-8   Multi-Step Problem Solving

15. 10.18   **17.** 3   **19.** 12

Page 189   Chapter Review

1. mixed number   **3.** reciprocal   **5.** denominator
7. improper fraction   **9.** simplest form

Page 190   Chapter Review

1. X; $13 \times \frac{1}{3} = \frac{13}{3}$ or $4\frac{1}{3}$ **3.** ✓   **5.** ✓

Page 191   Chapter Review

7. 9 more pancakes

Chapter 3 Operations with Integers

Page 196   Chapter 3   Are You Ready?

1. 9   **3.** 100   **5.** 19

7.

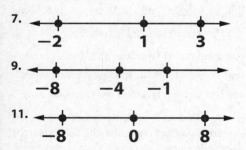

9.

11.

Pages 207–208   Lesson 3-1   Independent Practice

1. −38;

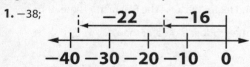

3. 16   **5.** 0   **7.** 1   **9.** −18   **11** green: profit of $1; white: profit of $3; black: profit of $3   **13.** Sample answer: In science, atoms may contain 2 positive charges and 2 negative charges. In business, a stock's value may fall 0.75 one day and rise 0.75 the next day.   **15.** a **17.** $m + (−15)$

Pages 209–210   Lesson 3-1   Multi-Step Problem Solving

19. D   **21.** 0   **23.** The other customer used 18¢ from the tray; Sample answer: After the first costumer added 6¢, there would be a total of 33¢ in the tray. So, 18¢ must have been used by the other customer to end up with 15¢ left. $27 + 6 + (−18) = 15$

Pages 219–220   Lesson 3-2   Independent Practice

1. −10   **3** −12   **5.** −30   **7.** 23   **9.** 104   **11.** −22   **13** He did not find the additive inverse of −18. $−15 − (−18) = −15 + 18$ or 3. The correct answer is 3.   **15a.** no; Sample answer: The Commutative Property is not true for subtraction. $2 − 7 \neq 7 − 2$ or $−5 \neq 5$.   **15b.** no; Sample answer: The Associative Property is not true for subtraction. $9 − (6 − 3) \neq (9 − 6) − 3$ or $6 \neq 0$.   **17.** Sample answer: The temperature of a deep freezer was −15°F. When the lid was opened, it lost −7°F. What was the resulting temperature after the lid was opened? $−15 − (−7) = −8$; −8°F

Page 222   Lesson 3-2   Multi-Step Problem Solving

19. D   **21.** According to her budget, Alisha has −$69 at the end of the month. Sample suggestions for saving money:
- Stop using credit card and try to pay it off.
- Cancel cable TV or get a cheaper package.
- Cancel gym membership or get a cheaper membership.
- Cut down on cell phone use or get a cheaper plan.
- Look into working overtime or get a part-time job.

Page 225   Focus on Mathematical Processes

1. 488 meters   **3.** 6

Pages 235–236   Lesson 3-3   Independent Practice

1. −96   **3.** 36   **5** −64   **7** 5(−650); −3,250; Ethan burns 3,250 Calories each week.   **9.** 5 black T-shirts
11. Sample answer: Removing sets of negative counters from a mat requires adding zero pairs which leaves only positive counters.   **13.** Sample answer: Evaluate −7 + 7 first. Since −7 + 7 = 0, and any number times 0 is 0, the value of the expression is 0.   **15.** −3 and 7

Page 238   Lesson 3-3   Multi-Step Problem Solving

17. A   **19.** $319

Pages 245–246   Lesson 3-4   Independent Practice

1. −10   **3** 5   **5.** −11   **7.** −2   **9.** −3   **11.** −6
13 −60 miles   **15a.** $−45 ÷ (−15) = 3$ **15b.** Sample answer: Start at −45. Subtract −15 repeatedly until you reach 0. Subtracting a negative moves to the right on the number line. You need to subtract 3 times, so the quotient is 3.
15c. Sample answer: Start at −40. Subtract −8 repeatedly until you reach 0. Subtracting a negative moves to the right on the number line. You need to subtract 5 times, so the quotient is 5.   **17.** −3   **19.** −143.5°F   **21.** no; Sample answer: When two integers are divided, the quotient is sometimes an integer. Other times it is a decimal. For example, $−5 ÷ −10 = 0.5$.
23. Sample answer: Over the course of 3 plays, a football team lost 27 yards. If they lost the same number of yards for each play, what was the change in yards during the first play? −9 yards

Pages 247–248   Lesson 3-4   Multi-Step Problem Solving

25. B **27.** 1.4°F **29.** negative; Sample answer: The quotient of two negative integers is positive. The quotient of two positive integers is positive. So, the quotient of a positive and negative is negative.

Pages 253–254   Lesson 3-5   Independent Practice

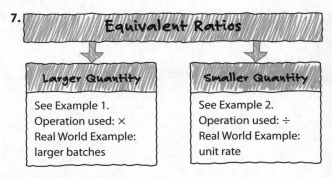 **1** −30 **3.** −8 **5.** 98 **7** 13 years; It would take (−15) ÷ (−3) or 5 years to erode to the grass line and then (−24) ÷ (−3) or 8 additional years to erode to the tree line. So, it would take 5 + 8 or 13 years total. **9.** Tom; Tom's total score is 1 + (−2) + 0 + 0 + 1 + (−1) + (−1) + 2 + (−2) or −2. Paida's total score is 0 + 0 + 1 + (−2) + (−1) + (−1) + 2 + 1 + 1 or 1. Since −2 < 1, Tom wins. **11.** 2°F **13.** Sample answer: The temperature in a freezer decreased 15°F an hour for 3 hours after being plugged in. The temperature in the freezer was 76°F when it was plugged in. What was the temperature in the freezer after 3 hours? 31°F **15.** Sample answer: −$15, $20, −$35, −$5 **17.** −9; Sample answer: These expressions contain quotients that are rational numbers, not just integers.

Page 256   Lesson 3-5   Multi-Step Problem Solving

19. 25 **21.** $225

Page 259   Chapter Review

1. additive **3.** integers **5.** opposites

Page 260   Chapter Review

1. X; $|-5| + |2| = 5 + 2$ or 7
3. X; $-24 \div |-2| = -24 \div 2 = -12$

Page 261   Chapter Review

5. Hollern, Thorne, Brigham; Sample answer: Find the score for each golfer. Thorne: −3; Hollern: −4; Brigham: −1; Then, order the scores from least to greatest: −4, −3, and −1.

Chapter 4 Understand Proportions

Page 266   Chapter 4   Are You Ready?

1. 29 **3.** 6 **5.** $\frac{1}{4}$ **7.** $\frac{13}{25}$

Pages 277–278   Lesson 4-1   Independent Practice

1. $\frac{3}{2}$; 1.5; For every 3 goggles, there are 2 snorkels.
3 $\frac{4}{7}$; There are $\frac{7}{4}$, or 1.75, times as many puppies as adult dogs.
5 12, 21 **7a.** $\frac{2}{5}$, 2 to 5, 2:5; For every 2 championships won by Australia, the United States has won 5. **7b.** $\frac{6}{35}$, 6 to 35, 6:35; The Australians have won 6 of the 35 championship matches. **9.** 1,440; The ratios of each two consecutive terms are 1:2, 1:3, 1:4, and 1:5.

Pages 279–280   Lesson 4-1   Multi-Step Problem Solving

11. 20 **13.** 2 **15.** Sample answer: There could be 4(3) blue circles to 5(3) total circles, or 12 blue circles and 15 circles in all. Multiply 4 and 5 by the same number.

Pages 289–290   Lesson 4-2   Independent Practice

1. $\frac{12 \text{ oz}}{1 \text{ steak}}$ **3** $\frac{5.1 \text{ gal}}{1 \text{ container}}$ **5.** 0.4 min per lap; Divide the time by the number of laps. Evans drove 2.3 minutes per lap and Loza drove 2.7 minutes per lap. 2.7 − 2.3 = 0.4 **7.** $4 per mile **9 a.** 268 miles **b.** about 2 h **11.** A unit rate has a denominator of 1. $\frac{\$108}{6 \text{ weeks}} = \frac{\$18}{1 \text{ week}}$ **13.** $1\frac{1}{3}$ min, or about 1 min, 20 s; 45 mph $= \frac{45}{60}$ mi per s, so $\frac{60}{45}$ gives the seconds per mile

Page 292   Lesson 4-2   Multi-Step Problem Solving

15. C **17.** Company C; $1.90

Pages 297–298   Lesson 4-3   Independent Practice

1

Stew (c)	8	4	24
Beef (lb)	2	1	6

; 6 lb

3

American Dollars	300	100	50
New Zealand Dollars	378	126	63

; 63 New Zealand dollars

5a.

People Served	6
Pasta (lb)	1
Meat (lb)	1.5
Cheese (c)	2
Sauce (c)	2

5b. 3 lb of pasta, 4.5 lb of meat, 6 c of cheese and 6 c of sauce

5c. 0.5 lb of pasta, 0.75 lb of meat, 1 c of cheese, and 1 c of sauce; Sample answer: Since 3 is half of 6, half the recipe that serves 6 people will serve 3 people. 1 lb ÷ 2 = 0.5 lb, 1.5 lb ÷ 2 = 0.75 lb, 2 c ÷ 2 = 1 c, 2 c ÷ 2 = 1 c.

7.

Equivalent Ratios

Larger Quantity
See Example 1.
Operation used: ×
Real World Example: larger batches

Smaller Quantity
See Example 2.
Operation used: ÷
Real World Example: unit rate

9.

Bulls	18	2	22
Cows	45	5	55

no; If 4 bulls and 4 cows are added, there would be 22 bulls and 49 cows on the ranch. Using the ratio table, there should be 55 cows for 22 bulls.

Pages 299–300 Lesson 4-3 Multi-Step Problem Solving

11. A **13.** Emperor penguin; 4.68 mph

15.

Blueprint (in.)	0.25	0.5	1.5	1.25	3.75
House (ft)	0.625	1.25	3.75	3.125	9.375

Pages 305–306 Lesson 4-4 Independent Practice

1 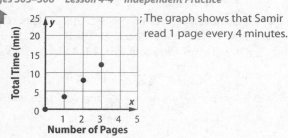 ; The graph shows that Samir read 1 page every 4 minutes.

3. Ken's Home Supply: $45; Wayne's Warehouse: $54; Sample answer: Ken's Home Supply charges $5 for every foot. So, 9 feet of fencing costs $5 × 9 or $45. Wayne's Warehouse charges $6 for every foot of fencing. So, 9 feet of fencing costs $6 × 9 or $54.

5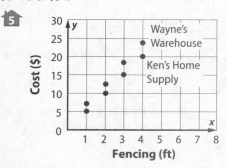

Sample answer: As the number of feet increases, the cost at Wayne's Warehouse increases at a faster rate than the cost at Ken's Home Supply. The cost at Wayne's Warehouse is shown on the graph as a steeper line.

7a.

Length (x)	Width (y)	(x, y)
1.618	1	(1.618, 1)
3.236	2	(3.236, 2)
4.854	3	(4.854, 3)
6.472	4	(6.472, 4)

7b.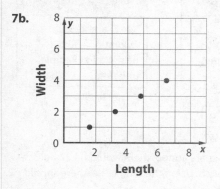

7c. The area of the first rectangle in the table is 1.618 square units. The areas increase to 6.472, 14.562, and 25.888. The areas increase at a slower rate as the dimensions increase.
9. (2, 2.5)

Pages 307–308 Lesson 4-4 Multi-Step Problem Solving

11. D **13.** 21 centimeters **15.** no; Sample answer: The line drawn showing Zoe's wages is steeper than the line drawn showing Felix's wages.

Page 311 Focus on Mathematical Processes

1.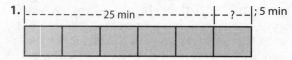

3. 100 miles

Pages 317–318 Lesson 4-5 Independent Practice

1. no; Since the unit rates, $\frac{\$0.20}{1\ donut\ hole}$ and $\frac{\$0.18}{1\ donut\ hole}$, are not the same, the rates are not equivalent.
3 no; $\frac{\$210}{3\ tires} = \frac{\$70}{1\ tire}$ and $\frac{\$250}{4\ tires} = \frac{\$62.50}{1\ tire}$. Since the unit rates are not the same, the rates are not equivalent. **5.** yes; The length to width ratio for the photograph and poster form equivalent fractions. **7** 28 beads; Sample answer: $\frac{68\ beads}{17\ inches} = \frac{4\ beads}{1\ inch}$ and $\frac{28\ beads}{7\ inches} = \frac{4\ beads}{1\ inch}$. Since there are 4 beads for every inch of wire, she will use 7 × 4 or 28 beads. **9.** 86.4 feet in 18 seconds; Sample answer: The other three are equivalent rates. **11.** 6 girls

Page 320 Lesson 4-5 Multi-Step Problem Solving

13. B **15.** 15 cents

Pages 329–330 Lesson 4-6 Independent Practice

1 27 cookies **3.** 15 instruments **5** 60 students; There were 6 + 3 + 4 + 7 or 20 responses. Three out of 20 choose science. Using a proportion, 60 students out of 400 might choose science. **7.** Sample answer: The advertisement could have only surveyed 6 students. If the company surveyed more students, the number of students that prefer talking on the phone over texting could be a different ratio. **9.** Elisa did not set up the equivalent ratios in the correct order. She should have set it up as $\frac{1}{12} = \frac{\blacksquare}{276}$. There are 23 teachers at the preschool. **11.** always; In order for the ratios to form equivalent ratios, they must be equivalent fractions, therefore reducing to the same fraction. **13.** 160.6 miles

Page 332 Lesson 4-6 Multi-Step Problem Solving

15. B **17.** 20

Pages 337–338   Lesson 4-7   Independent Practice

1. 6   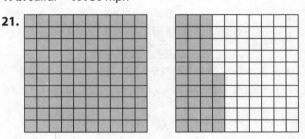 **3** 0.0065   **5.** $2\frac{1}{2}$ **7** 1,500 lb; Sample answer: Since the measurement was in fraction form, it is easier to use a unit rate.   **9.** $4\frac{4}{5}$ oz; $\frac{16 \text{ ounces}}{1 \text{ pound}} = \frac{\blacksquare \text{ ounces}}{3 \text{ pounds}}$. So, 3 pounds equals 48 ounces. $\frac{48 \text{ ounces}}{10 \text{ pork chops}} = \frac{\blacksquare \text{ ounces}}{1 \text{ pork chop}}$. So, one pork chop is $4\frac{4}{5}$ ounces.   **11a.** The *x*-value represents the number of quarts and the *y*-value represents the equivalent number of gallons.   **11b.** Sample answer: The point on the line whose *y*-value is equal to 2.5 is (10, 2.5), so 10 qt = 2.5 gal.   **11c.** $\frac{4 \text{ qt}}{1 \text{ gal}}$ **11d.** $\frac{4 \text{ qt}}{1 \text{ gal}} = \frac{\blacksquare \text{ qt}}{2.5 \text{ gal}}$ **13.** <; 16 in. is equivalent to 1 ft 4 in.; $1\frac{1}{2}$ ft is equivalent to 1 ft 6 in.; So, 16 in. $< 1\frac{1}{2}$ ft.   **15.** Sample answer: 5 pt; 80 fl oz

Pages 339–340   Lesson 4-7   Multi-Step Problem Solving

17. 3   **19.** 4   **21.** Method 2 is correct. In Method 1, the correct number of sq. cm was found, but the conversion to sq. m is incorrect. When converting square units, the conversion involves two dimensions. So, instead of dividing by 100, you must divide by 10,000 to convert sq. cm to sq. m.

Page 343   Chapter Review

1. rate table   **3.** *x* axis; *x* coordinate   **5.** rate   **7.** unit price; unit rate   **9.** graph   **11.** proportion

Page 344   Chapter Review

1. $\frac{1}{6}$ **3.** $\frac{2}{5}$ **5.** $\frac{2}{3}$

Page 345   Chapter Review

7. 25 cars

Chapter 5 Apply Proportions to Percent

Page 350   Chapter 5   Are You Ready?

1. 72   **3.** 477   **5.** $\frac{9}{20}$ **7.** 18 teeth

Pages 361–362   Lesson 5-1   Independent Practice

1 $\frac{1}{50}$ **3.** $\frac{17}{20}$ **5.** 20%   **7.** 35%   **9.** $\frac{7}{25}$ **11** $\frac{9}{50}$

13 do not prefer: 80%, prefer: 20%; The sum of the percents is 100.   **15.** Sample answer: $\frac{11}{20} = \frac{55}{100}$ or 55%, $\frac{3}{5} = \frac{60}{100}$ or 60%, $\frac{7}{10} = \frac{70}{100}$ or 70%   **17.** $\frac{8}{45}$; The other numbers are equivalent to $\frac{9}{20}$.   **19.** Sample answer: As a fraction, $33\frac{1}{3}\%$ is $\frac{1}{3}$ and 33% is $\frac{33}{100}$, which does not simplify.

Page 364   Lesson 5-1   Multi-Step Problem Solving

21. D   **23.** 1 hr

Pages 369–370   Lesson 5-2   Independent Practice

1. 0.57   **3** 0.31   **5.** 18%   **7** 10%   **9.** 0.04   **11** 12%   **13.** C: $59.50, A: $70, B: $87.50   **15.** $1.50   **17.** Sample answer: 26%; 0.26; $\frac{13}{50}$ **19.** Sample answer: Niko scored a 92% on his math test. Express this percent as a decimal.   **21.** 0.45; Sample answer: Written as decimals, the set is 0.4, 0.45, 0.35, and 0.375. So, 0.45 is the greatest number in the set.

Pages 371–372   Lesson 5-2   Multi-Step Problem Solving

23. C   **25.** $0.12   **27.** 12.5%

Pages 377–378   Lesson 5-3   Independent Practice

1. 3.5; $3\frac{1}{2}$ **3** 0.0015; $\frac{3}{2,000}$ **5.** 250%   **7.** 420%   **9.** 850%   **11.** 0.9%   **13** 140%   **15.** 0.003; $\frac{3}{1,000}$; 3 out of every 1,000 people are Japanese.   **17a.** 0.0005   **17b.** sulfur   **19.** 30 mph

21.

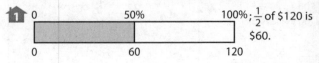

Sample answer: Since 135% > 100%, two 10-by-10 grids will be used. The first will be completely shaded and the second will have 35 of the sections shaded.

Pages 379–380   Lesson 5-3   Multi-Step Problem Solving

23. 121.5
25. 0.5%   **27.** 0.01%, 0.5%, 1%, 0.05, 0.500, 500%, 50

Page 383   Focus on Mathematical Processes

1. 1,440 hours   **3.** 420 pieces

Pages 393–394   Lesson 5-4   Independent Practice

1 0   50%   100%; $\frac{1}{2}$ of $120 is $60.
0   60   120

3.

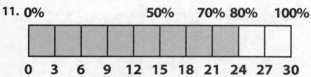

0 $33\frac{1}{3}\%$ $66\frac{2}{3}\%$ 100%;

0 100 200 300

$\frac{2}{3}$ of 300 is 200.   **5.** about 140 cards; $0.60 \times 700 = 420$, $700 - 420 = 280$; $420 - 280 = 140$ **7.** $67 + 67 = 134$ 🏠 about 260,000 people; Sample answer: $\frac{2}{5}$ of 650,000 is 260,000.   **11.** about 284; Sample answer: 18% is about 20% and 194 is about 200; 200 is 20% of 1,000; $1,000 - 194 - 522 = 284$ **13.** $\frac{1}{5}\%$ of 20, 10% of 20, 20% of 20   **15.** Sample answer: Melissa's homeroom has raised 63% of its goal to raise $500 for the school fundraiser. Matt's homeroom has raised 48% of its $1,000 goal. How much has each homeroom raised? Melissa's homeroom: $315; Matt's homeroom: $480

Page 396   Lesson 5-4   Multi-Step Problem Solving

17. A   **19.** about 225

Pages 403–404   Lesson 5-5   Independent Practice

1. 46   **3.** 92   5️⃣ 9   **7.** 336   9️⃣ $35.95

11. 0%   50%   70% 80%   100%

0 3 6 9 12 15 18 21 24 27 30

no; 70% of 30 is 21, not 24. 80% of 30 is 24. Sample model shown.

13. Sample answers given for examples.

Percent	Shared Concept	Fraction
A whole is represented by a percent that is equal to 100%. Example: 100%	Whole	A whole is represented by a fraction with a numerator that is equal to the denominator. Example: $\frac{3}{3}$
Part of a whole represented by a percent that is less than 100%. Example: 25%	Part of a whole	Part of a whole is represented by a fraction with a numerator that is less than the denominator. Example: $\frac{1}{3}$
An amount that is greater than one is represented by a percent that is greater than 100%. Example: 125%	more than one	An amount that is greater than one is represented by a fraction with a numerator that is greater than the denominator. Example: $\frac{4}{3}$

15. yes; 16% of 40 is 6.4 and 40% of 16 is 6.4   **17.** Sample answer: If a number n is 25% of a and 35% of b, it is a greater part of b than it is of a. So, $a > b$.

Page 406   Lesson 5-5   Multi-Step Problem Solving

19. D   **21.** $67.73

Pages 415–416   Lesson 5-6   Independent Practice

1.

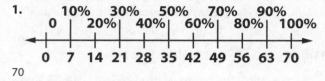

10%   30%   50%   70%   90%
0   20%   40%   60%   80%   100%

0 7 14 21 28 35 42 49 56 63 70

70

🏠 $\frac{22}{\blacksquare} = \frac{44}{100}$; 50   5️⃣ $50   **7.** 15 cups   **9.** 20 cups   **11.** Sample answer: $\frac{21}{25} = \frac{\blacksquare}{100}$; 84%   **13.** 18 karats; 24 is the whole and 75 is the percent, so $\frac{18}{24} = \frac{75}{100}$.   **15.** 5%

Page 418   Lesson 5-6   Multi-Step Problem Solving

17. A   **19.** 50%

Page 421   Chapter Review

1. percent   **3.** percent proportion   **5.** benchmark percents

Page 422   Chapter Review

3. $120\% = \frac{120}{100}$
$= \frac{6}{5}$
$= 1\frac{1}{5}$

Page 423   Chapter Review

5. 166.6 in²; Sample answer: Find the width of the placemat. $0.85 \times 14 = 11.9$ Find the area of the placemat. $11.9 \times 14 = 166.6$

Index

Copyright © McGraw-Hill Education

Kk

Ll

Mm

Pp

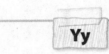

Modeling the Math

0　1　2　3　4　5　6　7　8　9

−11　−10　−9　−8　−7　−6　−5　−4　−3　−2　−1　0　1　2　3　4　5　6　7　8　9　10　11

Name

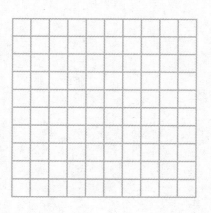 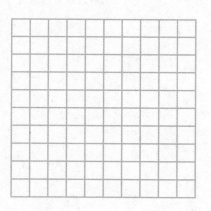

| 0% | 10% | 20% | 30% | 40% | 50% | 60% | 70% | 80% | 90% | 100% |

| 0% | 10% | 20% | 30% | 40% | 50% | 60% | 70% | 80% | 90% | 100% |

| 0% | 10% | 20% | 30% | 40% | 50% | 60% | 70% | 80% | 90% | 100% |

| 0% | 10% | 20% | 30% | 40% | 50% | 60% | 70% | 80% | 90% | 100% |

Name _____

What are VKVs® and How Do I Create Them?

Dinah Zike's
Visual Kinesthetic Vocabulary®

Visual Kinethestic Vocabulary Cards® are flashcards that animate words by focusing on their structure, use, and meaning. The VKVs in this book are used to show cognates, or words that are similar in Spanish and English.

Step 1

Go to the back of your book to find the VKVs for the chapter vocabulary you are currently studying. Follow the cutting and folding instructions at the top of the page. The vocabulary word on the BLUE background is written in English. The Spanish word is on the ORANGE background.

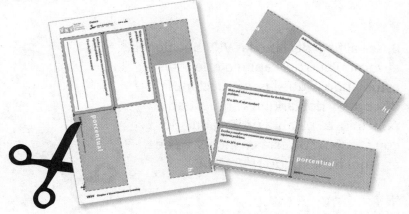

Step 2

There are exercises for you to complete on the VKVs. When you understand the concept, you can complete each exercise. All exercises are written in English and Spanish. You only need to give the answer once.

Step 3

Individualize your VKV by writing notes, sketching diagrams, recording examples, and forming plurals.

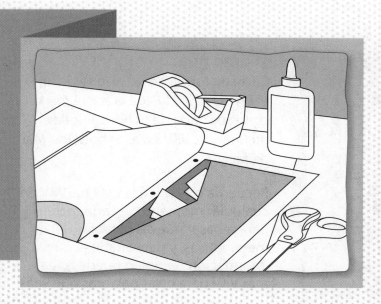

How Do I Store My VKVs?

Take a 6" x 9" envelope and cut away a V on one side only. Glue the envelope into the back cover of your book. Your VKVs can be stored in this pocket!

Remember you can use your VKVs ANY time in the school year to review new words in math, and add new information you learn. Why not create your own VKVs for other words you see and share them with others!

Las tarjetas de vocabulario visual y cinético (VKV) contienen palabras con animación que está basada en la estructura, uso y significado de las palabras. Las tarjetas de este libro sirven para mostrar cognados, que son palabras similares en español y en inglés.

Paso 1

Busca al final del libro las VKV que tienen el vocabulario del capítulo que estás estudiando. Sigue las instrucciones de cortar y doblar que se muestran al principio. La palabra de vocabulario con fondo AZUL está en inglés. La de español tiene fondo NARANJA.

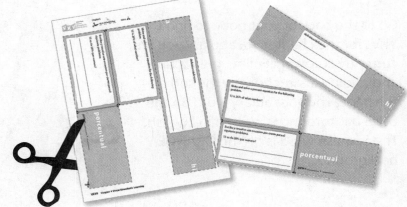

Paso 2

Hay ejercicios para que completes con las VKV. Cuando entiendas el concepto, puedes completar cada ejercicio. Todos los ejercicios están escritos en inglés y español. Solo tienes que dar la respuesta una vez.

Paso 3

Da tu toque personal a las VKV escribiendo notas, haciendo diagramas, grabando ejemplos y formando plurales.

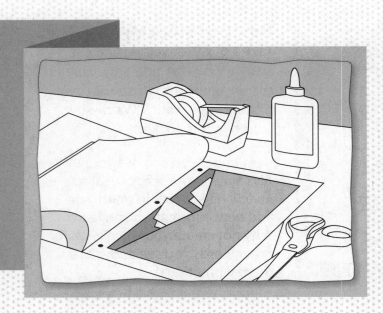

¿Cómo guardo mis VKV?

Corta en forma de "V" el lado de un sobre de 6" X 9". Pega el sobre en la contraportada de tu libro. Puedes guardar tus VKV en esos bolsillos. ¡Así de fácil!

Recuerda que puedes usar tus VKV en cualquier momento del año escolar para repasar nuevas palabras de matemáticas, y para añadir la nueva información. También puedes crear más VKV para otras palabras que veas, y poder compartirlas con los demás.

Dinah Zike's
Visual
Kinesthetic
Vocabulary®

Chapter 1

✂ cut on all dashed lines

🗋 fold on all solid lines

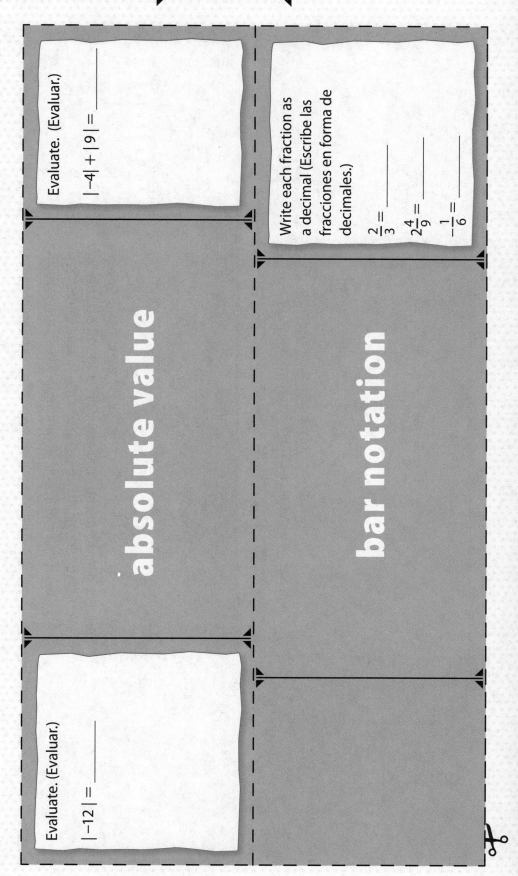

Evaluate. (Evaluar.)

$|-4| + |9| = $ _____

Write each fraction as a decimal (Escribe las fracciones en forma de decimales.)

$\dfrac{2}{3} = $ _____

$2\dfrac{4}{9} = $ _____

$-\dfrac{1}{6} = $ _____

absolute value

bar notation

Evaluate. (Evaluar.)

$|-12| = $ _____

de barra

absoluto

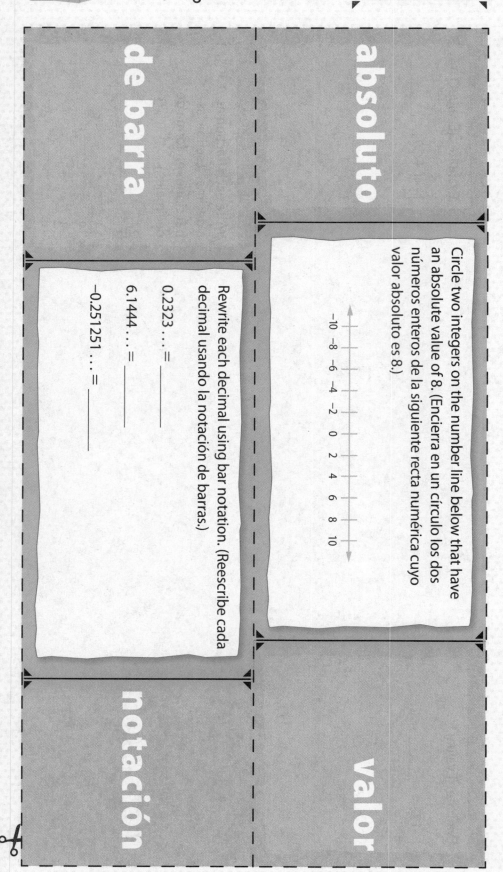

Rewrite each decimal using bar notation. (Reescribe cada decimal usando la notación de barras.)

0.2323 … = _____

6.1444 … = _____

−0.251251 … = _____

Circle two integers on the number line below that have an absolute value of 8. (Encierra en un círculo los dos números enteros de la siguiente recta numérica cuyo valor absoluto es 8.)

−10 −8 −6 −4 −2 0 2 4 6 8 10

notación

valor

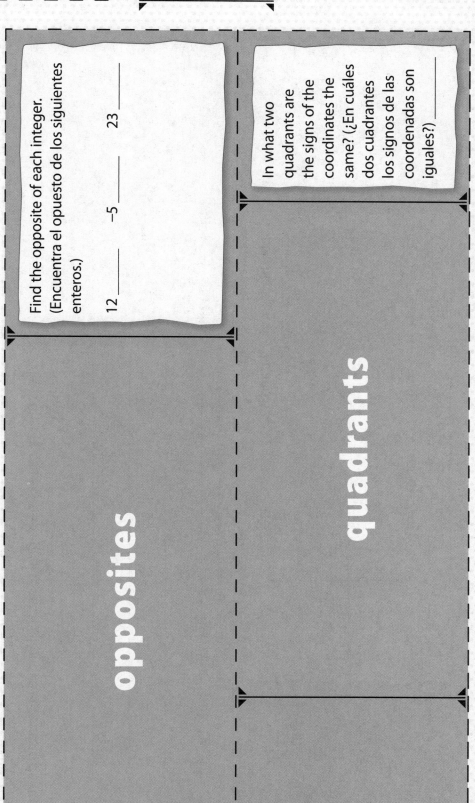

Find the opposite of each integer. (Encuentra el opuesto de los siguientes enteros.)

12 _____ −5 _____ 23 _____

In what two quadrants are the signs of the coordinates the same? (¿En cuáles dos cuadrantes los signos de las coordenadas son iguales?) _____

opposites

quadrants

es

uestos

Label Quadrants I, II, III, and IV.
(Rotula los cuadrantes I, II, III y IV.)

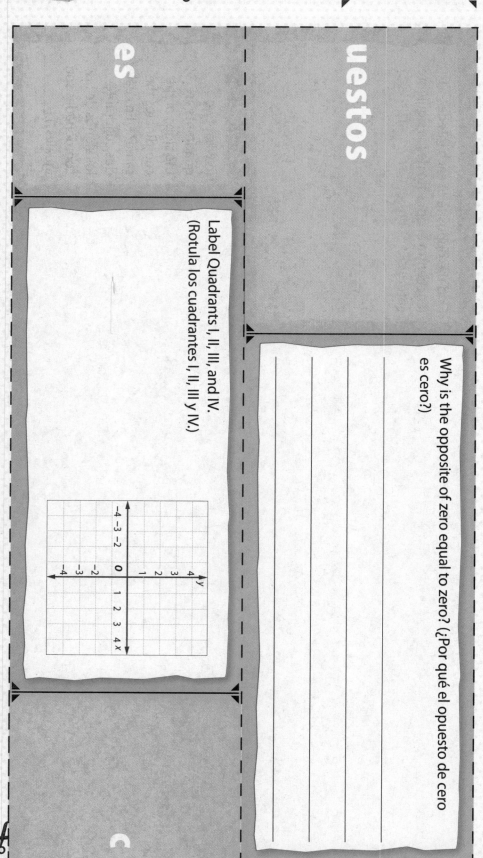

Why is the opposite of zero equal to zero? (¿Por qué el opuesto de cero
es cero?)

Commutative Property

Circle the word that is related to the Commutative Property. (Encierra en un círculo la palabra que se relaciona con la propiedad conmutativa.)

grouping   order

Define Commutative Property. (Define propiedad conmutativa.)

reciprocal

To solve $8 \div \frac{3}{4}$, multiply _____ by the reciprocal of _____. (Para resolver $8 \div \frac{3}{4}$, multiplica _____ por el recíproco de _____.)

Dinah Zike's
Visual Kinesthetic Vocabulary ®

íproco

conmutativa

Circle the operations that are commutative. (Encierra en un círculo las operaciones conmutativas.)

addition   subtraction

division   multiplication

Find the reciprocal of each number. (Halla el recíproco de los siguientes números.)

$$\frac{7}{12} =$$ _____ $9 =$ _____

$$1\frac{5}{8} =$$ _____ $$\frac{1}{6} =$$ _____

propiedad

Dinah Zike's
VKV
Visual
Kinesthetic
Vocabulary®

Chapter 3

✂ cut on all dashed lines

🗁 fold on all solid lines

Write the additive inverse of each number below. (Escribe el inverso aditivo de los siguientes números.)

13 _____

−2 _____

−25 _____

1 _____

Write the opposite of each number below. (Escribe el opuesto de los siguientes números.)

−54 _____

25 _____

12 _____

−16 _____

additive inverse

opposites

Define additive inverse. (Define inverso aditivo.)

_____
_____
_____

Dinah Zike's
Visual
Kinesthetic
Vocabulary®

✂ cut on all dashed lines

▭ fold on all solid lines

uestos

aditivo

inverso

Circle the word that has the same meaning as *additive inverse*. (Encierra en un círculo la palabra que significa lo mismo que inverso aditivo.)

negative integer   opposite

number line   absolute value

Explain why 6 and −6 are opposites. (Explica por qué 6 y −6 son opuestos.)

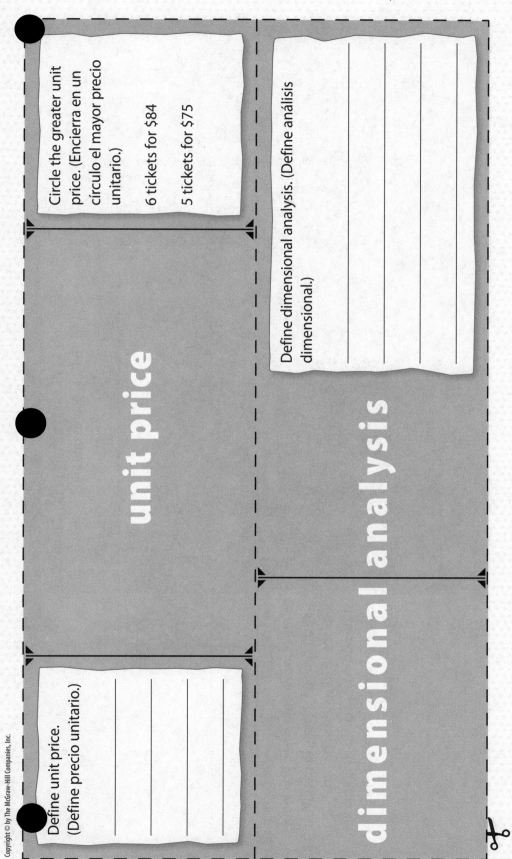

Circle the greater unit price. (Encierra en un círculo el mayor precio unitario.)

6 tickets for $84

5 tickets for $75

Define dimensional analysis. (Define análisis dimensional.)

unit price

dimensional analysis

Define unit price. (Define precio unitario.)

Dinah Zike's
Visual
Kinesthetic
Vocabulary®

✂ cut on all dashed lines

⬚ fold on all solid lines

unitario

análisis

Five chairs cost $110. Find the unit price. (Cinco sillas cuestan $110. Halla el precio unitario.)

Write about a time when you would use dimensional analysis to solve a problem. (Escribe sobre una situación en la cual podrías aplicar el análisis dimensional para resolver un problema.)

precio

Write about a time when it might be useful to know the percent proportion. (Escribe acerca de una situación en la cual podría ser útil conocer la proporción porcentual.)

percent proportion

Write the percent proportion. (Escribe la proporción porcentual.)

Dinah Zike's
V K V
**Visual
Kinesthetic
Vocabulary** ®

Chapter 5

✂ cut on all dashed lines

📄 fold on all solid lines

porcentual
(por ciento)

Circle the example of a percent proportion. (Encierra en un círculo el ejemplo de proporción porcentual.)

23% of 200 is 46.

$\frac{24}{96} = \frac{25}{100}$

$\frac{1}{4}$ of 360 is 90.

$\frac{3}{5} = \frac{27}{45}$

proporción

Grade 6 Mathematics Reference Materials

LENGTH

Customary			Metric		
1 mile (mi)	=	1,760 yards (yd)	1 kilometer (km)	=	1,000 meters (m)
1 yard (yd)	=	3 feet (ft)	1 meter (m)	=	100 centimeters (cm)
1 foot (ft)	=	12 inches (in.)	1 centimeter (cm)	=	10 millimeters (mm)

VOLUME AND CAPACITY

Customary			Metric		
1 gallon (gal)	=	4 quarts (qt)	1 liter (L)	=	1,000 milliliters (mL)
1 quart (qt)	=	2 pints (pt)			
1 pint (pt)	=	2 cups (c)			
1 cup (c)	=	8 fluid ounces (fl oz)			

WEIGHT AND MASS

Customary			Metric		
1 ton (T)	=	2,000 pounds (lb)	1 kilogram (kg)	=	1,000 grams (g)
1 pound (lb)	=	16 ounces (oz)	1 gram (g)	=	1,000 milligrams (mg)

Inches
0
1
2
3
4
5
6

AREA		
Triangle	$A = \dfrac{bh}{2}$ or	$A = \dfrac{1}{2}bh$
Rectangle or Parallelogram		$A = bh$
Trapezoid		$A = \dfrac{1}{2}(b_1 + b_2)h$

VOLUME	
Rectangular Prism	$V = Bh$